CLIMATOLOGY

The Matterhorn with its banner cloud

CLIMATOLOGY

TREATED MAINLY IN RELATION
TO DISTRIBUTION IN TIME
AND PLACE

By

W. G. KENDREW, M.A.,

READER IN CLIMATOLOGY,
UNIVERSITY OF OXFORD

BEING THE
THIRD EDITION OF *CLIMATE*

OXFORD
AT THE CLARENDON PRESS
1949

Oxford University Press, Amen House, London E.C. 4

GLASGOW NEW YORK TORONTO MELBOURNE WELLINGTON
BOMBAY CALCUTTA MADRAS CAPE TOWN

Geoffrey Cumberlege, Publisher to the University

FIRST EDITION   1930
SECOND EDITION   1938
REPRINTED   1942

PRINTED IN GREAT BRITAIN

PREFACE

In the eighteen years since this book was first prepared the large additions of observational material and the many developments of meteorological theory have made much revision of it desirable. The general scope of the book has been retained, but large sections have now been entirely rewritten, some curtailed, others enlarged, and nearly all rearranged. It was intended that this work should be published as a new, third, edition of *Climate*, but it became clear as revision proceeded that the necessary changes were such that a modification of the title was advisable, and *Climatology* was chosen as more suitable.

For the most part the climatology of the surface of the earth only is treated, the upper atmosphere being omitted as far as possible; obviously that would not be feasible if an attempt were being made to deal in any completeness with the meteorological basis of climatology, and even within the limits set the shortcomings of a surface treatment are many.

To quote from the Preface of the first edition, 'it is a pleasure to acknowledge the frequent use made of the work of those scientists and others whose observations and results are the foundation of a book of this character, as will be obvious from every chapter'. In particular the author's cordial thanks are tendered to the following for permission to reproduce diagrams, plates, and letterpress: the Director of the (British) Meteorological Office (all the British synoptic charts, by the authority of the Controller of His Majesty's Stationery Office, and Figs. 44 and 45 from the Meteorological Glossary); the Council of the Royal Meteorological Society (Figs. 4 and 5, and the quotation on page 333); the Director-General of Observatories, Poona (Figs. 52 and 53); Messrs. McGraw Hill Book Company, New York (Figs. 57 and 58); the persons and firms named on page 10, who hold the copyright of the Plates; and to several friends for advice and help which involved much time and work.

W. G. K.

CONTENTS

PART III

THE VAPOUR IN THE ATMOSPHERE AND ITS CONDENSATION. RAIN. CLOUD. SUNSHINE. VISIBILITY

PART IV

MOUNTAIN AND PLATEAU CLIMATE

CONTENTS

PART V
THE WEATHER OF THE WESTERLIES

PART VI
SOME CLIMATIC TYPES

LIST OF PLATES

INTRODUCTION

THE SCOPE OF CLIMATOLOGY

MODERN civilized life has become so artificial that our relations with and dependence on basal natural conditions are to a large extent masked. In primitive societies these relations are obvious; only the man who can adapt himself to his surroundings survives, and the community which is most richly endowed by nature, and able to take full advantage of its endowment, makes headway and secures pre-eminence over its neighbours. This romance of evolution is seen most clearly in the realms of plants and animals.

Climate is the most fundamental and far-reaching of the natural elements which control life. The vegetation of the earth is closely dependent on it, and the adaptations in the animal kingdom are numerous; among the climatic types in mankind we will mention only the Eskimos on the frozen margins of the Arctic, the fair-skinned races of the westerlies, the Arabs of the trade-wind deserts, and the negroes of the tropics. The adaptation to climate is both direct and indirect. Especially when men of any race are moved to a new environment, their specialized adaptation to their home climate, and their lack of adaptation to their new conditions, become clearly manifest. In spite of all his command of the resources of civilization, and his advances in scientific knowledge, the north European is unable to flourish for many consecutive years in the heat and moisture, the 'hot-house' atmosphere, of the Guinea coast, and the white race is as yet unable to establish itself in the humid tropics as colonists, reproducing its species; the human organism is debilitated by the direct influence of the new climate, and so falls a ready prey to sundry germ-diseases, such as malaria and yellow-fever, which haunt the region. This is an extreme case, but not exceptional. Some changes of climate seem to be stimulating when the change is not of great magnitude, but if a race can be permanently subjected to such new conditions it is likely that the type changes gradually, probably by a process of elimination.

In this work the important features of climate will be described, and some indication given of the physical principles underlying them. The regional distribution of the elements is kept prominently in view, since the influence of climate on the distribution and characteristics of the plant and animal inhabitants, and the economic development, of the earth is the most interesting and important aspect of applied climatology. It is outside the scope of this book to treat of applied climatology, but the attempt is made to provide an outline of the climatology required for the more extensive study.

Climate and Weather

'Climate' is a composite idea, a generalization of the manifold weather conditions from day to day throughout the year. Some small regions, most of them near the equator, have such constant weather that 'weather' and 'climate' are almost synonymous; any one day is a fair sample of the season. With increasing distance from the equator the variation becomes greater, at any rate from season to season, for astronomical as well as meteorological causes; and between the tropics and the poles the weather is so changeable—especially in the westerlies—that it is difficult to form a conception of the climate save as a complex of irregular changes. Certainly no picture of it is at all real unless it is painted in all the colours of the manifold variations of weather and the rounds of the seasons which are the really prominent features; it is quite inadequate to give merely the mean state of any element. The variations are much more frequent than the mean values themselves and they deserve description. To do full justice to this requirement demands a long treatment, so long perhaps as to be incapable of being grasped and used. The best course lies midway between unreal generalization through means, and excessive detail; in much of the world meteorological records are too few to tempt to over-detailed description.

In the study of climatology the primary interest lies in the facts of the climates of the earth in themselves, and as elements in the natural environment of life. The investigation of the physical causes underlying the facts is a valuable as well as an interesting side of the study, but it is to be regarded as subordinate. Climatology thus differs from meteorology, a physical science primarily concerned with the physical processes which go on in the atmosphere, from the surface of the earth up to the highest strata concerned in weather.

NOTE

THE units generally used in this book are those likely to be most familiar to readers—inches for rainfall, the Fahrenheit scale for temperature (but millibars for atmospheric pressure). Conversion tables, inches to millimetres, Fahrenheit to Centigrade, and millibars to inches of mercury, are given on pp. 377 to 379.

For convenience the division of the year usual in the temperate zone into winter (December, January, February, in the northern hemisphere), spring (March, April, May), summer (June, July, August), autumn (September, October, November) is sometimes extended to low latitudes.

The 24-hour reckoning of time is used in view of its convenience, e.g. 8.0 a.m. is indicated by 0800, 4.35 p.m. by 1635.

PART I
INSOLATION AND TEMPERATURE
CHAPTER I
THE DISTRIBUTION OF INSOLATION

TEMPERATURE is a fundamental element of climate, from many points of view the most important, in controlling the distribution of life on the earth, and in any treatment of the subject it must come first since most of the other elements are dependent on it directly or indirectly.

The analysis of temperature is somewhat complicated. The source of our heat is the sun (the internal heat of the earth is ignored as being uniform everywhere, except for the occasional and very local heating by volcanic eruptions). First the distribution of the insolation on the earth must be determined, then the effect on it of its passage through the atmosphere, and thirdly, a very important factor, the nature of the surface on which it falls, for the temperature of the air depends mainly on that of the surface on which it rests. If the atmosphere were still, we should then be well forward in our inquiry. But a new train of effects is started by the temperature differences themselves, in that they give rise to the winds which bring with them the temperature of their place of origin, possibly distant, modified by the surface traversed.

Source of Insolation

The sun emits into space a complex of energy, 'insolation', composed of radiations of a wide band of wave-lengths (see p. 24). The sun's diameter is about 864,000 miles, and its volume a million times that of the earth. So hot is it that the imagination is unable to form any conception of the conditions. The temperature of the surface is estimated at about 10,000° F., of the centre at 50,000,000° F. The whole mass consists of gases, and the intense activity of the blazing ball is strikingly visible in the prominences which are seen projecting through its corona during a total solar eclipse.

These gigantic tongues of brilliance have sometimes been observed to attain a height of half a million miles, and they dart forth at a speed of some 250 miles a second. From the surface, in comparison with which our hottest furnaces are cold, radiant energy is poured into space in all directions. The earth revolves at a distance of 93 million miles in the field of insolation, and intercepts a minute fraction (about 1/2,000,000,000) of it, but minute as it is all the life on the planet depends on it.

The solar energy that reaches the outer surface of the atmosphere, the 'solar constant', has been determined at about 1·94 g./cal. a minute on a square cm. normal to the rays, or 135 milliwatts; but the solar constant belies its name in being subject to appreciable variations. The important point for most of the present study will be not the absolute energy received, but its distribution over the earth, or rather, as a first element in the analysis, over the outer surface of the atmosphere.

The Intensity of Insolation at the Surface of the Atmosphere

This is a matter of mathematical calculation, the variables being the angle of incidence of the rays and the length of the day, or in other words the latitude and, a result of the tilt of the earth at $66\frac{1}{2}°$ to the plane of its orbit, the season; an additional seasonal effect is produced by the fact that the orbit is not a true circle, the earth approaching nearest to the sun (91,500,000 miles) on 20 December and being most distant (94,500,000 miles) on 21 June.

The following table gives the amounts of insolation received in 24 hours at the equinoxes and the solstices in kilowatt-hours per sq. dekametre, the solar constant being 135 kilowatts per sq. dekametre:

	Equator	20°	40°	60°	90° N.	90° S.
Mar. 22	1,038	980	805	532	30	0
June 21	915	1,085	1,150	1,135	1,249	0
Sept. 20	1,023	972	805	541	20	0
Dec. 20	977	702	371	58	0	1,331

The facts are shown graphically in Fig. 1. The seasonal change is least on the equator, where the noon sun swings from $23\frac{1}{2}°$ north of the zenith in June to $23\frac{1}{2}°$ south in December and is overhead at the equinoxes, and the day is 12 hours long throughout the year. The amount is greatest at the equinoxes, at a maximum at the spring equinox, when the distance from the sun is less than at the autumn equinox.

Everywhere between lats. $23\frac{1}{2}°$ N. and $23\frac{1}{2}°$ S. the sun is overhead on either one or two days each year. And the greater the distance from the equator the longer are the

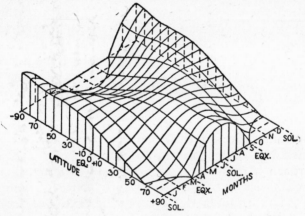

FIG. 1. Distribution of insolation on the earth (W. M. Davis)

summer days, so that the tropic receives more insolation on midsummer day than the equator in March when the sun is overhead there.

The summer day continues to lengthen as far as the polar circles. But, on the other hand, the angle of incidence of the rays decreases—on the polar circles the midsummer sun is 47° above the horizon at midday, and just skirts the horizon at midnight (but refraction increases the apparent altitude slightly). Between the polar circles and the poles the midsummer sun is above the horizon all the 24 hours, its noon elevation decreasing till at the poles it is only $23\frac{1}{2}°$. But what the sun loses in noon altitude it gains during the 'night' hours, the elevation remaining the same throughout the 24 hours at the pole. The net result is that on their midsummer days the poles receive more insolation than any other latitude in any 24 hours. The south pole is the more favoured since the earth is nearer the sun on 21 December than on 21 June.

To recapitulate by considering the insolation on 21 June, starting from the south pole, as far as the Antarctic circle the sun does not appear above the horizon. From there the length of the day and the elevation of the sun both increase to latitude $23\frac{1}{2}°$ north, and the insolation increases rapidly. Beyond $23\frac{1}{2}°$ north the sun's altitude decreases but the day continues to increase, the result being that a maximum of insolation is received about $44°$ north. North of that the diminishing altitude of the sun more than neutralizes the increasing length of the day nearly as far as the Arctic circle. Thence to the pole the day lasts for the whole 24 hours; the nearer the pole the greater is the altitude of the sun during the 'night', though not during the day. The pole itself has the maximum insolation for the whole globe.

The values given in this chapter are certainly interesting and striking. The polar figures are specially noticeable; the frozen Arctic and snow-covered Antarctica, where no month has a mean temperature above 32° and the highest temperatures do not rise much above freezing-point, receive considerably more insolation at midsummer than even the hottest lands inside the tropics, such as the Sahara where the sand is too hot to touch. Evidently the influences to which the insolation is submitted before it reaches the surface of the earth must be of great magnitude, and greater importance for climate than the mathematical factors which have been considered.

CHAPTER II

THE PASSAGE OF THE INSOLATION THROUGH THE ATMOSPHERE

OF the solar energy reaching the atmosphere over 40 per cent. is reflected, mostly from the clouds, back into space, and is lost to the earth, part is scattered by the molecules in the air and by minute solid and liquid particles, part is absorbed in the passage of the atmosphere, and part reaches the surface of the earth and is absorbed by it; this last is by far the most effective in controlling the temperature of the troposphere, and we may regard the part that is directly absorbed by the atmosphere rather as a loss from the available store. The important factor is the intensity of the insolation that actually reaches the surface of the earth.

The absorption of insolation by the atmosphere depends

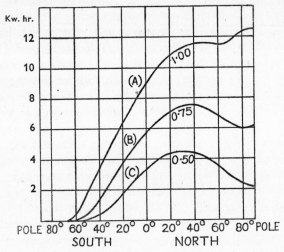

FIG. 2. Solar energy (kilowatt-hours) received by direct radiation in 24 hours on 21 June on 1 square metre of horizontal surface of the earth at sea-level: A, with a transparent atmosphere; B and C, with coefficients of transparency 0·75 and 0·50

on two factors, (1) the length of the passage, or, in other words, the angle of incidence of the rays, and (2) the transparency of the atmosphere to the various wave-lengths, which are intercepted and absorbed selectively by gases at the highest levels in which they are present in sufficient abundance (see p. 24 for a fuller treatment). (1) is capable of mathematical calculation and its importance is shown by the fact that for a given coefficient of absorption the energy decreases in geometrical progression when the mass of the atmosphere traversed increases in arithmetical progression. The long oblique path in the polar regions is one obvious cause of the discrepancy between the high insolation value and the low air temperature. The second factor is very variable according to time and place; the coefficient of absorption, and the proportion of the whole that will reach the surface, cannot be calculated without a detailed knowledge of the condition at the moment of the air through which the insolation has to pass, and this is not attainable.

Fig. 2 shows the influence of the increasing obliquity of the rays and the longer path through the atmosphere poleward of the tropic. The actual transparency is always changing; only very exceptionally as much as three-quarters of the insolation reaches the surface—77 per cent. has been recorded at Nice, 88 per cent. on Popocatepetl (17,500 feet); the mean is a little below 60 per cent. The total receipt consists of three components, (1) the direct radiation from the sun, (2) the scattered radiation from the sky, and (3) the 'return' radiation from the vapour in the very low atmosphere (mostly below 500 feet) which has absorbed the long-wave energy radiated from the surface (see p. 23). The second component, the sky-radiation, is relatively large when the sun is low, in winter in high latitudes; Ångstrom calculates that in latitude 60° N. it exceeds the direct radiation throughout the 5 winter months, October to February; the proportion is greatest for the shortest, ultra-violet, rays, and in middle latitudes the ultra-violet radiation from the sky exceeds that in the direct sunshine even at midday in summer, and is in enormous excess with a low sun (when, however, the total receipt is necessarily very small); this scattered sky-radiation consists mainly of the shortest wave-lengths, since, according to Rayleigh's law, the amount of light scattered in an atmosphere without solid or liquid particles is in inverse proportion to the fourth power of the wave-length; this explains the prevailing blue colour of the sky. The blue is deepest as seen from high altitudes; the solid and liquid suspensoids, most numerous in the lower levels, reflect light which dilutes the blue, the white component tending to increase in the afternoon when turbulence is at a maximum.

The last component, the return radiation from the lower atmosphere, forms a large part of the whole, especially in winter when it far exceeds the direct insolation everywhere outside the tropics, to become the only source of radiant heat inside the polar circles.

It is calculated that the percentages of the three sources for the earth as a whole in the year are: direct insolation, 19, scattered sky-radiation, 15, return radiation from the lower atmosphere, 66.

The long waves, 'infra-red', which are radiated from the surface heated by the incoming insolation and are most effective in heating the atmosphere, are absorbed (with some exceptions) chiefly by the water vapour and the solid and liquid particles in the lowest layers where they are most abundant. The water droplets are visible as cloud and no instruments are needed to show that clouds intercept the sun's heat. Even the finest film of cirrus which is hardly visible is an effective obstacle, and often the sky is overcast with masses of cloud miles deep. The passage of every cloud, especially on a bright summer day, depresses the temperature appreciably.

Water vapour also is a serious obstacle. At Montpellier, south France, 71 per cent. of the insolation penetrates to the surface in December, only 48 per cent. in the summer; for the less vapour in the air in winter more than compensates for the longer path of the insolation through the atmosphere.

Dust particles are most numerous in the low stratosphere, being blown up from the dry surface, particularly in arid lands, or thrown into the air by volcanoes. Salt from dried sea-spray is another large element, and a cause of widespread haze. A shower of rain removes most of the dust in its passage, but the finer particles float above the level of cloud and rain, as has been noted after great volcanic eruptions. The terrific eruption of Krakatoa in the Strait of Sunda in 1883 threw dust high into the stratosphere—so thick that it was dark at midday for hundreds of miles round about; and the finer particles were carried by the winds of the upper atmosphere right round the globe, and manifested themselves in brilliant sunset colours for three years after the eruption. These particles were high above the clouds, and therefore were not washed down by rain. Such dust from great volcanic eruptions may impede the solar radiation so seriously that the temperature of the air is appreciably reduced for some years, and this is perhaps a considerable factor in the production of unusually cold or wet seasons. The dust from the eruption of Mount Katmai (Alaska) on 6 and 7 June 1912 seems to have formed a haze all round the globe; observations indicate that the insolation in 1912 was 10 per cent. less than in the previous year, and the summer was abnormally cold in Europe. Some investigators incline to attribute glacial epochs in part to this cause working on a large scale.

Another important source of solid impurities is smoke, especially over great cities, and extensive tracts of grass-land such as the Sudan when the dead grass is fired in the dry season. The smoke may hang at low levels in the atmosphere, and collect till the sun is hidden. But without attaining such density it almost always covers large cities in sufficient volume to be of serious significance from the aesthetic and medical standpoints, and smoke trails may be carried for a hundred miles or more by the wind (see p. 280, Atmospheric Pollution).

The atmosphere as a whole is clearest over the tropical deserts, where clouds are few and thin and rain very rare. On the other hand, a consequence of the aridity is dust, and the strong winds sometimes sweep it up in dust-storms, but most of it is in the lowest layers of the atmosphere. These deserts are the hottest tracts on the globe in summer, the overhead sun pouring down its rays through the clear dry air throughout the long day. On the ocean the air contains no dust, save what is carried by the wind from the land, but more moisture, and much light cumulus cloud floats even in the blue skies of the trades.

The equatorial atmosphere has much vapour and abundant cloud, especially in the hottest hours of the day, and consequently the insolation does not reach the surface of the earth with the intensity found under the trade winds.

Poleward of the trade-winds the surface air is almost saturated with vapour, since it blows over comparatively warm seas, and frequent cyclonic disturbances produce abundant cloud. Insolation is much weakened, and in winter the air temperature is more strongly controlled by other influences than by the direct rays of the sun. In the far interiors of the continents the air is drier.

Inside the Arctic circle is an expanse of water partly open but mostly frozen. The air is vapour-laden and misty, and the sky cloudy. These facts, together with the long path of the rays through the atmosphere, explain the discrepancy between the high value of the insolation which reaches the polar atmosphere at the summer solstice and the low temperature of the air at the surface of the earth. Antarctica has less cloudy skies, and the plateau, 7,000–15,000 feet above the sea, is above the denser and more humid strata, so that the insolation is more intense than at lower levels.

The importance of altitude in this connexion is shown by the fact that on the average half of the vapour, and very much more than half of the solid particles, are contained in the lowest 7,000 feet; one-half of the whole mass of the atmosphere is below 17,500 feet, and above the tropopause (about 10 km. in middle latitudes) there are no clouds of the ordinary types. Hence the greater the altitude the more intense is the insolation.

The insolation that succeeds in passing the barriers in the atmosphere reaches the surface. About 40 per cent. of the incoming energy is reflected from atmosphere, clouds, and surface of the earth, and lost; the remainder is absorbed and heats the surface, which then radiates 'heat', long waves of 2 to 50 μ (see p. 24), which are absorbed strongly by the vapour in the lower atmosphere. The lower air, heated by this absorption and by conduction from the surface, rises, and is replaced by the cooler air above, so that the heat is spread through some depth. The long-wave radiation absorbed by the water vapour, mostly in the first few hundred feet, heats it, and the vapour itself then radiates at long-wave lengths. Part of this radiation is directed outwards from the earth, but much returns downward, and forms a large part of the heat absorbed by the surface, its 24-hour contribution exceeding the direct insolation over most of the winter hemisphere in midwinter, and being not much less than it even in the summer hemisphere at midsummer.

The Selective Absorption by the Atmosphere of Insolation according to Wave-length

For the understanding of the heating of the atmosphere the history of the insolation in its inward passage from space, and of the energy radiated outwards from the earth that is heated by the incoming radiation, must be examined. It was mentioned above (p. 15) that insolation, being emitted by an intensely hot body, is a complex of radiations of a wide band of wave-lengths; these are absorbed in the atmosphere selectively at different levels according to the gases present, or transmitted downwards. The complex may conveniently be divided into three groups of wave-lengths (usually expressed not in inches or mm., which are too long as units for these minute lengths, but in microns, a micron, μ, being 0·001 mm.):

(a) Short-wave (less than 0·4 μ) includes the ultra-violet rays, invisible but of strong actinic power, effecting chemical change in many substances; they form about 6 per cent. of the energy of the whole incoming insolation. They are largely absorbed by oxygen and ozone high in the stratosphere, oxygen absorbing all the shortest waves, less than 0·26 μ, at and above 50 km., and ozone most of the rest between 50 and 25 km.; this absorption is a main source of the remarkable heat in those levels.

(b) Medium-wave (0·4–0·8 μ); these are the 'light' waves which the eye perceives and differentiates into colours, from violet, the shortest, to red, the longest, the whole group in combination giving white; they form 52 per cent. of the insolation. They are in part reflected from solids and liquids (the water droplets of clouds) but otherwise reach the earth, being only slightly subject to absorption.

(c) Long wave (>0·8 μ), infra-red rays, invisible but perceptible as heat, include almost the whole of the radiation from bodies at a temperature below red heat; they form 43 per cent. of the energy of the incoming insolation, and most of the outgoing radiation from the heated surface. They are absorbed strongly, with the exception of those of about 10 and 15 μ, by water vapour, which is most abundant in the lowest atmosphere (half is normally below 7,000 feet), so that a large proportion of the earth's radiation is absorbed in the first 1,000 feet. The waves not absorbed there continue their passage outwards, to be absorbed in the stratosphere, those about 10 μ by the ozone, and those about 15 μ by the carbon dioxide, adding to the heat of those high levels.

The atmosphere as a whole is heated only very slightly by direct absorption, the chief absorbing gases being ozone, present in all levels in minute quantity but mostly in the stratosphere at 25 to 30 km. (in middle latitudes), and oxygen; most of the shortest waves are absorbed by them, becoming 'heat'. Water vapour is present in large amount, but almost entirely in the lowest levels; it is transparent to the short and medium bands, but is strongly absorptive of the long waves. Carbon dioxide exists in very small, but probably fairly constant, relative proportion up to great heights; it absorbs wave-lengths round 15 μ. Of the major constituents of the air, nitrogen is almost transparent to most wave-lengths, and oxygen to all but the very shortest.

Suspended in the atmosphere are water droplets and particles of dust and ice, but most are in the lower and middle troposphere. They are more or less opaque to all waves, and their main effect is to intercept and reflect the insolation; the upper surface of a cloud is dazzlingly white in the sunshine, and the under surface correspondingly dark.

When the absorbing gases are heated, they themselves emit long-wave radiation.

CHAPTER III

THE HEATING AND COOLING OF THE SURFACE
OF THE EARTH

YET another stage intervenes between insolation and air temperature. The lower atmosphere is heated hardly at all by the direct passage of the sun's rays, but mainly by conduction from the surface of the earth on which it rests, and by the radiation of heat from that surface. But conduction is again only a first step, for heated air rises and is replaced by cooler and, except on absolutely flat land, air cooled by conduction gravitates down the slopes. These and other movements are the next stage whereby the temperature of the solid surface is communicated to a large volume of air; without them a shallow layer would acquire excessive heat on a sunny day, and excessive cold on a clear night. Direct cooling, however, by conduction in still air during a night of active radiation may be appreciable in middle and high latitudes through a depth of 150 feet, though very slight above a few feet from the cold surface.

The surface of the earth, solid and liquid, is heated by the direct and the scattered insolation during the day; it loses heat by radiation both in the day and in the night, most rapidly in the day when it is warmest (the total radiation from a perfect radiator is proportional to the fourth power of its absolute temperature), but more noticeably at night in the absence of incoming insolation to compensate (or, in other words, though the absolute loss is greater by day, the net loss is smaller). For the present our main interest is the heating and cooling of the air *in situ* by the surface on which it is resting; 'advected' heat and cold, brought from outside in an air-mass, is treated in Chapter VII. Radiation depends on the nature of the radiating surface, though the total gain or loss of heat in a given time is also a function of the specific heat and of the conductivity of the medium below the surface.

The main types of surface, land, water, and snow or ice, are all very good radiators, but differ greatly in other qualities which affect their heating and cooling; the main differences between land and water may be summarized as follows:

1. Volume for volume water has a specific heat about 2·5 times that of average land, or, in other words, land heats more than twice as much as water under a given amount of insolation and cools more than twice as fast when the source of heat is removed.

2. Evaporation, with consequent cooling of the evaporating surface, is going on from the surface of the sea day and night, unless the air is saturated. But it is equally vigorous during the hot hours from wet ground, and in hot countries often more vigorous owing to the higher temperature; soon after sundown it ceases. Perhaps a liberal estimate might put the total evaporation from the sea at about twice that from land in the same region, with a similar difference in the cooling effect.

3. The depth to which the incident heat penetrates is a very large factor; the greater the depth the more the heat is 'diluted'. It depends partly on the transparency; short-wave insolation can penetrate water to some extent to a depth of the order of 25 feet, nearly all the absorption occurring in the topmost layers; strong light is perceptible down to over 500 feet. Land is opaque and the surface, if light-coloured, reflects a considerable proportion of the insolation back into the atmosphere.

4. A much larger factor is the mobility. Land does not admit of the transference of heat except by the very slow process of conduction, so slow that the diurnal range of temperature becomes inappreciable at a depth of a few inches. But water is mobile both horizontally and vertically; waves set up turbulence, which extends down to about 30 feet, to take an average figure for the oceans, and the insolation is spread through that depth. Differences of density also play a large part; at night the surface water cools and sinks, to be replaced by warmer water from below. The effect is seen on an impressive scale in the oceans in the Horse Latitudes and under the trades; evaporation is active in the dry air, and the surface water becomes more saline and sinks, carrying its heat down with it to the depths. In the sub-tropical North Atlantic the water even at 500 fathoms is about 10° warmer than the normal (Fig. 3); a smaller excess is found in corresponding regions in other oceans. Owing to the high salinity of the Mediterranean a strong undercurrent sets into the Atlantic over the sill of the Strait of Gibraltar; the high temperature and salinity of this water is very perceptible in the ocean outside from 500 down to 1,000 fathoms, and it can be traced through the South

Atlantic even to the Cape of Good Hope. A similar under-current removes the heated water from the Red Sea into the Indian Ocean, where it spreads at great depths.

Ocean currents help to mix the water, and they transport it horizontally for enormous distances. The range of temperature, and the depth to which a perceptible range penetrates, vary greatly with latitude and with the seasonal

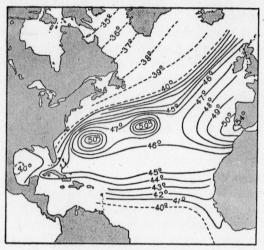

FIG. 3. Temperature of the sea at 500 fathoms

changes in currents and winds, which mask the direct effect of the changing local insolation. The annual range on the surface is least, 2°–4°, at the equator, increases to a maximum in the sub-tropics, and decreases thence polewards; in the northern oceans the largest range is about 16°, in the southern only 9°. Some range is perceptible to a depth of 60 fathoms or more in middle latitudes where the local thermal changes are not complicated by extraneous influences. On the other hand, the diurnal range on the surface is extremely small, the mean being about 0·5° in equatorial seas and in the Atlantic off the British Isles.

The mobility of water is by far the largest of the factors that combine to give the low range in the surface layer.

Land surfaces are of many varieties, and have very

III   HEATING OF EARTH'S SURFACE   29

different thermal reactions. Loose, dry, dark-coloured sand is one extreme; the air enclosed among the dry particles helps greatly to improve the insulation, so that the surface attains both very high and very low temperatures. From the many observations which show the intense heating of the bare surface under the high sun in the long summer days near the tropics of Cancer and Capricorn the following may be quoted: surface sand of a dune in the Sahara, 172°; sand on the Loango coast, lat. 5° S. 183°; even at Tucson, in the desert of Arizona, the sand probably attains a temperature of 180° at times in summer, in spite of the altitude of 2,390 feet; 151° has been recorded on dry fallow land at Giza, Egypt, lat. 30° N., and 133° on limestone in the same region. The high temperatures by day are paralleled by very low minima at night, often below freezing-point in winter in the middle and north of the Sahara, and very much below in higher latitudes, especially in the deserts of the far interior.

Compact clay or rock conducts better than sand, communicating the surface heat more rapidly to the layers below. Wet land shares the characteristics of water in a modified degree, and the percolating water carries the heat or cold down with it and spreads it. A grass-covered surface gives higher temperatures in the air resting on it by day, and lower at night, than bare ground, the longer the grass the more extreme being the readings; the main reason seems to be that the air is trapped among the stems (the large surface and low conductivity of which make them efficient sources of heat or cold), and is subjected to heating or cooling longer than on bare ground where it is always in motion. The roots of the grasses form a thick mat which, if dry, is a good insulator, and this favours extreme temperatures in the grass above; ground under trees and other vegetation susceptible to frost should be kept clear of grass. But the air 3 or 4 feet above the surface is not necessarily warmer by day over grass than over bare soil.

Leaf surface temperatures are difficult to take, and few examples are available; two readings on the Highlands of Kenya, altitude 5,500 feet, in December were 90° and 104°, the surface of adjacent patches of bare soil at the same time being at 97° and well over 140° (the limit of the graduations

of the thermometer used) respectively; these readings indicate, at any rate, the much lower temperatures of the foliage
of trees than of bare ground.

Dry powdery snow is a notably good reflector, reflecting
more than three-quarters of the incident light waves; wise
travellers over snow-fields are careful to protect their eyes
from snow-blindness by dark glasses. Snow is a poor con-
ductor of heat, and added insulation is given by the enclosed
air, a result being intense surface cooling at night in winter
and a large range of temperature. The conductivity of loose
powdery snow is estimated at about a fiftieth of that of solid
rock.

A snow surface cannot warm above 32° even under the
hottest sun, and much energy is required to convert snow
at 32° to water at the same temperature. After a spell of
frost ponds retain their ice long after the air temperature has
risen above the freezing-point. The thaw is a long process
unless the air temperature rises rapidly. In countries with
deep snow in winter the spring is much delayed; weeks of
slush and flood and cold air come to an end in a few days
when the snow is gone, for then the land is rapidly heated
by the sun, the air temperature rises fast, and spring comes
on apace. In the polar regions the ice is so thick that it never
melts completely; the sun's heat is used up in melting it
throughout the summer, and the surface remains at 32°—
a main reason for the discrepancy already noted between the
very liberal summer insolation at the poles and the inhospitable air temperature. As ice is slow to melt, so water
is slow to freeze. At night the air temperature may fall
considerably below freezing-point, and yet ponds have little
if any ice in the morning. Even when the water has cooled
to 32°, itself a slow process, there is a long interval before it
becomes ice, since in freezing much heat is liberated, and
this counteracts the general fall in temperature. The properties mentioned above explain in part the fact that spring
is cooler than autumn in many regions in the higher latitudes.

To sum up: a water surface is conservative, heating and

cooling slowly, so that its range of temperature, diurnal and annual, is small; the maximum temperature of the day occurs about 3 hours after noon; the warmest period is about 2 months after the summer solstice. Land heats and cools much more rapidly, has extreme temperatures, and large range; the daily maximum is reached within 2 hours after noon, and the warmest and coldest months are the next after the solstices; but different types of surface have different thermal reactions. Snow can never heat above freezing-point, and melting is a slow process, requiring much heat; cooling is intense on clear nights; thus maxima are low and minima very low, and the range of temperature large.

Till now we have considered the control of the surface temperatures by the nature of the surface. But evidently another, and almost equally important, control is the transparency of the atmosphere to radiation. Incoming short-wave insolation is largely reflected back to space by clouds. The outgoing long-wave radiation from the surface is effectively checked by dust, water-vapour, and clouds, which are always present; hence the nights are warmest when they are present in largest amount, and especially when the sky is overcast with low cloud, coldest when the sky is clear. High mountains rise above the levels that contain most of these obstructions, and on them we may be scorched by the powerful sunshine in the day and frozen by the sudden chilling after sundown.

In some orchard countries subject to damage by spring frosts advantage is taken of the blanketing effect of solid particles artificially produced; a smoke screen is generated by oil lamps on calm nights when frost is expected, and radiation is checked. The artificial heat helps by setting up convection which mixes the cold surface air with the warmer air above. The success of such methods depends on the topography, the intensity of the cold, and the general atmospheric conditions.

Dew (or hoar-frost in winter) is a good indicator of the intensity of the nocturnal radiation, for the amount of the deposit depends, other factors being constant, on the surface cooling. It is most copious in clear, cloudless, calm nights;

cloud hinders its formation by checking the loss of heat, and wind by mixing the layers of air.

The atmosphere may be likened, in respect of radiation, to a valve, not a very efficient one, which allows the downward passage of the incident insolation to the surface, but obstructs the outward passage of the dark rays from the heated surface.

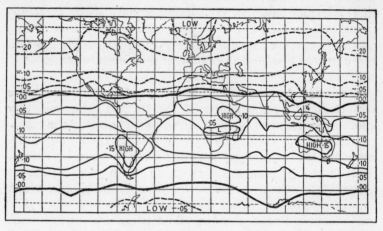

Fig. 4. Intensity of net radiation ($S-R$) in January; S = intensity of effective solar radiation, R = intensity of outgoing terrestrial radiation. Negative values are shown by broken lines (Simpson)

The Heat-balance of the Earth

The temperature of the earth as a whole remains almost constant from year to year, so that evidently the incoming insolation is balanced by the outgoing radiation. We have noticed the continuous loss of heat by radiation of long-wave energy from the surface by day and by night, a large proportion of it being intercepted by solid and liquid particles and vapour in the atmosphere. Return long-wave radiation from these to the earth largely restores the original loss. The intensity of this indirect source is greater than might have been expected, the average for the zone between 60° N. and 60° S. being about 700 g./cal. a day. Its value relatively to the direct insolation increases as the sun's altitude decreases, till within the polar circles in winter it is the only effective source of heat from the sky.

The mean annual temperature of the surface of the whole earth is about 58°, this being the temperature at which the loss is just equal to the gain from the insolation, a heat

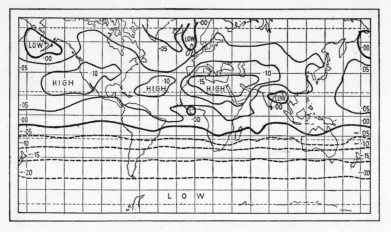

FIG. 5. Intensity of net radiation (*S–R*) in July (Simpson)

balance being maintained. The two sides of the account, incoming and outgoing, are very different in different latitudes. Figs. 4 and 5 show the results of calculations by Sir G. C. Simpson of the balance in January and July; the lines marked ·00 separate those regions in which incoming insolation is in excess from those in which loss by radiation from the earth preponderates. It will be noticed that incoming insolation is in excess in temperate latitudes of the summer hemisphere as well as in the tropics.

CHAPTER IV

THE MEASUREMENT OF AIR TEMPERATURE. ISOTHERMS

IN order that the records may be comparable thermometers must be of standard pattern, and exposed under standard conditions; otherwise discrepancies are introduced which

are merely adventitious and without general climatic significance. In most countries the thermometers are enclosed in
a 'Stevenson Screen', a well-ventilated wooden box with a
double top, and double-louvred sides, the whole painted
white. The air can circulate freely, but the direct radiation
from outside cannot penetrate. The bulbs of the thermometers are 4 feet above the ground, and the screen is in a
fully open position, away from trees and buildings; the
ground should be turf-covered. Unfortunately this standard
screen is not used universally even in Europe. In parts of the
tropics other forms have been used, one consisting of a roof
shelter, usually of thatch, under which the instruments are
hung, freely exposed to the air but well protected from the
rays of the sun; but the Stevenson screen is replacing the
thatched shelter. In hot deserts so intense is the sunshine
that extra ventilation should be provided in the screen to
prevent excessive heating.

The screen should contain four thermometers. Two are
standard mercury thermometers of identical pattern, one of
which has its bulb covered with thin muslin kept wet by a
wick from a small vessel of water; the dry-bulb instrument
gives the air temperature, and the difference between the
readings of the dry-bulb and the wet-bulb enables the
humidity of the air to be determined by means of tables.
The other two thermometers are self-recording, maximum
and minimum. All readings must be corrected for any
instrumental error.

First-order meteorological stations in Great Britain maintain hourly readings of temperature and other elements;
their readings and those of 'telegraphic reporting stations',
taken at 0000, 0600, 1200, and 1800, are used in the preparation of the daily Weather Report. At least two readings
a day are desirable at all stations; 0900 and 2100 are the
hours adopted for 'Normal Climatological Stations' in the
British Isles. The maximum and minimum thermometers
are read and set every day. Not only are the highest and
lowest temperatures important in themselves, but they also
enable the mean temperature of the day to be readily
obtained, for the mean of the maximum and minimum gives
a good approximation to it.

If possible the screen should contain a thermograph, or self-registering thermometer, which, by means of a pen resting on a chart, gives a continuous record of the temperature (e.g. Fig. 15, p. 58). The ordinary forms of the instrument are less accurate than mercury thermometers, but they can give valuable information about temperature changes which would escape notice if only two or three eye-readings of the mercury thermometers each day were available, and for many purposes it is more interesting to know when the temperature changed, and by how much, than to have the exact readings at stated hours.

A grass minimum is a useful addition to the equipment. It is a minimum thermometer without back or frame, and is set on the ground with its bulb just clear of the grass in a fully exposed position. Its records, including the number of days of ground frost, are valuable for agricultural studies.

In climatic descriptions quantitative statements of the elements are essential. Mean values must be stated, and, since weather is very variable, a long series of records is necessary to establish them, 35 years being generally considered desirable for middle and high latitudes; the arithmetical mean of the 35 yearly values is the annual mean for the period. Similarly monthly and seasonal means are obtained. Means for shorter periods, weeks for example, are not usually given, by reason of the practical difficulties of such numerous statistics, but it must be remembered that many significant weather periods are shorter than a month, or fail to coincide with calendar months, and may be lost to view in a monthly grouping of data.

Account must be taken of extremes as well as of means, including at any rate the mean highest and lowest daily temperatures in each month (the 'mean daily maximum' and 'mean daily minimum' temperatures) and the mean highest and lowest temperatures in the whole month (the 'mean monthly maximum' and 'mean monthly minimum'). The former are the means of the maxima and minima respectively for each day in the month for the period of observations, the latter the means of the one highest and one lowest readings in the month for the period. But the actual readings may depart considerably from the means. A more useful statement is the percentage frequencies of readings within stated intervals at stated hours, or of maxima, minima, or daily means within stated intervals, but the computation is laborious, and the tables too voluminous for convenience. An example quoted by Conrad is:

MEAN PERCENTAGE FREQUENCIES OF TEMPERATURES (°F.)
AT VIENNA AT 1400 IN SUMMER

under 50·0	< 1	between 68·0 and 76·9	46
between 50·0 and 58·9	6	„ 77·0 „ 85·9	14
„ 59·0 „ 67·9	34	„ 86·0 „ 94·9	< 1

The average deviation of the individual items from the mean may be given, expressed statistically, usually as the standard deviation, at the cost of a considerable lengthening of the tables.

The highest and lowest readings ever recorded in each month should be included. They are the 'absolute maximum' and the 'absolute minimum', and are useful provided that the period is long enough; the longer the period the higher the maximum and the lower the minimum will tend to be; 10 years is too short to give comparable extremes.

The range of temperature is the difference between the highest and lowest readings in the period, the mean range the difference between the mean maximum and the mean minimum. Thus the mean daily range for a month is the difference between the mean daily maximum and the mean daily minimum. The mean annual range is the difference between the means of the warmest and the coldest months. Similarly the extreme ranges may be obtained; the absolute (extreme) annual range at Kew is 85°, being the difference between the absolute maximum 94° and the absolute minimum 9°.

The table on p. 37 gives long-period data for Oxford. But thirty-five years' observations are not available for all stations. Shorter records are of less value in proportion to their length and the variability of the climate, but 20 years' records may have to be accepted. Means for even 5 years suffice for temperature near the equator, but are liable to considerable error in the variable temperate latitudes. It is possible to obtain a close approximation to the true means for a station with, say, only 10 years' records, by comparing them with those of another station which has records for 35 years including the 10 years of the first station, if the second station is in the same meteorological region and not far distant from the first. From the records for the 10 years common to the two series the differences are established for

RADCLIFFE OBSERVATORY, OXFORD, Altitude 212 feet
1881–1945
TEMPERATURE

	Jan.	Feb.	Mar.	Apr.	May	June	July	Aug.	Sept.	Oct.	Nov.	Dec.	Year
Mean . .	39	39	42	46	53	58	61	61	56	49	43	40	49
Mean daily max. .	44	45	50	53	62	67	71	70	65	57	49	45	57
„ min. .	34	34	35	39	44	50	53	53	49	43	38	35	42
„ range .	10	11	15	14	18	17	18	17	16	14	11	10	15
Mean monthly max.	53	55	61	67	76	80	82	81	76	66	58	55	..
„ min. .	22	23	25	29	33	41	45	44	37	31	26	23	..
Abs. max.(1881–1948)	58	64	72	81	87	90	93	95	92	81	66	58	95
„ min. („)	6	3	12	23	29	34	41	38	31	23	16	8	3
„ range („)	52	61	60	58	58	56	52	57	61	58	50	50	92

the year and the several months, and on the assumption that the differences for the whole 35 years are the same as for the 10 years, the full-period means can be obtained for the first station. This procedure is justified by the examination of many simultaneous long-period records; but if the two stations are in different meteorological regions it fails, for no necessary parallelism links the records.

Isotherms, Uses and Limitations. Kind of Heat

Comparison with other places is implied, even if not expressed, in most climatic descriptions, and comparisons of temperature are most easily shown by means of isotherms, lines drawn on a map through places with the same temperature (usually after correction for altitude) for any period,

the whole year, a season, or a month. The position and run
of the isotherms are determined by wide influences, latitude,
prevailing winds, distribution of land and sea, but local
conditions, chiefly topographical, impose modifications.
Among mountains even neighbouring valleys have differences, which are not constant but vary with the hour, the

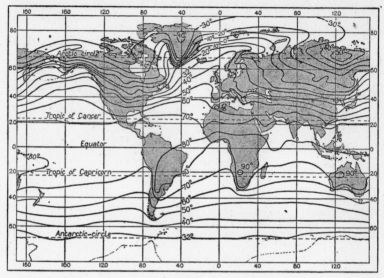

FIG. 6. Mean isotherms (reduced to sea-level), January

season, and type of weather, according to the slope and
exposure of the ground and the topographical obstacles to
the movements of the air. Again, the neighbourhood of a hot
desert may be liable to hot dusty winds; and continental
interiors may pour floods of cold air in winter over regions
which usually enjoy warmth.

Isotherms show the temperature at any given time, or for
any given period, a day, a week, a month, or the mean
temperature for any period; mean monthly and mean annual
isotherms are most used. They may indicate the actual
temperatures as observed, or temperatures 'reduced to sea-
level'. The effects of altitude are explained in Chapter XXX;
on the average the mean is about 1° lower for 300 feet of
altitude; this control is stronger than any other, and unless

it is eliminated the isotherms follow the contour lines closely. For many purposes it is convenient to eliminate it by adding to the observed reading. 1° F. for each 300 feet; isotherms based on the corrected figures show the effect of the factors which are masked by altitude, and such isotherms are valuable especially in theoretical investigations; Figs. 6 and

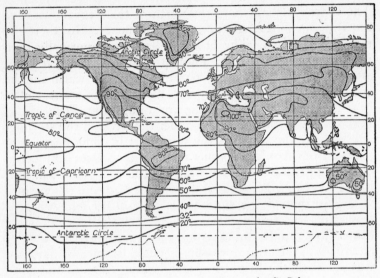

FIG. 7. Mean isotherms (reduced to sea-level), July

7 show mean isotherms, reduced to sea-level, for January and July. But it must not be forgotten that except in low-lands they give little indication of the actual climate since the all-important effect of altitude is ignored. Over great areas of plateau in Asia and Africa the actual temperature is at least 10° lower than the values of the sea-level isotherms. The correction for altitude is at best approximate; in many regions observations show that the mean gradient between high and low stations varies seasonally, a fact commonly ignored in the reduction. However, even for purely climatological purposes reduction to sea-level is desirable, for the intricacies of topography prevent 'actual' isotherms being other than rough generalizations except on large-scale maps.

Isotherms are so graphic that they may give erroneous impressions in other ways, and a warning is necessary as to the limitations of what they express. Two stations on the same mean monthly isotherm certainly have the same temperature for the month, after allowance for altitude. But the actual sensible temperatures as experienced from day to day may have more points of difference than of resemblance. The Orkney Islands and the north of the Aegean Sea have the same mean temperature, 40°, in January. But there the resemblance ends. The Orkneys have an abnormally high mean because of their prevailing strong SW. winds, arriving after a long passage over an ocean remarkably warm for the latitude. The sky is cloudy and the sunshine scanty; little heat is gained in the daytime from sunshine, little lost at night through radiation; the duller the sky and the stormier and damper the weather, the warmer it is. The heat is imported from tropical regions in both air-masses and ocean currents; great extremes of heat and cold are unknown. But in the Aegean a day without sunshine is rare, and the warmth is largely that of the sun's rays, both direct and reflected from the sea; the nights are correspondingly cold, since heat is lost rapidly by radiation in that region of clear skies and dry air; the typical weather is much warmer by day (and warmer with the bright and exhilarating rays of the sun), and colder at night than in the Orkneys. Moreover greater variations may occur, for cold waves sweep down from the steppes of Hungary, and snow and frost are prominent and unwelcome visitors on the sunny coasts of the Aegean. Or again, the sirocco, originating far south in the Sahara and charged with moisture from its passage of the Mediterranean, may bring muggy weather, unpleasantly damp and warm. To say nothing of the other elements of climate, the differences in the temperature conditions are more important than the one similarity that the means of the readings for 30 Januarys are the same at the two places.

This same isotherm of 40° for January is responsible for incorrect ideas on the climate of the British Isles. The fact that it crosses the north of Scotland and the Isle of Wight does not indicate that the actual temperatures from day to day in the two districts are the same. Again, it is not the case that months with mean temperature of 80° in the Congo basin and in the Sahara have even approximately the same conditions.

Isotherms necessarily mask the peculiarities of local climates which are too small to appear on the scale of the map, and many larger ones are smoothed out since the local effect is prominent only in part of the day, and is possibly reversed in the other part.

Some outstanding features of Figs. 6 and 7 may be noted: the marked divergence of the isotherms from the parallels of latitude, except over the Southern Ocean; their wider spacing in the tropics than in higher latitudes, vast areas of the tropics having similar means; the rapid cooling north-ward in winter over Asia, North America, and Greenland, the 32° isotherm for January being about 2,000 miles farther north over the north-east Atlantic than in the east of Asia; the intense heat in summer in the deserts about Cancer and Capricorn. The thermal gradient between equator and poles is much steeper in winter than in summer, especially in the north hemisphere; the mean gradient for the year is about 1° F. in one degree of latitude.

CHAPTER V

LOCAL CONTROLS OF AIR TEMPERATURE.
CONTINENTALITY

The temperature of the air is controlled partly locally, partly by the importation in air-masses of the conditions that pre-vailed in the region of origin, as explained in Chapter VII. The local effects concern us now, and they are: altitude of the sun, length of day and night, nature of the surface in respect of topography (the main distinction being between concave and convex) and type (the main types being bare rock or sand, snow, ice, vegetation; vegetation may be forest, bush, or grass, all of which may be subdivided into humid, with water surfaces in rivers and swamps, and dry).

Temperature is normally lowest just before sunrise, when radiation without compensating insolation has had its longest

effect, and highest not at noon but about 1400 on land,
1500 at sea, the surface continuing to heat for some time
after the sun begins to decline. The warmest and coolest
months are 1 month after the solstice on land, 2 months
after at sea. But weather imposes many irregularities in
individual days and years; in middle and high latitudes not
infrequently the night is warmer than the day, and other
features will be mentioned later.

Topographical Control of Air Temperature. Inversion of Temperature

Among mountains the dependence of climate on altitude,
not least the general fall of temperature with increasing
height, is prominent (see Part IV). But the local effects of
even the subdued topography of the more populous lowlands are worthy of study, and will now be described.

As the air is heated and cooled chiefly by contact with the
ground, its temperature range tends to be largest when the
surface of contact is largest, in basins and valleys, less over
a convex surface, and at a minimum on a sharp mountain
summit. The bottoms of mountain valleys thus resemble
land-masses in having extremes of heat and cold, and the
small range of air temperature on mountain peaks (this must
not be confused with the temperature of solid objects exposed to the sun's rays) is suggestive of oceanic conditions.
The free atmosphere a mile above the surface (two miles
above in low latitudes) has very little change of temperature
from day to night.

Air chilled by a surface which is rapidly losing heat at
night gravitates to the lowest possible level where, in the
absence of wind to cause turbulence, an 'inversion of
temperature' results, temperature rising with altitude instead
of falling. The inversion is largest on low ground surrounded
by extensive slopes (e.g. see p. 44), but even where the
differences of level are small, hollows ('frost hollows') fill
with cold damp air on calm clear nights, as can easily be felt
when we come down in the evening from the higher ground,
where the air is still warm and dry, into 'lakes' of cold air in
the valleys. In the long winter nights the low ground may
be covered with a cold fog, so thick that it is not dispersed

even in the daytime (but additional factors are then usually involved). The condition described constitutes a climatic difference of no little significance for agriculture between lowlands and uplands even in regions of such small relief as the south-east of England. Unfortunately most towns are

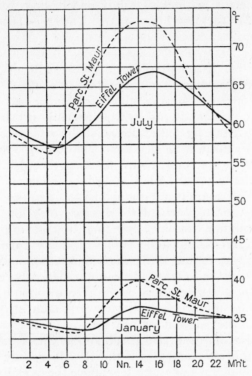

FIG. 8. Mean diurnal temperature curves for Parc St. Maur, Paris, and the top of the Eiffel Tower

in the valleys and are often enshrouded in cold damp or foggy air at night, while neighbouring elevations, though only two or three hundred feet higher, are warm and dry; and the smoke adds its effect by discolouring the fog almost to blackness in large industrial districts.

Observations on the top of the Eiffel Tower, Paris, are available for comparison with those in Paris itself (Fig. 8), the former giving the conditions of the free atmosphere 990 feet above the city except for the slight influence of the ironwork of the structure itself. The mean range is much less aloft, both in summer and winter. The higher station is warmer in the night than the lower, in July between 2200 and 0500, and in January between 0100 and 0800; on calm clear nights the higher station is more favoured, but the lower station is warmer in windy and cloudy weather. In summer the warmest hour on the Tower is 1600, but in Paris 1400.

Similarly with topographical differences of altitudes, the mean night temperature in winter may be lower at low levels than on slopes or plateaux which are higher but so placed that the chilled air drains away, especially in calm regions often dominated by anticyclones, such as Central Europe. The January mean is 34° at Lugano, altitude 902 feet, on the southern slopes of the Alps overlooking the plain of Lombardy, but only 32° at Milan, altitude 482 feet, on the plain. The night inversion is often much larger than the means for the month indicate, particularly in calm anticyclonic spells in winter; mountain summits may then be enjoying cloudless skies, with intense sunshine by day, and dry warm air with bright stars at night, while the valleys thousands of feet below are filled with stagnant fog, unrelieved by a beam of sunshine, at a temperature below freezing-point (Chapter XXX). The following readings were taken in Auvergne, France, on the summit of the Puy-de-Dôme, an isolated volcanic cone, altitude 4,823 feet, and at Clermont-Ferrand in the bottom of the valley of the R. Allier, only 10 miles from the mountain and 1,280 feet above the sea; the weather was controlled by a large anticyclone giving fog on the low ground:

0600, 20–28 December 1879

	Temp. °F.	Rel. humidity
Puy-de-Dôme	39	38%
Clermont-Ferrand . . .	8	91%

One of the early investigations of inversions by Hann, amplified by Conrad, illustrates the conditions in hollows among the eastern Alps, the stations being in the bottom and up the sides of a depression in Carinthia:

MEAN TEMPERATURE IN JANUARY

	Alt. (ft.)	Temp. °F.
Klagenfurt . .	1,444	21
Althofen . . .	2,356	26
Hüttenberg. . .	2,569	27
Lölling . . .	2,756	28
Lölling Berghaus .	3,619	29
Stelzing . . .	4,626	25

Fig. 9 shows a remarkable frost hollow, also in Carinthia, but it is an extreme case.

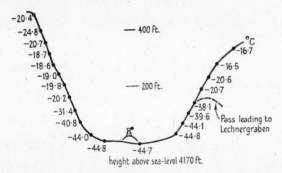

FIG. 9. Temperatures (°C.) in the morning of 31 March 1931, showing a remarkable inversion in the Gestettner Alm, a deep enclosed hollow in the Alps, 80 miles west-south-west of Vienna; the district was snow covered (Schmidt)

Fig. 10 illustrates a frequent case of inversion in winter in the Oxford district, which is representative of the lowlands of south and east England. An extensive anticyclone covered England and the neighbouring parts of the Continent, and by 12 February the region was enveloped in a thick fog, the air being calm. The temperature in Oxford at 0600 was 30°; but Shotover Hill, an upland 350 feet above the city and 3 miles east, was high enough to project above the lake of fog, the air was clear and comparatively warm, temperature 40°, the grass sparkled with hoar-frost and the stars twinkled brightly in the sky. The bottom of a combe on the south side of the hill, only 180 feet below the top and hardly half a mile distant, was filled with fog and the temperature was down to 26°.

To illustrate further the conditions in the south of England, a region of weak relief, observations are available

from Oxford, 208 feet above the sea in the midst of the wide
expanses of flood-plain in the middle Thames valley, and
Leafield, 612 feet, on an open limestone plateau of the
eastern Cotswolds, 15 miles to the north-west. The mean

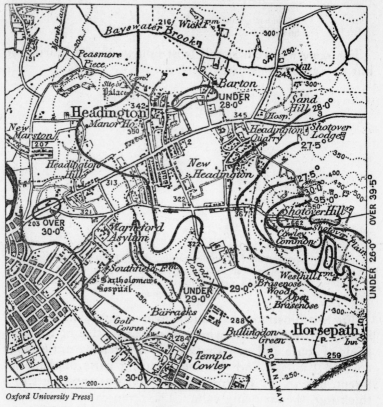

Oxford University Press]

Fig. 10. Air temperature, 0600 13 Feb. 1913. (Based upon the Ordnance Survey
map with the sanction of the Controller of H.M. Stationery Office)

monthly temperatures are always higher at the former
station, but the excess in the mean daily minimum is less in
winter (1° in December) than in summer (2° in August);
calm winter nights sometimes give an inversion of temperature, Leafield being 10° or more warmer than Oxford in
extreme cases. The day maxima are almost always higher at
Oxford, the mean excess being about 3° all the year.

The lowest minimum in the U.S.A., −65°, was recorded

at Miles City in the bottom of the valley of the Yellowstone River, altitude 2,371 feet. Braemar, in the valley of the Dee, has the record, — 17°, for the British Isles.

The lowest temperatures on the globe near sea-level are at Verkhoyansk, altitude 330 feet (and in similar frost hollows such as Oimekon) in north-east Siberia, where the January mean is — 58° and a reading of — 94° has been recorded.

The action of severe cold on everything about you is certainly striking. You take a glass of water and dash it high into the air, the liquid will come down in the form of ringing crystals of ice. All live things seek deep shelter during the winter. Partridges dig themselves far into the snow and stay there. There have been cases of their falling like stones while in flight, freezing to death in the air. . . . Live wood becomes petrified, and when one chops it sparks fly as if from flint. . . . The air one exhales issues forth to the accompaniment of a feeble crackling sound in the air, the result of a rapid contraction of the warm breath. . . . I covered my face with my fur headpiece and left only my eyes exposed, but I felt the unpleasant sensation of the freezing of the moisture on my eye-balls; it was rather painful to have little icicles stuck in the eyes. . . . One of the strangest phenomena was the rumbling of the earth in the burning cold. The ground seemed to crack underneath, with a sound that resembled artillery blasts; the dull roars reverberated in the still air. (Zenzinof, on Verkhoyansk.)

These intensely cold districts are near the polar circle, in the bottoms of steep-sided valleys deeply incised in plateaux surrounded by mountain ranges. The air is chilled by the snow in the clear dry atmosphere of the long polar nights, and drains into the depressions, giving extraordinarily low readings, which are thus isolated inversion effects. On the higher, atmospherically well-drained, slopes the cold is much less intense; Semenovski mine, 3,300 feet above sea-level on an open south-facing slope in this same region, has a January mean about — 20°.

Snow is a very good radiator, and the lowest readings known are on loose dry powdery snow after long clear winter nights; the surface becomes the colder by reason of the insulation given by the large volume of air in the interstices. In strong contrast the ground underneath is well blanketed, and may be little below freezing-point; even a shallow layer of snow is effective; for example, at 2240 on 16 January 1926 at a station in the south of England the temperature of the surface of the snow was 4°, on the ground under the 5 inches of snow 29°. The effect is much larger in the far interior of a continent in high altitudes, where the snow is deeper and more continuous and the nights longer. This blanketing is one of the advantages of snow for agriculture.

Even in low latitudes the ground cools fast at night, notably on highlands under a clear dry atmosphere. At Simla, altitude 7,232 feet in the Himalayas, ice fit for skating is available in December, though the screen temperature has never been known to fall below 40°. Baguio, alt. 4,800 feet, lat. 16·5° N., in the Philippine Islands, has ground frost in the hollows not infrequently in winter, and ice forms on shallow water when standard air temperature on the flat plateau is as high as 45°.

Inversions of temperature other than the simple surface type described above are mentioned in later chapters.

It is a general rule, then, that very low temperatures are liable to occur during long winter nights in valley bottoms and other hollows, and on low levels, especially when the ground is snow-covered, the atmosphere calm, and the sky clear. These frost hollows are evidently unsuitable for dwelling-houses, and for orchards and other trees sensitive to frost (which is likely to be most injurious in spring); even in São Paulo, on the tropic in Brazil, coffee-growers avoid the bottoms and plant on the slopes which, though many hundred feet higher, are preferable. But it is otherwise in spells of cold, polar, general winds, which may blow for days with a temperature below freezing, since high and open ground is more exposed than the bottoms, and all possible protection by wind-breaks, high walls, or screens of trees is desirable. Lowlands have the advantage of higher day temperatures, especially in summer, than uplands.

In the hot hours of the day the vertical temperature gradient tends to be the opposite of the inversion described above, the surface layers being heated instead of cooled by contact with the ground. But this causes instability; the air rises—the shimmering of the landscape on a hot day is the effect, in part, of the currents—and cool air descending from above, or coming in horizontally, takes its place, to be warmed in its turn. Thus both convection and turbulence in the moving air bring about heat interchange, and instead of the lowest layers being heated excessively a considerable depth of atmosphere is warmed moderately. Vigorous convection results from not only abnormal heat below but also abnormal cold above; in the polar air in rear of a depression of the westerlies the sky may be at first cloudless and the insolation powerful, but the temperature remains low, and the strong wind helps to diffuse the heating by turbulence. The vigorous convection becomes visible in the cumulus clouds, and possibly showers. The warmer the surface air becomes, the more rapidly it brings about its own removal. Cold, on the other hand, tends to persist and be intensified by the stable equilibrium; in winter, anticyclones build up over the continents in high latitudes, and their clear air and cloudless skies favour further loss of heat by radiation; but in this case, too, the process provides its own check in that the high pressures cause outblowing winds which remove the cold air.

If the higher atmosphere is unusually warm it forms a ceiling which checks, or stops ascent, and the heating is restricted to the surface layers, which attain high temperatures. An actual increase of temperature with altitude is not required for this; an isothermal layer (that is, a layer with the same temperature through some depth) or an appreciable reduction of lapse-rate is enough. An example occurred in July 1926; on 11 July maxima of 81° and 82° were recorded in the south of England; the 12th was warmer, and the 13th still warmer, the sky being almost cloudless, and many parts of the country had more than 12 hours of sunshine. Next day, 14 July, was again almost cloudless, and the sunshine even longer; in the south of England it was the warmest day of the spell. An anticyclone had spread north-eastward from the Azores, and covered France and much of central Europe, becoming centred over north Germany and the

North Sea on the 12th, 13th, and 14th. The wind in
England was light from the south-east (Fig. 11), bringing
warm air from the Continent. But an additional cause of the

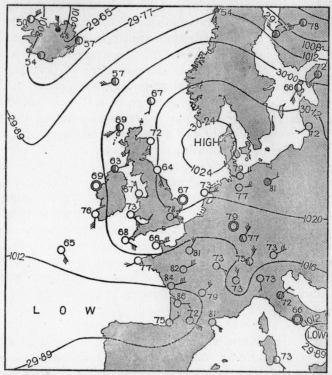

BAROMETER.— *Isobars are drawn for intervals of four millibars.*
TEMPERATURE.— *Given in degrees Fahrenheit.*
WIND.— *Direction is shown by arrows flying with the wind. Force, on
the scale 0 to 12 by number of feathers.   Calm* ◯
WEATHER SYMBOLS.— ◯ *clear sky;* ◐ *sky ¼ clouded;* ◑ *sky ½ clouded;*
◕ *sky ¾ clouded;* ⦿ *overcast sky;* ● *rain falling;* ✳ *snow;*
▲ *hail;* ≡ *fog;* ≡˙ *mist;* T *thunder;* ℞ *thunderstorm.*

FIG. 11. A very hot day in north-west Europe; synoptic chart, 1800,
13 July 1926

heat was the abnormal warmth of the upper air; on 12 July
the air between 7,000 and 16,000 feet over the south of
England was warmer than ever before observed, and next
day warmer still, the temperature being 47° at 12,500 feet
over Lympne, 25° above the mean for the month. In the
absence of convection the heated surface air was not removed

by ascent, and the usual cumulus clouds of summer failed to appear, so that the sun shone powerfully all day, intensifying the already high surface temperature.

Thus the surface air temperature is controlled not only by the transparency, but also by the temperature of the upper atmosphere thousands of feet above.

Extreme Heat and Cold

The highest temperatures on the earth occur in summer in the trade-wind deserts, and the lowest in winter in the land-masses in high latitudes. The latter fall more below the annual mean than the former rise above it, for two main reasons. Firstly, inside the polar circles on at least one day of the year the sun does not rise, and the loss of heat continues throughout the 24 hours; in lower latitudes no season has a correspondingly long period of heating, for however fierce the rays of the summer sun may be they are interrupted by the oncoming of night, when the clear sky that gave passage to the insolation by day is equally favourable to the loss of heat. Secondly, cold air is in stable equilibrium, the more so the colder it is, and remains stagnant in the lowest levels unless it is displaced by still colder air draining down the surrounding slopes. Only the turbulence of a strong wind in the higher atmosphere can mix it with the warmer air above. These lakes of cold surface air may thus become colder and colder, and extraordinarily low temperatures are attained in north-east Siberia, north Canada, Greenland, and Antarctica. The conditions in the regions of great heat are quite different; as the surface heats equilibrium becomes unstable, the hot air rises, and is replaced from the higher atmosphere which is at a more normal temperature. The hotter the surface air becomes under the rays of the sun, the more vigorously is it carried up by convection. The heat, instead of being confined to, and intensified in, a shallow layer, like the cold in the polar winter, is diffused through thousands of feet of the atmosphere, and removed by the strong winds. Hence, in spite of the powerful rays of the midday sun, the air temperature rises much less above the mean than the polar winter minima fall below the mean for the latitude.

These facts are illustrated by Verkhoyansk, just inside the Arctic circle in north-east Siberia, the station with the lowest temperatures recorded, and Insalah, an oasis in the Algerian Sahara, one of the hottest parts of the globe in summer; but the difference in latitude between the stations is a factor. At Verkhoyansk the mean temperature for the year is 3°, the mean for January − 58°, and the lowest record −94°. At Insalah the mean for the year is 78°, the mean for July 99°, and the highest record 129°. While at Verkhoyansk the mean of the coldest month is 61° below the mean of the year, and the absolute minimum 97° below, at Insalah the mean of the warmest month is only 21° above the mean for the year, and the absolute maximum only 51° above.

Abnormal heat and cold are explained by the same considerations. The following conditions conduce to very high day maxima: season summer, with its high sun and long days; sky clear and cloudless, allowing the insolation to reach the surface in strength; atmosphere calm, or with a slow drift of tropical air from a hot land surface; lapse-rate (p. 69) less than the adiabatic, and preferably reversed at no great altitude; ground dry, sandy, and already warmed by preceding hot days; topography concave, such as the bottom of a steep-sided valley or other depression. And for great cold the favourable conditions are: season winter, with low sun and long nights; sky clear and cloudless, facilitating rapid loss of heat; atmosphere still; air polar and already cold; surface grass-covered, or, better, snow; lapse-rate reversed ('inversion of temperature'); topography concave to collect and retain the coldest air. On the other hand, damp air, cloudy skies, and strong winds are likely to give low maxima, high minima, and small range.

Shelter

A north wind sometimes blows so strongly in spring that even the unclouded sun hardly tempers the piercing cold. But a high wall or a screen of trees gives shelter from the wind and at the same time intensifies the heat of the sun by reflection. The old gardeners understood this when they made the walled gardens that are so prolific. On a larger scale in nature a range of hills or mountains may modify the climate appreciably.

The Mediterranean provides many important instances; in several respects the region is suitable for invalids and holiday-makers in the cooler half of the year, but a serious disadvantage on parts of the northern coasts is the liability to strong cold winds from the interior of Europe, for the prevailing winds are between north-west and north-east. Fortunately the Mediterranean Sea is almost enclosed by mountain ranges and where they rise steeply from the sea they give the necessary protection from the wind, while the direct rays of the sun, together with the reflected light and heat from the hill-sides of white limestone and from the azure waters of the sea, make these favoured shores veritable suntraps. The French and Italian Rivieras, the Dalmatian coast, and the Italian lakes are well-known winter resorts, thanks largely to the mountain shelter; the cold winds which are turned aside rush through with the greater rigour where the coast lacks a rampart (p. 368). The popular resorts are on the sheltered littorals except those on the southern shores such as Algiers. In summer the mountain background so intensifies the powerful sunshine that all who can do so retreat to cooler places. The north-east shore of the Lake of Geneva owes to its mountain shelter and southward exposure the climatic advantages that attract a large health- and pleasure-seeking population.

The Himalayas form a mighty screen for the plains of India against cold winds in winter from the deserts of the interior—such winds as are a scourge in China. The south of the United States in the same latitudes as the north of India, being without shelter, suffers seriously from cold waves which often sweep down in winter from Canada.

In high summer a strong wind is welcome, promoting evaporation and tempering the physiological temperature. The furnace heat of the Sahara and similar deserts would be very trying and almost impossible for human life but for the strong and dry wind that is usual during the hottest hours. But strong winds can be injurious for agriculture both in desiccating effects and in removing the fine surface soil (as

in America in the drought years 1934–5, when great clouds
of it were carried across the continent from the Middle
West to the Atlantic). A remedy applied in dry and windy
regions is the planting of shelter-belts of trees or shrubs in
parallel lines athwart the prevailing winds; for market-
gardening intervals of 50 to 100 feet are usual. A screen of

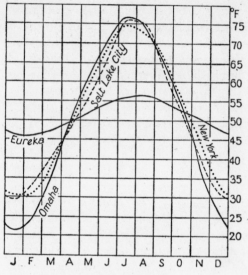

FIG. 12. Mean temperature

trees gives useful shelter to a distance of twenty to thirty
times its height.

Continentality

The range of temperature, best the annual range (Fig. 25,
p. 78), is an indicator of 'continentality', that is, the magnitude of the influence of distance from the windward ocean.
As an illustration Fig. 12 gives the curves of mean temperature for a series of stations in the same latitude in North
America. Eureka has a pronounced oceanic climate, with
the warm winters and small range to be expected on a windward western seaboard; its cool summers are due largely to
the frequent fogs of the cool California current. Salt Lake
City, though 4,366 feet above the sea, is as warm in summer

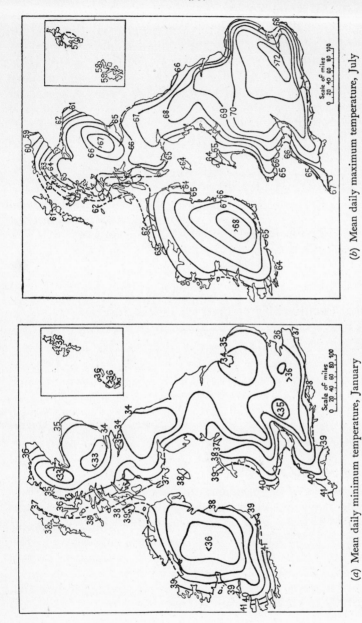

(a) Mean daily minimum temperature, January

(b) Mean daily maximum temperature, July

Fig. 13. Mean daily extreme temperatures in the British Isles (by permission of the Director, Meteorological Office, London)

as Omaha (1,103 feet, in the middle of the continent) owing
to the clear dry air and strong sunshine, and in winter considerably warmer, partly owing to being nearer the Pacific,
partly thanks to the influence of the Lake; both have
strongly continental climates. New York on the east coast
and Salt Lake City have very similar curves, for New York
has prevailing off-shore winds most of the year which carry
the continental extremes with them. Even the British Isles
are large enough to exhibit continentality, the interior
having warmer days and cooler nights than the coasts (Fig.
13).

Continentality asserts itself also in the interdiurnal
variability of temperature, that is, the difference between the
mean temperatures of pairs of days; its mean annual value
is 2·0° in the Scilly Isles, 2·4° at Southport (Lancs.), 4·1° at
Vienna, about 6·5° (9·0° in January) in west Siberia; it is
much less in low latitudes, e.g. 1·1° at Georgetown, British
Guiana.

Local Peculiarities of Meteorological Stations

Observations are representative of the immediate environment of the station, a small area, possibly of specialized
topography such as a valley bottom, a wind-swept ridge or
cape. For climatology this is in some ways no disadvantage,
in so far as the detailed conditions of the site are required;
but care must be taken not to generalize from such local
data. For meteorological purposes, requiring the general
conditions of the surface air, only observations at stations
fully exposed, and free from local irregularities, are suitable;
many meteorological services issue a gazetteer of their
stations, describing the sites and any resulting peculiarities
in the readings, so that they may be allowed for in com-
parative studies, as in using synoptic charts.

CHAPTER VI

DIURNAL CURVES OF TEMPERATURE

EVERYWHERE outside the polar circles day is warmer than night in ordinary weather, but the form and amplitude of the temperature curves vary greatly. The range is much larger

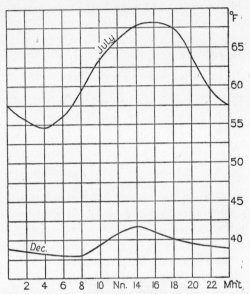

FIG. 14. Mean hourly temperature at Oxford in December (month with least diurnal range) and July (month with largest diurnal range)

on land than at sea, the nights being colder, the days warmer; the maximum is at about 1400 on land, 1500 on the sea. The curve depends on the season and on the weather. In temperate latitudes the mean range is larger in summer than in winter (Fig. 14), a result partly of the finer weather and clearer skies, a clear sky favouring hot days and cold nights, but chiefly of the stronger solar control in summer, for in summer a night is rarely warmer than the preceding or following day, but it is not infrequently so in winter, when the weather control may be stronger than the solar control, the general weather conditions, mainly the cloud cover and the direction and force of the wind, being more effective than the direct rays of the sun in determining the temperature. Thus on 15 November 1929 (Fig. 117, p. 352) the temperature remained low during the day, and the maximum was in the night owing to a change of wind. Cold gloomy days are only too frequent in temperate latitudes, especially near the oceans; east winds and overcast skies may continue day after day, and the sun has little or no direct effect on the temperature, which is hardly higher by day than by night. The thermogram in Fig. 15 from the

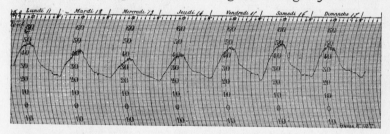

FIG. 15. Temperature (° C.) at Touggourt, Algerian Sahara, 11–18 August 1912

Sahara reflects the intensity of direct insolation, the weather remaining constant and the solar control being strongly marked in the trade-wind desert. The effect of altitude is shown in Fig. 8 (p. 43).

In the westerlies temperature may rise in winter nights owing to clouds forming and checking the loss of heat by radiation, or to a calm giving place to wind which mixes the chilled surface air with the warmer atmosphere above it, or to the arrival of a warmer air-mass. On the other hand, it may fall during the day, though the altitude of the sun is still increasing, with a change in the wind or the state of the sky. Such large irregularities are not usual, but frequent enough to make the mean diurnal range of temperature notably less in winter than in summer.

An interesting relation between pressure and temperature changes may be observed, especially in winter. As a depression approaches, with its tropical air and cloudy skies, temperature rises while the pressure falls, and after the passage of the cold front polar winds bring a fall in temperature as the pressure rises, the barogram and thermogram moving inversely (Fig. 117, p. 352; 0100, 12 November, and 1200, 15 November). These effects are noticeable where-ever the weather is under a strong cyclonic control, that is, speaking generally, poleward of the thirtieth parallels. In the tropics the range is least in the cloudy and rainy months, largest in the dry season, especially in the hottest months (Fig. 16).

The mean daily range is larger if it is taken as the difference between the maximum and minimum tempera-

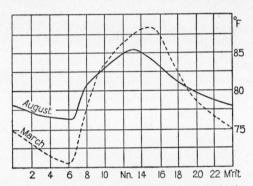

FIG. 16. Mean hourly temperature at Manila in March (dry season) and August (rains)

tures irrespective of their hours of occurrence ('aperiodic range'), than as the difference between the means at the mean hours of maximum and minimum ('periodic range'). The former is only slightly in excess in low latitudes; the excess increases rapidly with latitude, particularly in winter, being about three times as large in mid-winter in the British Isles and eight times as large in Norway.

Topographical influences may be strong enough to counterbalance the solar control, as we shall see later is the case with föhn winds, the mistral, and the scirocco.

Two types of diurnal curve are characteristic of large areas. On the warmer coasts, roughly between the equator and latitude 40° (Britain[1] is hardly warm enough, but the south of Europe is included), the wind alternates from land-

---

[1] See, however, Bilham, E. G., 'The sea breeze as a climatic factor', *J. State Medicine*, 42, Lond. 1934.

breeze at night to sea-breeze by day (p. 118). The sun's rays are powerful, and the rapid heating of the land leads to its own undoing, for about 1000 the sea-breeze of cool air sets in, and the rising temperature curve is checked and often reversed, the maximum for the day occurring as early as 1000 or 1100 (Fig. 17); the highest portion of the diurnal

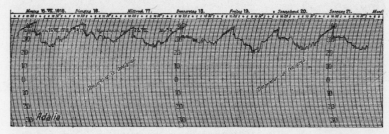

FIG. 17. Temperature at Adalia, south coast of Asia Minor, 15–22 July 1918

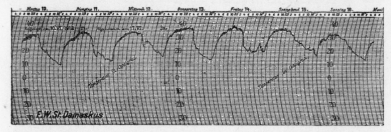

FIG. 18. Temperature at Damascus, Syria, 10–17 June 1918. The thickening of the trace in the midday hours is due to the rapid oscillations in temperature associated with convection currents

curve is cut off, and the coasts enjoy a great advantage over the interior, where the curve goes on rising and the heat becomes excessive in the afternoon.

The rising temperature is often checked to some extent in the interior also. In humid climates convection currents give rise to heavy cumulus clouds which screen the ground. Arid districts do not enjoy this alleviation, but the convectional mixing of the surface air with the cooler winds aloft has some effect (Fig. 18). Here, again, very high temperatures on the surface are prevented by the ascending currents which the heat itself sets in motion. The contrast with the persistence of excessive cold has been pointed out (p. 51).

The polar regions have a 24 hours' day in summer and
a 24 hours' night in winter, and at the poles themselves
the mean diurnal temperature graph should be a straight
line. For lower latitudes inside the polar circles records are
available, one for McMurdo Sound, 78° S., in Antarctica
(Fig. 19), but they are too short to establish the true means.
The range in summer seems at first surprisingly high, as the

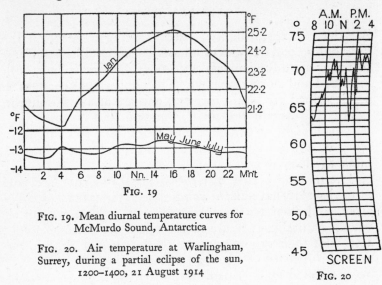

FIG. 19

FIG. 19. Mean diurnal temperature curves for
McMurdo Sound, Antarctica

FIG. 20. Air temperature at Warlingham,
Surrey, during a partial eclipse of the sun,
1200–1400, 21 August 1914

FIG. 20

sun is above the horizon continuously, but the difference
between the noon and midnight altitudes explains it. The
winter curve has two striking features, the rise between 0800
and 1500 and the minimum at 0200, although the sun never
appears above the horizon, and the slight, but apparently
real, secondary maximum at 0400.[1]

Observers on the middle of the ice cap of Greenland, at
Eismitte, alt. 10,000 feet, lat. 71° N., were surprised at the
rapid fall in temperature on clear evenings in summer as the
sun declined though not to disappear; large crystals of rime
and hoar-frost formed on objects exposed to the sky under
the midnight sun, and the daily range of air temperature
under clear skies in early summer amounted to 30°.[2]

[1] Simpson, *British Antarctic Expedition*, vol. i, ch. 2.
[2] Loewe, *Q. J. R. Met. Soc.*, 1936, July.

An interesting, though not common, temperature curve (Fig. 20) shows the effect of an eclipse of the sun. In this case the eclipse was not total, a maximum of 0·65 of the sun's disk being covered; the sky was cloudless.

CHAPTER VII

AIR-MASSES

AIR-masses are introduced here as being a factor in the distribution and changes of temperature; it will be seen later that they are a fundamental feature of the atmosphere, both in settled and stormy weather. The temperature changes so far described are local processes, and are at a maximum in calms. But usually the air is in motion, and brings with it the qualities of structure, temperature, humidity, and visibility which it has acquired elsewhere, and these imports mask the local effects.

The moving bodies of air—air-masses as they are now termed—may have been 'conditioned' thousands of miles away, and then taken several days on a journey, during which, naturally, they are more or less modified. To consider first their origin, suppose that a mass of air, with an area of a quarter of a million square miles and a depth of 10,000 feet at least, remains stationary for some time, which is most likely to occur in the semi-permanent anticyclones in the sub-tropics, in the polar regions, Greenland and Antarctica, and in winter on the cold land-masses of Asia and North America. During its sojourn of days, or weeks, the air is 'conditioned' mainly from the surface (some of the controlling factors have been described in Chap. V), becoming warm or cold, humid or dry, first at the base and then higher and higher, rapidly if vertical movement is going on; it thus becomes largely homogeneous. The main types of air-mass are 'tropical' and 'polar'. Most tropical air originates in the sub-tropical anticyclones; it is always warm, but its vapour-content varies, being high when the source is on the ocean, low when on land. Polar air is cold, and its vapour-content therefore low. But precise temperatures and humidities cannot be laid down, as they vary with the character of the source and the duration of the sojourn.

After some time a change in the distribution of pressure may occur, the gradient compels movement and the air sets off in the direction and at the speed imposed, under-

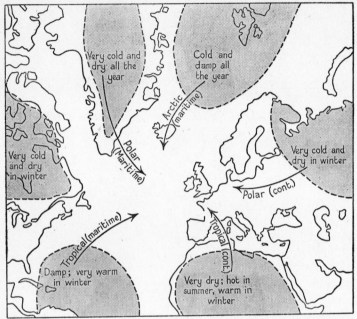

FIG. 21. Source-regions of air-masses which frequently reach the British Isles

going modifications according to the temperature and humidity of the surface passed over, and with any ascent or subsidence in pressure systems it may enter, but retaining recognizable characteristics derived from its birthplace for remarkably long periods. The qualities, physical and physiological, which we associate with air-masses are largely relative to our place of observation; tropical air appears warm and humid in temperate latitudes, but cool and fairly dry in low latitudes; polar air appears cold when it invades a warm region. The sources of some main air-masses (see table below) that reach the British Isles are shown in Fig. 21.

An air-mass does not necessarily, or usually, make a direct passage from its source, but curves in accordance with the

barometric gradient, sometimes even returning on its track.
Polar air from high latitudes may move south over the North
Atlantic perhaps to latitude 40° N., and then recurve and
approach the British Isles from the south-west; as 'returning

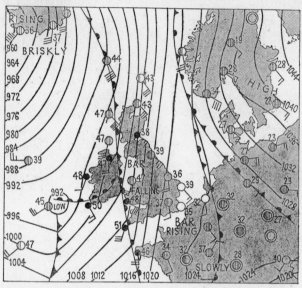

WIND: arrows fly with wind. A full length feather indicates two
steps on the Beaufort Scale, and a short feather one step. Calm
is indicated by circle outside weather symbol :– ○
TEMPERATURE: is given in degrees F.
WEATHER SYMBOLS: ○ Clear sky. ◔ Sky less than ³/₁₀ clouded.
◑ Sky ⁴/₁₀ to ⁶/₁₀ clouded.   ◕ Sky ⁷/₁₀ to ⁹/₁₀ clouded.
◉ Overcast sky.   ● Rain falling. ✳ Snow. △ Hail. ≡ Fog
〜〜〜 Warm front on the surface. ▲▲▲▲ Cold front on the surface.
▲●▲●▲● Occluded front (or Occlusion)

FIG. 22. Synoptic chart, 0600, 3 January 1947

polar air' it will be more modified than if it came direct, but
may still be very different from tropical air arriving with the
same wind direction. Fig. 22 illustrates another case; for
some days an anticyclone covered Europe, radiation had
been favoured by clear skies and the calm air had become very
cold—a large polar continental air-mass had been formed;
at the time of the synoptic chart a deep depression in the
Icelandic region was giving southerly winds over the British

MAIN TYPES OF AIR-MASS IN NORTH TEMPERATE LATITUDES

TYPE	SOURCE REGION	FEATURES (ON REACHING BRITISH IS.)
Arctic	Arctic Ocean	Cold; unstable; much cu. cloud, showers.
Polar, continental	(a) Greenland, Canada	Cold and dry, unstable; in summer much cu. cloud and showers.
	(b) Siberia	In winter, very cold and very dry; stable; cloud st.-cu., but often little cloud.
		In summer, warm and dry; little cloud.
Polar, maritime	North of North Atlantic and North Pacific	Cold and damp; unstable; cu. cloud, showers; but becoming stable, with st.-cu. cloud, on colder land.
Tropical, continental (subsiding air)	Sub-tropical anti-cyclones on continents	In winter, warm and dry; cloud st.-cu., but usually little cloud; stable.
		In summer, hot and dry; little cloud, hazy.
Tropical, maritime (subsiding air)	Sub-tropical anti-cyclones on oceans	Warm, moderate to high vapour content; cloud variable in amount and kind. Liable to give persistent sea-fog in spring and early summer, but may become unstable on land in summer and give afternoon thunderstorms.

MAIN TYPES OF AIR-MASS IN THE TROPICS

TYPE	SOURCE REGION	FEATURES (IN LOW LATITUDES)
Tropical, continental (subsiding air) (NE. and SE. trades on land)	Sub-tropical anti-cyclones on continents	Stable, except near surface in daytime; very little cloud but much dust; very hot and dry in summer, warm and dry in winter
Tropical, maritime (subsiding air) (NE. and SE. trades on oceans)	Sub-tropical anti-cyclones on oceans	Stable; warm and dry (but cool and humid near surface); light cu. cloud, but liable to give heavy cloud and rain on reaching hot lands or mountains
Equatorial (usually rising air)	Equatorial trough	Unstable, hot, moist; massive cu. and cumulo-nimbus; liable to give heavy frontal and convectional rain

Isles, which brought polar air and a temperature of 35° to east Kent, but tropical air with a temperature of 51° to the Scilly Islands. Not infrequently in winter the east of England is 20° colder than the south-west coasts because they are under different air-masses.

The mean temperatures in tropical and polar air-masses in the British Isles in winter have been determined by Belasco[1] from upper-air soundings at various stations, and the following extracts from his results illustrate some of the points mentioned above:

MEAN TEMPERATURES, WINTER

	Height, ft.				
	1,000	2,000	5,000	10,000	20,000
In tropical air, all classes . . .	43	43	40	27	−8
In polar air, all classes . . .	34	31	22	5	−34

MEAN SURFACE AIR TEMPERATURES AT KEW, WINTER

	Daily max.	Daily min.	Mean for day
In tropical air, all classes	51	42	46
In polar air, all classes	42	33	38

MEAN FALL IN TEMPERATURE IN 1,000 FT., WINTER

	Between levels (in thousands of ft.)					
	15 and 20	10 and 15	5 and 10	3 and 5	2 and 3	1 and 2
In tropical air . .	−3·9	−3·3	−2·6	−1·4	−0·2	+0·5
In polar air . .	−4·1	−3·8	−3·3	−3·4	−3·5	−2·7

Evidently a statement of air-mass has advantages over one of wind direction for most climatological purposes, though the direction and force of the wind are also important. Air-mass data indicate the quality of the air, its temperature and humidity, and to some degree the weather; the wind expresses movement but is not a safe guide to the origin and the quality of the air. If a region has a definitely dominant air-mass in any season the air-mass quality (which is known) will be persistent. If it has several air-masses changeable weather with stormy periods may be expected. Trade-wind air-masses, with their uniform qualities, are persistent in much of the tropics, and the weather tends to uniformity. Polar (Siberian) air is very persistent in winter in north China, and this fact explains, as well as expresses, the climate. North-west Europe, on the other hand, exposed to invasion by air-masses of very different character and variable direc-

[1] Q.J.R. Met. Soc., 1945, July.

tion and speed, and often in conflict, has notably changeable
weather; in winter tropical air brings abnormal warmth,
returning polar air cool fresh weather, polar maritime air
cold, and polar continental air from east Europe or Asia very
dry and frosty weather which may continue for many days
or weeks; in summer continental interiors are hot, and their
air-masses, very warm and dry, give the warmest spells.
Thus SE. winds bring the coldest spells in winter, but the
hottest in summer when the dry heat is in strong contrast to
the very cool, fresh, showery weather of polar maritime air.

Contrasted air-masses are responsible for the noted variability of temperature in the U.S.A. The 'cold waves' of
winter consist of very cold and dry polar continental air from
north-west Canada, where the temperature may have fallen
to $-20°$ or lower; in its passage southward in rear of a
depression the air is warmed somewhat, but it is still an
extremely cold visitation on the shores of the Gulf of Mexico,
and zero has been recorded only a few miles from the
coast; open water soon warms such air—even the short
passage over the Great Lakes may raise the temperature $20°$.
The 'heat waves' of summer, on the other hand, are of tropical
maritime air, very warm and moist by origin, and little
modified by its passage along the Gulf Stream; the enervating sultry heat claims many victims.

Adjacent cool or warm surfaces of land or water cannot
have much effect on air temperature unless the air blows in
over them. The temperature of west Europe is controlled
strongly by the Atlantic Ocean since the prevailing winds
are from the west. The warm waters of the Kuro siwo bathe
the coasts of China, but they have little moderating influence
in the cold dry winters, since the winds are generally from
the north-west. But on the other side of the Pacific the
westerlies, warm and damp from the ocean, give the North
American coast mild open winters. The Great Lakes of
North America warm their leeward, eastern, shores appreciably; the mean date of the first killing frost of autumn in
the interior of the peninsula of Michigan is 21 September,
but on the east shore of Lake Michigan 11 October.
Generally speaking, a warm ocean current extends its

influence farther inland than a cold, since the latter is in most cases only a narrow strip off the coast, and the on-shore winds do not penetrate far inland; the Benguela current off South-west Africa is a very cool current, but the cool damp air from over it does not make its way more than 50 miles inland, usually not so far, being of the nature of a sea-breeze. The warmth of the North Atlantic Drift, on the other hand, carried inland by the westerlies, is felt strongly over most of Europe and can be traced in western Asia.

CHAPTER VIII

THE UPPER AIR. LAPSE-RATE OF TEMPERATURE

CLIMATOLOGY is concerned essentially with the weather on or near the surface of the earth (the climatology of aviation is not included here), but since that is in many ways at the mercy of the upper air the conditions there cannot be ignored; by the upper air is meant the atmosphere between about 3,000 feet and the tropopause. Some of the influences of the upper air on surface weather have been already mentioned, such as the effect on surface temperature of the temperature many hundreds or thousands of feet above (p. 49). Of more general importance is the control of the ascent and subsidence of the air on which cloud and precipitation depend. Though an adequate treatment of the upper air is the concern of meteorology rather than of climatology, some consideration of certain fundamental facts and processes is necessary, in particular the vertical gradient of temperature as favouring or checking ascent or descent, and conversely, the changes of temperature in a rising or subsiding body of air.

Our knowledge of the upper air was formerly dependent on the regular observations made at mountain observatories; one was maintained on Ben Nevis, 4,406 feet, from 1884 to 1903, and higher ones are on Mount Blanc, 14,300 feet, Mount Misti, 19,000 feet, in Peru, and many other summits. In the last fifty years investigations have been vastly extended by the use of various methods of sending instruments up to great heights. At first kites were used, but they were difficult to manage, and could not attain more than 20,000 feet, and they rarely went nearly so high. Unmanned balloons took their place, and carried self-recording instruments to much greater heights, often 70,000 feet; the instruments fell to the ground when the balloon burst, and many were recovered and their records measured; but the loss of many and the delay in receiving the others were disadvantages. Small 'pilot-balloons', filled to a diameter of 3 to 5 feet, however, are still used; they are released from the surface, and their tracks are followed by theodolite observation, so that the direction and velocity of the wind at the levels traversed are at once known. With the advance of air navigation personal observations have been made from aircraft used for the purpose, a method which has the advantages that more elements can be observed, and that the results are available by radio or when the aircraft lands. A recent and promising development is the application of radio and radar; radio-sonde instruments carried up by unmanned balloons automatically signal the pressure, temperature, and humidity at the moment, and the signals are picked up at the surface station; radar systems locate free balloons equipped with reflectors, which normally rise to about 30,000 feet (on one occasion in 1947 echoes were received from 80,000 feet), and the upper winds are calculated. These methods have the advantage that they are practicable in all weathers by day and night, on land, and on the oceans wherever ships are suitably equipped, as are the 'weather ships' now maintained internationally in the North Atlantic and North Pacific. Upper-air work is a regular part of the routine of meteorological stations in almost all countries. Of upper-air observations temperature alone will be treated here, as being fundamental for the study of climatology in relation to the vertical movements of the air.

Average values being taken, temperature decreases upward, and the rate, called the 'lapse-rate', is remarkably uniform above the lowest layers, at about 3° in 1,000 feet, all the world over, whatever the surface temperature may be. The decrease continues to a height which diminishes from about 18 kilometres at the equator, to 6 kilometres, and at times less, at the poles. At this level, which is known as the tropopause, the decrease stops abruptly; the exact height of the tropopause, like all other atmospheric phenomena, varies somewhat from day to day. Above it temperature remains almost constant, or increases slowly up to about 35 kilometres, so that the tropopause is the base of a most remarkable world-wide inversion of temperature. Above it

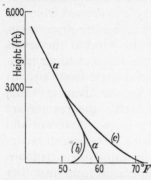

FIG. 23 a. Generalized lapse-rates on land: (a) mean, (b) at night, (c) in afternoon

is the 'stratosphere', below it the 'troposphere'. Though for most purposes the processes of the surface weather are considered to be restricted to the troposphere it seems likely that the stratosphere may exert a wide influence on the troposphere and its weather, though little definite knowledge has yet been attained.

The troposphere, though much shallower than the stratosphere, contains about three-quarters of the mass of the atmosphere. It is convenient to divide it into a lower layer, up to about 5,000 feet, in which the lapse-rate is variable from hour to hour, and a higher, in which the lapse-rate is fairly constant. In the lower troposphere the gradient may even be reversed, as occurs on most clear calm nights (p. 42). Normally the troposphere is top-heavy, warmer below than above, since the effective source of its heat is the long-wave radiation and conduction from the surface, not the direct, short-wave, insolation. On sunny days the lower layers are strongly heated, and the lapse-rate may exceed the adiabatic ('super-adiabatic') in the first few feet (Fig. 23a); in parts of the tropics insolation is so intense that the gradient is super-adiabatic up to about 500 feet on most afternoons in the dry season, and convection, setting in abruptly with some violence, may start dust-devils. On the other hand, the rapid cooling through long clear calm nights gives a gradient much less than the adiabatic. Additional variability may result from the presence at different

levels of air-masses moving with different velocities and
directions. Thus the lapse-rate is always changing, and it
can be discovered at any time only by observation as described above.

The changes of temperature in air when it rises or descends
have now to be considered. Rising air undergoes decrease of
pressure, expands, and in doing so cools adiabatically (that
is, simply as the result of its expansion); the rate is constant
(except near the surface) at $5.4°$ for 1,000 feet of ascent,
which is known as the 'dry adiabatic lapse-rate'; descending
air is heated adiabatically at the same rate. It must be noted
that some interchange of heat between the air and the
environment is necessarily added to the adiabatic effect.
In most cases another factor soon intervenes, for the rising
air is cooled to its dew-point, and the 'latent heat of vaporiza-
tion' is liberated on condensation of the vapour; this counteracts the adiabatic cooling to an extent depending on the
amount of vapour condensed, which is much larger at high
than at low temperatures. The net rate of cooling with ascent
of the air after it is saturated (the 'saturated adiabatic lapse-
rate') is at first, if saturation occurs while the air is still fairly
warm, only about half the dry adiabatic, but the rate increases
as the temperature falls with increasing height, till at about
40,000 feet the vapour-content is so small that the saturated
rate is little less than the dry.

In the above facts we have the main explanation of the
decrease in temperature with altitude in the troposphere.
Since the heating of the atmosphere is applied at the base,
convection is set up; additional vertical movement results
from the turbulence always present in the winds. The
whole troposphere is churned and assumes a mean lapse-rate
between the dry and the saturated rates, the atmosphere
being in part dry, in part saturated and condensing its
vapour. But minor influences are present, one being the
distribution of water-vapour, its amount decreasing rapidly
upward; the direct incoming insolation is hardly checked by
it, but the outgoing radiation, which, it must be remembered,
is removing heat always, more by day than by night, is a
much less effective cooling agent at low levels, where its long

waves are checked by the water-vapour and suspensoids, than at high, where the obstacle is much less. Thus the immediate source of heat, the surface of the earth, is at the base of the atmosphere, and the loss of heat by radiation into space increases with altitude; this is another powerful cause of the fall in temperature aloft.

Most cloud, and all thick cloud giving heavy rain, is the result of the adiabatic cooling of ascending air below its dew-point. Hence a weather forecaster has to judge whether ascent will take place; the factors involved are the dry and the saturated lapse-rates, and the temperature of the surrounding air (the 'environment'); a fire-balloon heated to 80° will rise through air at 75° but not through air at 85°. The lapse-rates are known, but the environment must be found by observation by any available method. Air is unstable, buoyant, and will rise as long as it is warmer than its environment, otherwise it is stable, dead, and unable to rise.

Often the lapse-rate of the environment is less than the dry and more than the saturated adiabatic, and the air is stable as long as it is not saturated; but if condensation takes place, its lapse-rate becomes less than that of the environment. Such air is 'potentially unstable' inasmuch as, though otherwise stable, if it is raised by some mechanical influence (e.g. a mountain-barrier in certain circumstances) in the beginning, and carried up past its dry and early saturated stages until it is warmer than the environment, it will then go on rising, with continued condensation, since its saturated lapse-rate is less than the lapse-rate of the environment.

The observed temperatures of the environment, and the lapse-rates of rising or descending air, may be plotted on a height (or pressure)–temperature diagram, and this enables an estimate to be made of the likely magnitude of the ascent or descent of the air at any level, either at the time of observation, or later in the day, anticipated changes of temperature being allowed for, or after the arrival of some expected airmass; and a forecast of the cloud and rain, or it may be the clearing of the sky, which should result, can be made.

The points that have been mentioned are illustrated in Fig. 23 *b*, in which altitudes are shown on the right, pressures on a logarithmic scale on the left. The sloping lines marked February and August give the mean lapse-rates in the atmosphere at Duxford near Cambridge for the extreme months, and the coldest and warmest soundings on record

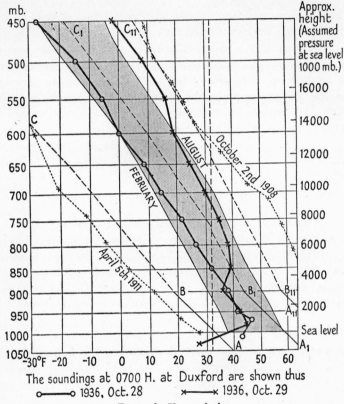

The soundings at 0700 H. at Duxford are shown thus
o——o 1936, Oct. 28   ×——× 1936, Oct. 29

FIG. 23 b. Upper air data

are the lines marked 5 April 1911 and 2 October 1908, respectively. The lines ABC, $A_1B_1C_1$, and $A_{11}B_{11}C_{11}$ show adiabatic lapse-rates, starting, for convenience of reference, at different surface temperatures; the parts AB, A_1B_1, $A_{11}B_{11}$, are the dry adiabatics—parallel since the lapse-rate is the same everywhere; saturation is assumed to occur at 3,000 feet, and BC, B_1C_1, $B_{11}C_{11}$ are the saturated adiabatics with a smaller gradient which increases with height, and gradually approaches that of the dry adiabatics. The heavy lines in the diagram are actual soundings on two consecutive mornings; as is usual they are less regular than the means or the adiabatics, especially in the lower levels with its large inversion, the temperature rising from 28° on the surface to 44° at 1,200 feet on 29 Oct.

For a more complete study the humidities as well as the temperatures, both in the environment and in the rising air, are required, and a more elaborate 'grid' than the one in Fig. 23ƒ must be used; of the several that have been devised the 'tephigram' is most common in Britain. It is a necessary tool for analysing and forecasting stability conditions, on which depend largely the temperatures and the cloud formations at night and still more in the day.

CHAPTER IX

OCEAN CURRENTS

CURRENTS exert so strong a control on ocean temperatures that some knowledge of them is required for climatology. The surface-currents are driven forward by the wind systems about 45° from their own directions, left or right according to the earth's rotational deflexion for the hemisphere. Differences in the density of the water add their effect.

On the east sides of the oceans between the fortieth and twentieth parallels the surface water is urged equatorward by the trades, and forms the California and the Peru currents in the Pacific, the Canaries and the Benguela currents in the Atlantic, and the West Australia current in the S. Indian Ocean; these appear as cool currents since they advance into warmer latitudes and lag in temperature. Another, and more effective, cause of their low temperature is the up-welling of cool water (see p. 278). The currents from the two hemispheres converge as they approach the equator, and they set towards the west as two wide 'Equatorial currents' (separated by a smaller, very warm, 'counter-current' setting east on, or near, the equator itself). In the east of the oceans the Equatorial currents are still cool from their origin, but they warm rapidly on their equatorial passage, and when they diverge to north and south against the western shores their direction keeps them warmer than their environment. These mighty ocean streams carry the heat of the tropics into the temperate and polar zones—the Gulf Stream in the North Atlantic, the Brazil current in the South Atlantic, the Kuro siwo in the North Pacific, the East Australia current in the South Pacific, the East African current (in summer only) in the North Indian, and the Mozambique and Agulhas currents in the South Indian Ocean. Having skirted the coasts to about the fortieth parallel they strike east as extensive ill-defined 'drifts' under the westerlies, crossing the oceans to be caught up in the trade-wind currents with which our description started (but much of the drift water returns equatorwards in more or less well-defined streams in mid-ocean).

In the North Atlantic the shape of the basin complicates the movements, the main drift setting east and north-east from Newfoundland, between Iceland and the British Isles and past the North Cape of Norway and the north Russian coast into the Arctic. The Gulf Stream, from which the North Atlantic Drift is fed, is a massive current for the size of the ocean, since it originates in both the Equatorial currents; for owing to its position and shape the north-east of Brazil turns much of the South Equatorial current into the North Atlantic. The great volume of this warm water is the ultimate cause of the open winters of north-west Europe; for the warmer the surface the lower the atmospheric pressure over it tends to be, as is seen in the persistent Icelandic low pressure system; the low pressures in turn intensify the SW. winds, and consequently the drift of warm water to the coasts of Europe. In the North Pacific the drift seems to consist of a mixture of the warm Kuro siwo and the cold Oya siwo water; it divides on approaching the American coast in about latitude 45° N., part going north off British Columbia as a warm drift for the latitude, and part south as the cool California current.

In the Southern Ocean, north of about 60° S., a great westerly drift circles the globe under the influence of the westerlies; it helps to feed the Peru, Benguela, and West Australia currents.

Of lesser currents mention must be made of the East Greenland and Labrador current. It originates as the out-flow from the Arctic which compensates the inflow of the North Atlantic drift, and sets southward as the Greenland current, very cold and carrying great masses of pack-ice and icebergs through Denmark Strait; having rounded Cape Farewell into Davis Strait, it turns south as the Labrador current to Newfoundland and the Grand Bank (where the ice finally disappears) and thence as a narrow current between the 'Cold Wall' and the shore as far as Cape Hatteras.

The Oya siwo (or Okhotsk current) is a similar but much smaller cold current, which sets southward between the Kuro siwo and north-east Siberia; most of it probably comes from the Bering Sea.

The thermal conservatism of water makes warm currents specially valuable in middle and high latitudes in winter when they pour warmth and moisture into the air over them; cold currents, on the other hand, are most significant in summer in chilling the air and condensing its vapour into fog. On-shore winds carry these temperatures and vapours over the lands, in some regions, including Europe, to great distances, in others not far beyond the littoral.

An interesting feature of the oceanic circulation is the existence of sharp discontinuities of temperature and salinity. They are prominent where warm and cold currents run alongside each other for great distances, as do the tropical Gulf Stream and the polar Labrador currents, and a similar but less marked discontinuity separates the Kuro siwo and Oya siwo in the north-west Pacific. In the south hemisphere the south-going Brazil, Agulhas, and East Australia currents bring warm water into contact with the cold Antarctic drift; in places the two interdigitate, and ships have long reported very abrupt changes of tempera-ture, at times up to 10°, off the south of Africa, between tongues of tropical and polar water. Elsewhere the dis-continuity seems to be more regular for long distances; a difference of about 8° marks the sub-tropical convergence in the South Atlantic (Fig. 24), but the line of convergence is liable to swing north and south through several degrees of latitude. In the Antarctic convergence, which persists with little change in position about latitude 50° S. in the Atlantic and Indian Ocean sectors of the Southern Ocean, and 55° S. in the Pacific sector, the discontinuity amounts

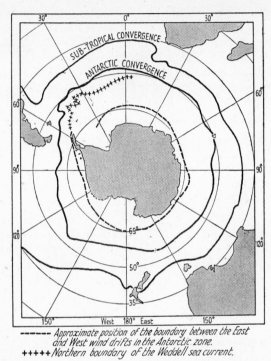

------ Approximate position of the boundary between the East
      and West wind drifts in the Antarctic zone.
+++++ Northern boundary of the Weddell sea current.

FIG. 24. Convergences in the waters of the Southern Ocean (Deacon)

to some 4°; it is within the Antarctic drift itself, and occurs where the cold and less saline surface water from off Antarctica sinks beneath the sub-Antarctic water. Appreciable modifications are to be expected in air-masses crossing these oceanic discontinuities. The convergences in the Southern Ocean have been elucidated by the investigations of the *Discovery*, and they are described by G. E. R. Deacon in *Discovery* Reports, 15 (1937).

(78)

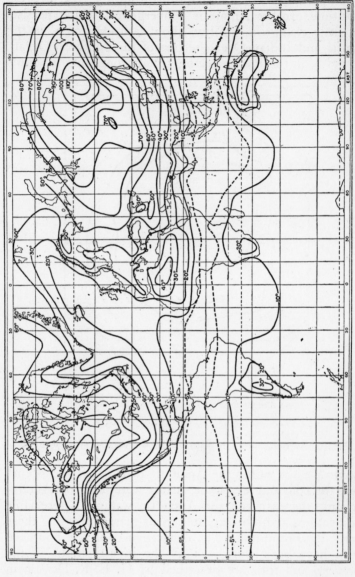

FIG. 25. Mean annual range of temperature (Haurwitz and Austin: *Climatology*. McGraw-Hill Publishing Company, London and New York).

CHAPTER X

REGIONAL DISTRIBUTION OF TEMPERATURE

REFERENCE should be made to Figs. 6 and 7 (pp. 38, 39) for the mean isotherms, and to Fig. 25 for the mean annual range of temperature. The modifications due to altitude, which become prominent above 1,500 feet, are not considered here, but are described in Chapters XXX and XXXIII. The latitudes given as boundaries of the temperature 'belts' are merely convenient approximations.

The Equatorial Belt

Temperature data for representative stations are given on the next page.

Situated roughly between the parallels of 5° N. and S., except where deformed by irregularities of winds or ocean currents, this belt covers an enormous area, extending degree after degree round the globe where degrees are most spacious; any variation from the normal conditions here is likely to have more influence on the rest of the atmosphere than a similar variation in a belt of the same breadth in high latitudes.

As is shown by the wide spacing of the isotherms, the mean temperature is notably uniform, very similar in all the lands, and with only small differences between land and sea, the latter being a little cooler. Everywhere the monotony of the temperature is an outstanding feature; the range between the means of the warmest and coolest months is about 4° on land and less than 1° on the oceans. The temperature of any month rarely differs appreciably from the mean.

On the other hand, the mean range from day to night is between 10° and 15°, about the average for the globe; it is far larger than the mean annual range, this being contrary to what is usual in other zones. The days are not specially hot; a more notable feature is the warmth of the nights, the minimum rarely falling below 67°; many places have never recorded a reading as low as 65°.

Temperature data for representative stations:

Station	Alt., ft.	Mean daily			Mean monthly		Mean temp.		Mean annual range	Abs. extreme		
		Max.	Min.	Range	Max.	Min.	Warmest month	Coolest month		Max.	Min.	Range
Lagos												
Jan.[1]	22	88	74	14	91	68						
Jun.[2]		85	74	11	88	71						
							83	78	5	104	60	44
Léopoldville												
Apr.[2]	1,066	87	80	7	96	67						
Jul.[1]		81	64	17	88	58						
							80	73	7	97	59	38
Mombasa												
Mar.[3]	52	91	77	14	94	75						
Aug.[4]		82	71	11	85	68						
							84	77	7	96	66	30
Kabete (near Nairobi)												
Mar.[3]	5,971	77	57	20	84	46						
Jul.[4]		69	52	17	77	40						
							67	61	6	86	41	45
Nauru (Gilbert Is.)												
May[1]	26	91	76	15	93	72						
Dec.[2]		90	75	15	93	72						
							83	83	<1	97	68	29
Pará												
Apr.[2]	42	87	73	14	90	71						
Oct.[1]		89	71	18	92	69						
							81	79	2	98	64	34
Manáos												
Mar.[2]	144	88	74	14	91	69						
Aug.[1]		91	75	16	95	69						
							84	80	4	101	66	35
Singapore, see below												

[1] Month with least rain. [2] Month with most rain.
[3] Warmest month. [4] Coolest month.

Singapore (Fig. 26, p. 86) illustrates the equatorial climate; the actual records for one year are more instructive than mean values. The warmest month was June, the coolest February, but the temperature difference was only 4°. The highest maximum, 92°, was recorded in May, but in no month did the thermometer fail to reach 88°, and in none did it fall below 70°. The mean diurnal range varied between 11° in December and 13° in March.

KANDANG KERBAN, SINGAPORE

Alt. 33 ft., lat. 1° 18′N.

TEMPERATURE °F.

1925	Mean	Highest maximum	Lowest minimum	Mean diurnal range	Highest wet bulb
Jan.	78·8	89·0	70·0	12·7	81·0
Feb.	78·2	88·0	70·0	12·0	80·0
Mar.	79·7	89·5	70·0	13·4	81·0
Apr.	81·3	90·5	72·5	13·2	82·0
May	82·1	92·2	72·8	13·3	82·5
June	82·6	91·0	73·5	10·9	82·0
July	81·9	91·0	71·0	12·4	82·0
Aug.	81·6	90·4	71·0	12·8	82·0
Sept.	81·2	91·5	72·0	12·3	82·0
Oct.	80·6	89·8	72·2	13·1	82·0
Nov.	80·3	90·8	72·0	13·0	82·0
Dec.	78·8	88·0	71·8	10·8	80·5
Year	80·6			12·5	82·5
Range	4·4	22·2		—	—

The total insolation is more intense in low than in high latitudes, but few useful records are available from the former. Possibly the composition of the insolation which reaches the surface differs appreciably in different equatorial regions; in South America and the East Indies heat-stroke is hardly known, and topees are not used, but in south India and equatorial Africa it used to be much feared, and topees are still used by many residents. Experience suggests that the difference is rather in the habits and health of the European residents than in the insolation; where the physique is much weakened by a long sojourn in an unhealthy environment the susceptibility to heat-stroke is greater, though the quality of the insolation may be the same. Infrared rather than ultra-violet rays are responsible for the heating which causes heat-stroke.

Astronomical and terrestrial conditions combine to produce the monotony of this climate. The mean altitude of the sun for the year is greatest at the equator, where it is overhead twice in the year; but the days are always only 12 hours long. Between the equator and the tropics the sun is overhead twice a year, but the summer days are longer, 13½ hours on the tropics, and therefore hotter. In the neighbourhood of the tropics (mostly trade-wind desert on the lands) the atmosphere tends to be dry and cloudless, and most of the surface is bare sand or rock; the equator, on the other hand, has damp air and much cloud, and the surface is moist, with forests and other dense vegetation, and many water expanses in rivers, lakes, and swamps. The sun's altitude in winter is less, and the day much shorter, in the outer equatorial belt than in south England in summer, but the former enjoys the protection of hundreds of miles of ocean at a high and uniform temperature, a secure defence against the cold of high latitudes. The damp, sultry, calm nights, week after week throughout the year, are perhaps the most trying feature for north Europeans, in whose native land the warmest weather is tempered by cool nights, a minimum as high as 65° being very exceptional.

Monotony characterizes not only the means but also the day-to-day temperatures. Unknown are those irregular variations of high latitudes, where they are often so large as to be unpleasant; with hardly any change each day conforms almost exactly to the mean for its month. Differences that do occur in the 'physiological' temperature result rather from the amount of cloud, an excess making the day cooler by cutting off the sunshine, and the nights warmer by the blanketing effect. And the wind may be a factor, as in the case of the sea-breeze on the shores of the sea or large lakes, a strong breeze giving cool, fresh days.

The monotony is injurious to the health of white men, and unfavourable for high intellectual development of the natives; white men lose both mental and physical vigour, and a change to a bracing climate is desirable each year and essential after a few years. Many regions are hotter, many lands are damper and rainier for part of the year, but they enjoy the great advantage of a cool and dry season. In no month is the mean temperature in the equatorial belt the highest on the globe; far hotter days and nights are frequent in summer in the trade-wind deserts (see p. 85), and even within the Arctic Circle in Canada and Siberia higher maxima are known, but they are rare and confined to the warmest months, while on the equator 85° or higher is recorded on almost every day of the year.

The Inner Tropics (between the equatorial belt and 12° N. and S.)

Temperature data for representative stations:

Station	Alt., ft.	Mean daily			Mean monthly		Mean temp.		Mean annual range	Abs. extreme		
		Max.	Min.	Range	Max.	Min.	Warmest month	Coolest month		Max.	Min.	Range
Kano												
Jan.[1]	1,552	86	55	31	96	49						
Aug.[2]		86	70	16	92	66						
							89	71	18	114	44	70
Elizabethville												
Feb.[2]	4,170	82	61	21	86	57						
Jul.[1]		79	43	36	85	38						
							75	61	14	99	33	66
Darwin												
Jan.[2]	97	90	77	13	96	72						
Jul.[1]		87	67	20	92	61						
							84	77	7	105	56	49
Port of Spain (Trinidad)												
Mar.[1]	72	87	67	20	91	63						
Aug.[2]		87	71	16	90	67						
							79	76	3	101	52	49

[1] Month with least rain.   [2] Month with most rain.

With increasing distance from the equator the mean annual temperature becomes lower and the winters cooler in the land-masses, but the summers warmer; the seasonal change is more prominent. The increasing range may be illustrated from islands of the Pacific far from land (see table on p. 84); on the mainland the increase is more rapid, and depends both on latitude and on the local conditions, being larger in a dry region with little cloud, where it exceeds 10°. But the cool season is not nearly cool enough to be the equivalent of winter in temperate latitudes, and the European finds little advantage over the equatorial belt except in the longer and drier dry season.

The Outer Tropics (latitude 12° to 25°)

Temperature data for representative stations:

Station	Alt., ft.	Mean daily			Mean monthly		Mean temp.		Mean annual range	Abs. extreme		
		Max.	Min.	Range	Max.	Min.	Warmest month	Coolest month		Max.	Min.	Range
Dakar												
Jan.[1]	105	82	64	18	93	59						
Aug.[2]		88	76	12	94	71						
							83	72	11	109	53	56
Wadi Halfa												
Jan.[4]	412	75	46	29	88	38						
Jul.[3]		106	74	32	115	69						
							89	58	31	127	28	99
Walvis Bay												
Feb.[3]	24	74	60	14	85	54						
Aug.[4]		68	46	22	88	38						
							67	57	10	104	25	79
Calcutta												
Jan.[4]	21	77	56	21	83	49						
Jul.[2]		89	79	10	93	75						
							86	64	22	108	44	64
Hyderabad												
Jan.[4]	1,778	85	59	26	90	54						
Jul.[2]		87	73	14	95	70						
							91	69	22	112	49	63
Rio de Janeiro												
Jul.[1]	201	75	63	12	85	58						
Dec.[2]		81	71	10	93	65						
							78	69	9	102	50	72

[1] Month with least rain.   [2] Month with most rain.
[3] Warmest month.   [4] Coolest month.

Data for island stations:

	Lat.	Mean temperature					
		Warmest month	Coolest month	Annual range	Max. for year	Min. for year	Extreme range
Nauru (Gilbert Is.)	0·5° S.	83	83	<1	97	74	23
Malden Is.	4·0° S.	83	81	2	97[1]	65[1]	32[1]
Jaluit Is.	6·1° N.	81	80	1	96	71	25
Guam	13·4° N.	81	77	4	94[1]	64[1]	30[1]
Honolulu	21·3° N.	78	70	8	87	57	30
Midway Is.	28·3° N.	78	65	13	91	46	45

[1] Absolute, not mean, extremes.

The range of temperature becomes still larger, as may be seen from the data for island stations, all near sea-level in the Pacific, far from any continental influence.

The contrast between sea and land (particularly the great areas of semi-arid and desert land) is prominent. In summer the sun is almost overhead, and the days are more than 12 hours long (nearly 14 hours at midsummer in latitude 25°), but in winter the nights are correspondingly longer than the days. The mean temperature exceeds 65° in every month.

The poleward limit of the belt is taken to be latitude 25°, because the lands beyond, in their winter temperature and weather, resemble the sub-tropics more closely, but the trade-wind deserts extend to the thirtieth parallel and in places farther, and in summer the outlying areas are similar to the outer tropics.

The deserts are furnaces of heat in summer; the mean temperature in July exceeds 90° in much of the Sahara. Day after day the thermometer rises above 120°, and the rocks and sand, the clay houses and walls, are so heated that night brings little relief, for even with a drop of 40° it is still extremely hot. But alleviating factors are the very low humidity and the usually strong wind, which cause vigorous evaporation, reducing the temperature 30° or 40° in the hot hours; thanks to this and also to the fairly cool winters the climate is not unhealthy, and provided he has abundance of water man finds even the summers not intolerable. But words fail to portray the horrors of the desert for the traveller who is without water in the heat of summer—the pitiless glare of the unclouded overhead sun, the sand too hot to touch, the air often full of fine dust. Over thousands of miles in the north of the desert of Australia maxima have exceeded 100° on 64 consecutive days. At Azizia, 25 miles south of Tripoli, 136°, the highest reading under standard conditions known on the globe, was recorded in September 1922, and readings above 110° are to be expected in every month from May to September. Death Valley, California, has a record of 134°; the station is 276 feet below sea-level, and this intensifies the normal heat of the trade-wind deserts.[1]

[1] Harrington, M. W., *Climate and Weather of Death Valley, Calif.* U.S. Dept. of Agriculture, Weather Bureau, 1892.

Winter is a distinctly cool season, with a mean for the coolest month of about 75° on the equatorial, 65° on the polar side of the belt; the air temperature may fall to freezing-point beyond latitude 20° on calm cloudless nights, and ground frosts are not uncommon, and towards the polar limits may be keen enough to freeze standing water. The summer heat has little intermission, but in winter polar air-masses appear at irregular intervals and give cold spells,

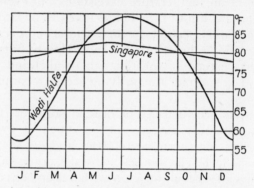

FIG. 26. Mean temperature at Singapore (lat. 2° N.) and Wadi Halfa (lat. 22° N.)

with rain, and in the higher latitudes snow, which, however, does not lie long; it is extremely rare near the south-east shores of the Mediterranean except on the few mountains; on the other hand, in tropical air the thermometer may rise to 100° on sunny afternoons even in mid-winter. In the outer tropics we are already in a region of extremes.

Fig. 26 shows the contrast between Wadi Halfa and Singapore; the absolute range at the former is 99°, at the latter only 31°; with increasing latitude the seasons become strongly differentiated; in the inner tropics the chief difference is in rainfall, but beyond, in the almost rainless deserts, the difference in temperature is pronounced.

Bombay (Fig. 27) is typical of the better-watered lands in the outer tropics where the rainy season begins in the middle of summer with overcast skies, thick clouds, and heavy downpours. So effective are the cloud screen and the

deluges of rain in cooling the air that the temperature curve
shows two maxima, one just before, the other just after, the
rains, and the year is divided into three seasons, the cool
season, the hot season, and the rains. Such are the conditions in the monsoon lands (but only inside the tropics) and
in lands with the Sudan type of climate, where the equatorial
rain-belt is in its extreme position, as at Khartoum and
Timbuktu. The diurnal range is much less during the rains

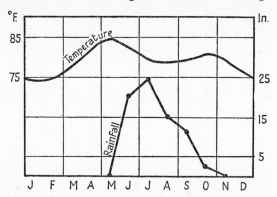

FIG. 27. Mean temperature and rainfall, Bombay

than in the rest of the year owing to the overcast skies and
damp air.

On the oceans the range is far less than in the arid lands
described above. The mean monthly temperature is between 75° and 80° in summer, and rather lower in winter,
and no great extremes can occur; frost is quite unknown.
In the Hawaiian Islands, despite the slight land influence,
frost probably never occurs below 2,500 feet, but the
mountains rise into colder levels, and the tops of Mauna
Loa and neighbouring cones may be snow-covered at midsummer.

The Sub-Tropics (latitude 25° to 45°)

Temperature data for representative stations are given on
the next page.

On land the summers, while much cooler than in the
trade-wind deserts, are not much cooler (in respect of mean

Temperature data for representative stations:

Station	Alt., ft.	Mean daily			Mean monthly		Mean temp.		Mean annual range	Abs. extreme		
		Max.	Min.	Range	Max.	Min.	Warmest month	Coolest month		Max.	Min.	Range
Algiers												
Jan.[4]	194	59	49	10	67	41						
Jul.		83	70	13	97	64						
							78	54	24	112	28	84
Johannesburg												
Jan.[2,3]	5,925	76	56	20	86	48						
Jul.[1,4]		60	41	19	68	31						
							66	51	15	94	23	71
Baghdad												
Jan.[4]	120	59	38	21	68	29						
Jul.[1,3]		109	79	30	116	73						
							95	49	46	123	19	104
Shanghai (Zi-ka-wei)												
Jan.[4]	23	46	33	13	62	19						
Jul.[3]		90	74	16	98	67						
							82	39	43	104	10	94
Chungking												
Jan.[1,4]	755	50	41	9	58	35						
Jul.		92	76	16	102	69						
							85	45	40	111	29	82
San Francisco												
Jan.[2,4]	155	55	45	10	63	39						
Jul.[1]		65	53	12	78	50						
							61	50	11	101	27	74
New York												
Jan.[1,4]	314	37	24	13	58	9						
Jul.[3]		82	66	16	94	55						
							74	31	43	102	−14	116
Buenos Aires												
Jan.[3]	82	85	63	22	97	50						
Jul.[1,4]		57	42	15	72	28						
							74	49	25	103	22	81
Cape Town												
Jan.[3]	40	80	61	19	95	52						
Jul.[4]		63	48	15	76	37						
							71	56	15	105	32	73

[1] Month with least rain.　　　　[2] Month with most rain.
[3] Warmest month.　　　　[4] Coolest month.

temperature) than on the equator, and even higher maxima occasionally occur (e.g. 110° at Toulouse, south France, on 9 August 1923). But in the interior and east of N.

America and Eurasia the winters are cold, with severe frost and snow, and frequent bitterly cold polar winds; the west coasts are favoured by warm winds from the ocean. The pressure-systems of the westerlies are prominent, especially in winter, bringing large variations of weather, including temperature, which are increased locally by the topography, as with winds of the föhn and mistral types. The duration of sunshine and exposure to it as determined by slope, and shelter from polar winds, are important considerations for living things, and differ much from place to place. On the other hand in summer a free exposure to the wind, especially the sea-breeze, gives a welcome alleviation of the heat.

The annual range of temperature increases with latitude, but is largely determined by continentality also, being about 30° in the west (less than in the trade-wind deserts), and between 40° and 70° in the interior and east of Asia and rather less in North America; the continents of the south hemisphere have about 30°, 20° on the coasts.

The seasons are marked as much by temperature as by other elements; nearly all the lands have at least 4 months with a mean above 70°, and at least 4 below 60°. Hot summers (dry and sunny in the west, moist and rainy in the east of the land-masses), cool or cold winters, are the prominent features of the yearly rhythm. Owing to the strong control by continentality three stations, representing the west, the interior, and the east, are required to give even a rough picture (Fig. 28); Algiers is a 'Mediterranean' station in the west, Shanghai is in the east, and Baghdad in the arid interior. The winters are warmest on the west coast, the Mediterranean region having oceanic winds and cyclonic weather, much colder in the east, where the winter monsoon blows from the very cold and dry steppes and deserts of Mongolia. In summer Baghdad is distinguished by its great heat which it shares with the trade-wind deserts; no clouds cut off the sunshine that beats down with fierce intensity on the arid plains; in July the mean daily maximum is 109°, and 123° has been recorded. Underground chambers are a refuge, not very effective, from the heat of the day, and at night the house-top which catches the breeze is a favourite sleeping-place, for the air temperature does not usually fall below 80°.

Land and sea influences, including the sea-breeze, are prominent, even in the small peninsulas and islands; the mean annual range at Lisbon is 21°, and rises to 38° at Madrid. Weather is a prominent element of the climate since the

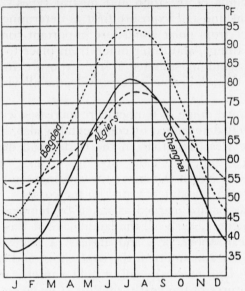

FIG. 28. Mean temperature in the sub-tropics

pressure irregularities of the westerlies invade the region. The Mediterranean lands often suffer severely from cold winds from the north, and the temperature falls well below freezing-point except in the islands and on the south shores; in the very severe winter of 1891 the inner harbours of Toulon and Lisbon were ice-bound. Snow is not uncommon, and it has fallen even in the north of the Sahara; but in spring and autumn it is the heat of the south wind in front of depressions which is a serious visitation (p. 159). The south of the U.S.A. is invaded by cold waves which may bring freezing temperatures to the shores of the Gulf of Mexico. These polar visitations are far more intense in the interior and east of the continents, but less noticeable in the cold winters there.

In the sub-tropics—and still more in the higher temperate latitudes—the annual range of temperature is so large that the transition seasons, spring and autumn, are important divisions of the year.

The cold-water coasts, an interesting part of the outer- and sub-tropics, are described in Chapter XXVIII; they are notable for their cool summers, rainless but with damp air and frequent fog, and their small range of temperature.

The Temperate Belts (latitude 45° to 66½°)

Temperature data for representative stations:

Station	Alt., ft.	Mean daily			Mean monthly		Mean temp.		Mean annual range	Abs. extreme		
		Max.	Min.	Range	Max.	Min.	Warmest month	Coldest month		Max.	Min.	Range
Kew												
Jan.[1]	34	45	36	9	53	22						
Jul.[2]		71	55	16	82	47						
							63	41	22	94	9	85
Semipalatinsk												
Jan.[1]	525	8	−7	15	30	−35						
Jul.[2]		81	57	24	96	47						
							69	1	68	101	−47	148
Vladivostok												
Jan.[1]	420	13	0	13	29	−13						
Jul.		71	60	11	85	53						
							69	7	62	96	−22	118
Victoria, B.C.												
Jan.[1]	228	43	35	8	52	22						
Jul.[2]		69	52	17	83	47						
							60	39	21	91	7	84
Montreal												
Jan.[1]	187	21	6	15	42	−16						
Jul.[2]		78	61	17	89	52						
							70	14	56	97	−29	126

[1] Coldest month.   [2] Warmest month.

This belt is temperate only in the sense that in its mean annual temperature it is between the equatorial and the polar zones. In other respects the name is unsuitable, for the temperature ranges from high to very low, indeed the lowest recorded, and larger and more sudden fluctuations occur than anywhere else, with rises or falls of 20° or more in a few hours even in the mild oceanic division. The oscillations may be of long duration, whole seasons being abnormally cold or warm. Lying between the cold polar zones and the warm tropics, these latitudes are liable to be invaded by air-masses from both sides in the pressure irregularities of the westerlies. The temperature has a large range from summer to winter, so that a statement of the annual mean conveys little useful information; Valencia, in south-west Ireland, has almost the same annual mean as Peiping (Peking), but the mean range is only 15° at the former, 55° at the latter.

More than in the sub-tropics, position in relation to land and sea exerts so strong a control that no one station can be regarded as typical, and we must examine at least three, one in an ocean or on its eastern, windward coast, one in the interior, and one on the east of a continent with winds from the land in winter, from the sea in summer. The north hemisphere contains extensive regions in all three categories, but most of the zone in the south hemisphere is unbroken ocean, save for the narrow extremity of South America.

In addition to the data in the table on p. 91, some details for Valencia, latitude 52° N. in the south-west of Ireland, are given here. At Valencia, in view of the high latitude and consequent large range in the sun's altitude and in the length of the day, the notable features are the remarkably warm winters (no month has a mean below 45°), the cool summers, and the small range of temperature. The warmest month is August, the coolest February, the long 'lag' behind the sun being typical of an oceanic climate. Spring is much cooler than autumn, the mean for March being 45°, for September 57°. The diurnal range, always small, is least in winter (only 7° in January), but even in May, the month with the largest range nearly everywhere in this belt, it is only 10°; extreme cold and heat are unknown. Frost is rare—rarer than on the north shores of the Mediterranean Sea—and the temperature has not been known to fall below 20°. A few sub-tropical plants flourish, the strawberry tree, fuchsia, and laurel, but the cool damp summers preclude true Mediterranean vegetation. Continental features appear within a few hundred miles of the western seaboard; off the south-east of England the inshore waters have been ice-covered in occasional very severe winters, and drifting ice-floes have hindered navigation in the south of the North Sea.

The long transition seasons in oceanic temperate climates are noteworthy. Spring is said to begin with March, but some years give signs of its approach in February, and the season continues, in a succession of bursts of warmth and returns to cold, till June, the cold being more prominent than the warmth in most years. In middle and high latitudes spring is the most interesting season of the year, and May the most variable of the months. With a few exceptions both the mean air temperature and the precipitation are much lower than in the autumn months which correspond astronomically. It is a season of contrasts. The polar regions are still snow-covered, and in lower latitudes snow lies on mountains and on some continental lowlands; in the Peace River valley, Alberta, lat. 58° N., the winter snow is melted by the beginning of April, and wheat may be sown in the middle of that month, to ripen within 90 days. The days are already hot in spring on the plains in the south, for the sun's altitude is increasing fast, and insolation is powerful even where the air temperature is low; strong winds make the temperature contrasts the more sensible physiologically, and the change from cloudy skies to full sunshine is prominent. Cyclonic activity is vigorous, and warm air-masses from the tropics may find themselves adjacent to polar air of almost winter type; cold fronts sweep down with their frowning rolls of black cloud, and give fierce, though short, squalls, at times with heavy rain, snow, hail, and thunder. Spring is the snowiest season in much of the westerlies (16 inches of snow fell in Oxford as late as 25 April in 1908), and the sudden returns of winter frosts remind us that summer is still many weeks away; spells of gloomy skies overcast with strato-cumulus, and bleak NE. winds, alternate with warm and bracing days of cumulus cloud dazzlingly white in the sunshine and blue sky. In many years a final, and sometimes severe, return of the sharp cold of winter works havoc with the young fruit about the second week of

May (the days of the 'Ice Saints'). Despite some discomforts spring is much more exhilarating than autumn, the season of damp air and fog, and few weather incidents save gales, heavy rains, and fogs.

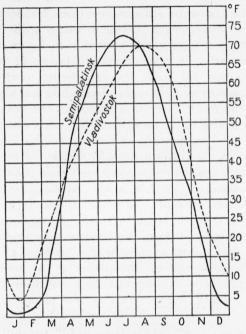

FIG. 29. Mean temperature

The winters become rapidly colder and longer eastward into the great land-masses. Semipalatinsk (Fig. 29) has a decidedly continental climate, though by no means so continental as the east of Siberia; five months (November–March) have a mean below 32°, the mean for January, the coldest month, being 0°, and during the whole the ground is snow-covered and the rivers ice-bound. The summers are warm for the latitude, with monthly means well over 60° in June, July, and August (72° in July, 10° warmer than in the south of England); the mean annual range is 71°. The change from week to week in the transition seasons is rapid —the mean is 19° higher in May than in April, and the drop in autumn is equally fast; early September is still summer, but the rigours of winter set in before the end of October.

Vast areas in the north of Canada and of Russia and Siberia have permanently frozen ground beneath the surface layer which thaws in summer. In Russia the area extends between the Arctic shores and roughly a line from the north of the White Sea to L. Baikal and thence east to the mouth of the Amur; the depth and thickness of the layer of frozen ground vary regionally, but it lies approximately between 20 feet and 70 feet below the surface.

The steppe lands of Russia, Siberia, and North America are included in this region. The rapid transformation in spring is graphically described by Brehm:

Even before the last patches of snow have vanished, the bulbous plants, and others which live through the winter, put forth their leaves and raise their flower-stalks to the sun. Among the sere yellow grass and the dry grey stems of all herbs which were not snapped by the autumnal storms the first green shimmers. From the apparently sterile earth herbaceous and bulbous growths shoot up; buds are unpacked, flowers unfold, and the steppe arrays itself in indescribable splendour. Boundless tracks are resplendent with tulips, yellow, dark-red, white, white and red. It is true that they rise singly or in twos or threes, but they are spread over the whole steppe-land, and flower at the same time, so that one sees them everywhere. Immediately after the tulips come the lilies, and even more charming colours appear wherever these lovely children of the steppes find the fit conditions for growth; they completely dominate wide stretches of country.

The deserts of central Asia are notable for their intensely cold winters, with rivers frozen to the bottom, but they are comparable with the Sahara in their summer heat; latitude, altitude, and continentality conspire to give the enormous range of temperature.

Vladivostok (Fig. 29) is 9° of latitude south of Valencia (and slightly outside the limit we have chosen for this belt). The Pacific Ocean is to leeward in winter and provides little heat, the winter air-masses being brought from the steppes of the interior by the winter monsoon. The cold is intense for the latitude. The rivers are frozen for 15 weeks, and the harbours on the coast closed to navigation from mid-December till

the beginning of April unless kept open by ice-breakers.
The coldest spots are where valleys open on the coast, giving
passage to the bitter blasts from the interior. The land is
snow-covered, sledges are the usual transport, and heavy fur
garments are worn. The thermometer may fall to − 20°.

Summer is much warmer than at Valencia, thanks partly
to the latitude, partly to the summer monsoon from the
warm waters of the Pacific. But it is not so warm as at Semipalatinsk in the far interior. This is the rainy season, damp
and cloudy; the summer heat, though not excessive, is
enervating, with small range of temperature from day to
night. The mean annual range is 62°. Autumn is warmer
than spring, the excess of October over April being 9°, but
the transition seasons are short—summer passes rapidly
into winter, September being as warm as the English July,
November much colder than the English January. Spring
is really reduced to the one month of May; April is still
winter, June already summer.

The Tundra Lands

Temperature data for representative stations:

Station	Alt., ft.	Mean daily			Mean monthly		Mean temp.		Mean annual range	Abs. extreme		
		Max.	Min.	Range	Max.	Min.	Warmest month	Coldest month		Max.	Min.	Range
Coppermine (68° N., 115° W.)												
Jan.[1]	coast	−12	−26	14	10	−45						
Jul.[2]		58	42	16	78	34						
							50	−19	69	87	−54	141
Wrangel Island (71° N., 179° W.)												
Jan.[1]		−3	−18	15	16	−37						
Jul.[2]		42	32	10	55	27						
							37	−10	47			

[1] Coldest month.   [2] Warmest month.

Most of the tundra lands are just inside the Arctic circle,
the corresponding latitudes in the south hemisphere being
either ocean or everlasting snow and ice. Winter is without
effective sunshine for several months, and the cold is intense

both by day and night, though not so intense as farther
inland where continental influence more than balances the
lower latitude. The monthly mean is below zero from
November to April and minima of − 60° are frequent. In
many tracts snow and ice remain unmelted in summer, and
everywhere the subsoil is permanently frozen; the coasts are
ice-bound most of the year. The winters are polar, but the
summers distinguish the tundra from the polar regions,
having at least 1 month with a mean above 40°. July and
August may be pleasantly warm or even hot, with midday
temperature above 80° at some distance from the sea, but
the ground a few feet below the surface is frozen solid. Slope
is all-important owing to the low sun; on sunward slopes the
snow melts, the water drains away, and the ground is warmed
enough to produce a hardy xerophytic vegetation with over
100 species of flowering plants, but the flat ground is sodden
and marshy.

The tundra is favoured over the polar region in having
some summer—short and cool, but enough to make vegetation possible. On the other hand, the shortness and coolness
of the summer, no month having a mean much above 50°,
together with the permanently frozen subsoil, the water-
logged surface, and above all the strong winds, preclude the
forest growth which characterizes the lands on the south,
and condemn even the most favoured slopes to a stunted
shrubby growth; large expanses remain for ever wastes of
snow, mud, and marsh, frozen hard for half the year.

The Polar Regions

Representative data are given on page 100.

North Hemisphere

The Arctic Ocean fills most of the area, thousands of
square miles completely ice-covered in winter except where
the North Atlantic Drift enters, but with a good deal of open
water in summer. It is surrounded by Eurasia, America,
and Greenland, and their island groups. The winters are
much less cold than in Antarctica; temperature falls fast in
autumn, and changes little in the months January to March.
The January mean is estimated at about − 40° at the pole,

and between −40° and −20° over most of the basin, but it
increases rapidly over the Atlantic Drift towards Spitzbergen
(0°) and Norway. The lowest record, taken by the *Fram* in
March in 80° N., 135° E., was −62°. Peary recorded
−40° near the pole in April. The surrounding lands are
much colder than the ocean in winter. The mean monthly
air temperature over the whole ocean in summer is about 32°,
with a large and abrupt rise on the continental coasts, where
the land heats up in the long polar days. The mean annual
range is thus 60° or 70°—a remarkable high figure for an
oceanic climate, but understandable in view of the alternation
of months of continuous day and months of continuous
night, of almost unbroken ice in winter and much open water
in summer. The summers are the bleakest and coldest
known at sea-level in the north hemisphere, but they are less
cold than in Antarctica.

The ice-cap of Greenland is cold in summer, extremely
cold in winter. At Eismitte, latitude 71° N., altitude
10,000 feet, in the year 1930–1 the mean monthly temperature ranged from 7° in July to −60° in February. −84°
was recorded in January, February, and March, so it is likely
that the middle of the ice-cap has the coldest winters on the
globe; and the winters are very long as well as cold, for
−60° was recorded as early as 10 October and as late as
12 April. Even in summer the highest reading was 28°, and
−30° occurred in June and August. A very prominent
feature was the strong inversion of temperature which was
always present except in the strongest winds, and as soon as
the wind fell and the sky cleared after such a break the inversion formed again at once; on ten occasions in the winter the
temperature fell more than 35° in 24 hours. Inversions are
the more natural as the surface at 10,000 feet in these latitudes is not far below the tropopause.

South Hemisphere

In the south hemisphere most of the polar zone is land,
the lofty snow-covered plateau of Antarctica rising steeply
from the sea to over 6,000 feet and attaining at least
15,000 feet in the interior. The winters are very cold, for the

dry powdery snow efficiently insulates the surface from the warmer land beneath, and the sky is clear and the air dry; the middle of the plateau must be one of the coldest tracts on the globe in winter with temperatures falling below − 80°, but records are not yet available. Temperature can change little from day to night where the sun never appears above the horizon; and large fluctuations of temperature from day to day are unlikely. At the pole the sun rises in September, and climbs higher each day to an altitude of 23½° at the solstice; but the air does not nearly reach freezing-point despite the 24-hour day, since the snow is not melted. In the four days 16–20 January 1912, when Scott's party was at the south pole or within 30 miles of it, the highest reading was − 19°, the lowest − 27°. The altitude, about 9,000 feet, is in itself a cause of the great cold, but even with the usual correction to sea-level the January mean is probably not above 15°. The annual range, unlike the daily, is very large, though probably much less than in Siberia and north Canada with their warmer summers.

Even at sea-level on the shores of Antarctica the summers are remarkably cold, no month having a mean above 32°. On the south coast of the Ross Sea the January mean is probably about 20°, and on the shores of the open Southern Ocean about 30°. A result, and at the same time a cause, of the low temperature is that even here no ground is bare of snow; no animals (except birds) or flowering plants can live. The sun is above the horizon the whole of the 24 hours at midsummer, but its altitude ranges (in latitude 70°) from 44° at noon to 4° at midnight, and the diurnal range of temperature is about 10°. The highest temperature in 4 years on Ross Island was 42°, and most summer nights had a minimum below 20°. The warmest month is December, the month with the highest sun (the usual lag in air temperature behind the curve of insolation is absent).

The winters, with little if any sunshine, are cold; the mean temperature in August, the coldest month, is about − 15° on Ross Island, and on the Great Barrier it is estimated at below − 35°. The lowest minimum in Antarctica, − 76°, was recorded on the Barrier near Ross Island on 6 July 1911.

On the coasts of the Southern Ocean the August mean is about − 10°.

On and around Ross Island temperature falls fast after the summer solstice, and then the monthly mean remains at − 12° from April to September, when the even more rapid rise to the summer maximum starts. The daily range is considerable, least in summer, about 10°, and increasing to 17° in winter. The rises and falls have little relation to the time of day, but depend on the direction and force of the wind and on the state of the sky.

Temperature data for representative stations:

Station	Alt., ft.	Mean daily			Mean monthly		Mean temp.		Mean annual range	Abs. extreme		
		Max.	Min.	Range	Max.	Min.	Warmest month	Coldest month		Max.	Min.	Range
Green Harbour (Spitzbergen)												
Jan.¹	36	10	−4	14	32	−30						
Jul.²		46	38	8	53	33						
							42	−3	45	60	−57	117
Gaasefjord (77° N., 89° W.)												
Jan.¹	coast	−29	−41	12	−10	−53						
Jul.²		46	35	11	54	32						
							41	−35	76	56	−61	117

¹ Coldest month.   ² Warmest month.

PART II
ATMOSPHERIC PRESSURE AND WINDS

CHAPTER XI
THE MEASUREMENT OF PRESSURE

Barometers. Pressure Changes

Two forms of barometer are in common use. For accurate measurements the mercury barometer is employed. In it a column of mercury adjusts its length automatically so that it balances the weight of a column of the atmosphere of equal section. The instrument is graduated to give readings of precision, and is usually read to 0·1 millibar (or 0·002 inch; the scale of inches refers to the length of the column of mercury, the millibar scale to units of pressure, 1,000 millibars being equivalent to 29·53 inches of mercury at 32° F. in latitude 45°).

A more portable and convenient, but less accurate, instrument is the aneroid, the essential element of which is a spring which is compressed more or less as the pressure of the atmosphere changes. The spring is contained in an air-tight box almost exhausted of air, the upper lid of which rests on the spring and, being flexible, is free to move as the pressure on it changes; if the box were not air-tight the changing pressure would not produce any movement in the lid, since both sides of it would be equally affected.

Continuous self-registered records of pressure are most valuable in the study of the atmosphere, and both types of barometer can be arranged to give them. The instrument in commonest use is the barograph, in which the reading of an aneroid is registered by a pen on a revolving drum. A good instrument of this pattern, kept in good order, gives records accurate enough for most purposes of climatology, and is useful and instructive.

Several distinct types of pressure change occur in the atmosphere. In temperate latitudes the most noticeable and

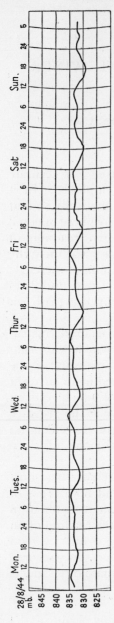

frequent is a fairly steady 'cyclonic' rise or fall which may last for only a few hours or as long as several days (Fig. 119, p. 355); such changes are associated with the pressure-systems which exert a strong control on the weather. Another type is a semi-diurnal oscillation, which has no direct connexion with weather but depends on the time of day; pressure increases to a maximum about 1000, falls to a minimum at 1600, rises to a second maximum at 2200, and falls to a second minimum at 0400 (Fig. 30). The amplitude is greatest, 3 to 4 millibars, at the equator, where this oscillation, being the only appreciable change, is the more prominent; Humboldt remarked long ago that it is so regular that we can tell the time by the barometer. With increasing latitude it diminishes, till in middle latitudes it is hardly noticeable except during settled anticyclonic weather, being masked at other times by the weather irregularities.

Yet another type is seen in the jerks, usually upward, in the trace, of as much as 3 millibars. They are often associated with the violent phenomena, squalls of wind, heavy showers, thunder and lightning, of a cold front.

Sometimes a generally level trace has oscillations of small amplitude and short period, continuing for perhaps 6 or 9 hours (Fig. 31), which often seem to be independent of weather changes.

Despite these irregularities the mean pressure is nearly constant for any given place and season. It is low, about

FIG. 30. Barogram, Nairobi (alt. 5,450 ft.; lat. 1·2° S.)

1,010 millibars (29·8 inches) at sea-level, near the equator, and gradually rises polewards to a maximum in the 'horse latitudes' about 35° N. and 30° S., where it exceeds 1,020 millibars (30·1 inches). Thence it falls to a minimum of about 1,005 millibars (29·7 inches) in the neighbourhood of 60° N. and S., and rises slightly again to the poles.

In temperate latitudes the pressure ranges from about 60

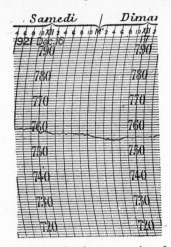

FIG. 31. Barogram showing a succession of oscillations of pressure

millibars below to 30 millibars above the mean. In the British Isles the mean is 1,012 millibars (29·9 inches) and readings below 927 millibars (27·4 inches) and above 1,050 millibars (31 inches) have been recorded. The variations decrease toward the equator, where the extreme range is less than 15 millibars.

The Velocity of the Wind

This is measured at well-equipped stations by self-recording instruments, the most common being the Dines Pressure-tube Anemometer, a large and elaborate instrument, a description of which may be found in *The Meteorological Observer's Handbook*. But most observations are estimates, without instrumental aid, on the Beaufort scale, which was laid down in 1805 by Admiral Beaufort for use at sea, and was soon used on land also; the effect of the wind on surface objects, the waves on water, the leaves, twigs, and branches of trees on land, is noted, and the appropriate number found on the scale according to the accepted table of equivalents. The scale is:

BEAUFORT SCALE Number	WIND VELOCITY m.p.h. (at 33 ft. above the surface)
0	less than 1
1	1–3
2	4–7
3	8–12
4	13–18
5	19–24
6	25–31
7	32–8
8	39–46
9	47–54
10	55–63
11	64–75
12	above 75

It has recently been extended to 17, to cover the higher velocities found in the upper atmosphere. The scale is easily learnt and used, and is satisfactory in practice within its limits.

Pressure Differences due to Differential Heating

In Fig. 32, (1) represents a section of the atmosphere; the temperature is the same along horizontal planes and the air is at rest. In (2) the column above BC is enclosed by air-tight walls and is warmed from the base; the air expands, and being unable to move sideways, rises; in spite of the heating there is no change in the pressure on BC, since all the air that was in the column before heating is still present. Let the partition be removed, (3); the air on the top of the column above BC will at once flow sideways, and a difference in pressure is set up, since the flow removes air from above BC and adds air outside. The lower layers now flow from AB and CD towards BC, the heated, low-pressure area, rising currents above BC feed the outflow above, and descending currents above AB and CD feed the surface winds. The upper and lower winds are separated by a 'neutral plane' without horizontal movement. As long as the heating of BC is continued the circulation is maintained.

This thermal circulation is found round the coasts of an island which is warmer than the sea by day, cooler at night,

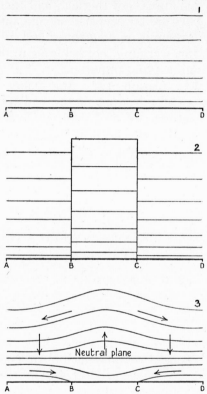

FIG. 32. Air-movements and pressure changes due to differential heating

and it gives rise there to a daily rhythm (sea- and land-breeze), and on a larger scale round a continent where the rhythm is seasonal with monsoonal winds.

Similarly high-pressure systems may be formed above cold surfaces; they are known as 'cold anticyclones', and prominent examples are those in the north-east of Asia and the north of Canada in winter, in Greenland, and in the polar regions. In them the air descends to feed the outblowing surface winds, but cold anticyclones are shallow systems,

the cold layer not exceeding some 10,000 feet in depth; the
descending air is warmed adiabatically but the warming is
more than neutralized by the intensely cold surface. The
other large anticyclones on the globe, 'warm anticyclones',
are dynamic structures, not thermal, and their home is the
sub-tropics. They are far deeper than cold anticyclones; the
air subsiding in them is much warmed and dried and except
in a few cases this warming, not being neutralized by a cold
surface, is prominent and important.

The general circulation of the atmosphere as a whole depends on the greater heating of the equatorial zone; but
many of the features are evidently not due to differential
heating, and in particular most of the temporary irregularities, depressions and anticyclones, call for some other
explanation.

CHAPTER XII

DECREASE OF PRESSURE WITH INCREASE OF ALTITUDE. PHYSIOLOGICAL EFFECTS

THE human body is not sensible to the small changes of
pressure mentioned in the last chapter. Much larger
changes are experienced in ascents in the free atmosphere
or on a mountain, as shown by the following table of pressures at different levels in the atmosphere taken as average
by the International Commission for Air Navigation, temperature being assumed to decrease in the troposphere
approximately 1° in 300 feet:

Sea-level	1,013 mb.		10,000 ft.	697 mb.
2,000 ft.	942 ,,		20,000 ,,	465 ,,
4,000 ,,	875 ,,		30,000 ,,	301 ,,
6,000 ,,	812 ,,		40,000 ,,	187 ,,
8,000 ,,	753 ,,			

The lowest layers are the densest owing to the pressure of
the layers above, and the fall in pressure in any interval is
more rapid near sea-level than at greater altitudes; at
17,500 feet the pressure is only about half that at sea-level.

At considerable altitudes the much-reduced pressure may
cause 'mountain-sickness', a malady well known on the

plateau of the Andes. At first the respiration quickens and
the skin gets blue; the mental powers begin to fail, and at
very low pressures paralysis of the limbs, and finally death,
may occur. Prolonged exposure to a moderate decrease of
pressure may lead to headaches, sleeplessness, and sickness,
owing to the decrease in the oxygen-pressure in the lungs;
but if the change in altitude is effected slowly the body may
be able to acclimatize itself so as to suffer no ill effects. The
party of the Duke of the Abruzzi reached 24,600 feet in the
Himalayas with such immunity from discomfort that they
concluded that mountain-sickness must really be due to
causes other than mere change of pressure, probably to
fatigue, but these climbers had probably been acclimatized
by their slow ascent. The trials of the British Everest expedition of 1924 show the effects on new arrivals; after a
climb of 50 feet, a member of the expedition writes, 'you fall
exhausted on the snow. It seems touch and go whether by
rapid panting you will ever catch up the deficit of oxygen in
the lungs the exertion has caused. . . . Above 27,000 feet
[during a climb] you may aim at doing 20 consecutive paces
before you pause, arm on bent knee, to pant and rest. You sit
down for some minutes at least every 100 feet.' When the
change of pressure is rapid the results may be fatal, as in
the balloon ascent of Croce-Spinelli, Sirel, and Tissandier in
1875. They attained 24,600 feet in some 2 hours without
serious discomfort, ballast was then thrown out and the
balloon rapidly rose higher, the altimeter registering a
maximum height of 28,600 feet. Soon all three occupants
were paralysed and unconscious. Tissandier alone recovered
consciousness when the balloon fell to 20,000 feet; his two
companions were dead. They were all provided with oxygen
apparatus, but apparently they succumbed so suddenly that
they had no time to adjust it before they lost their faculties.
Muscular exertion is not an essential factor in mountain-
sickness, but it may hasten it. Men in good physical training
are less subject than others. The preventive is the artificial
provision of oxygen, and apparatus for this purpose is regularly used by the crews of aircraft above 15,000 feet. Some
reference to the effects of reduced pressure on plateaux is
made on p. 312.

CHAPTER XIII

THE MOVEMENTS OF THE AIR

For climatology the important aspect of the distribution of pressure is its control of the winds. The air moves from higher pressure to lower, at a speed depending on the pressure gradient, which is defined as the decrease of pressure in unit distance in the direction of greatest decrease, that is normal to the isobars.

The pressure distribution is shown on maps by means of isobars, lines along which the pressure, 'corrected to sea-level', is the same (as contour lines are lines of equal height on a topographical map). The correction to sea-level is necessary, since without it the meteorological differences are masked by those due to altitude, and the map shows little except the relief of the country; the amount of correction depends on altitude and air temperature. The closer the sea-level isobars the steeper is the gradient and the stronger the winds.

No clear picture of the movements of the atmosphere, either the mean circulation or the conditions at any moment for synoptic studies, is possible unless the upper as well as the surface winds are included, and for many practical purposes, including aerial navigation, both are required. But in this book, which is devoted to surface climatology, attention is given mainly to the surface winds.

The movement of the air is not directly down the gradient, for, owing to the rotation of the earth, moving bodies appear to be deflected relatively to the surface, towards the right in the north hemisphere, towards the left in the south; in reality it is the earth that is deflected by its rotation under the atmosphere, the air continuing to move in a straight line. The deflexion (or Coriolis force) increases polewards, from zero at the equator, with the sine of the latitude, and its effect is prominent in all charts of the winds; for convenience only the north hemisphere is referred to in this chapter.

Thus the air moves under two forces, the pressure gradient and rotational deflexion; above the friction layer (i.e. the lowest 1,500 feet, in which the effect of friction with the surface is appreciable) steady motion is attained, in the case of straight isobars, with the air moving along, not across, the sea-level isobars, towards the right of the gradient direction with velocity depending on the gradient and on the latitude; it is called the geostrophic wind, and is the wind appropriate to the pressure distribution on the surface when surface friction is eliminated, that is, at an altitude of about 2,000 feet (Fig. 33). At greater altitudes other factors, particularly the distribution of temperature in the atmo-

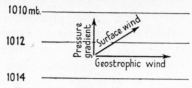

FIG. 33. Pressure-gradient and wind directions

sphere between the surface and the altitude considered, which may give rise to a 'thermal wind' as a component, come in to modify it, even to the extent of reversing the direction.

It should be noted that a wind must blow steadily for some time before it can become strictly geostrophic, and that is possible only if the isobars remain unchanged long enough, which is rarely the case. The isobars shown on any one synoptic chart do not usually indicate the track that an air-mass has followed for any length of time, but give only a good approximation to the movement at the hour of the chart, since isobars are always changing position, often rapidly.

A scale can be constructed to show the velocity of the geostrophic wind, and is useful in reading synoptic charts; Fig. 34 shows the scale for the British daily charts. The surface winds are much weaker than the geostrophic given on the

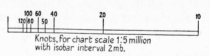

Knots, for chart scale 1:5 million with isobar interval 2 mb.

FIG. 34. Geostrophic wind scale for the following conditions: pressure 1,000 mb., air temperature 50° F., latitude 55°

scale, about one-third as strong on average land, two-thirds as strong at sea (with normal lapse rate of temperature), and they blow across the isobar, some 30° towards the low pressure on land, 10° to 15° at sea.

The same gradient gives a much stronger wind in low than in high latitudes, about four times as strong in latitude 10° as in latitude 50°, but the gradients are usually less steep in the tropics and the winds are lighter than in the temperate belts except in occasional storms. At the equator there is no rotational deflexion, and therefore strictly no geostrophic wind.

Isobars are often rather curved than straight, enclosing high- and low-pressure systems, and the curvature introduces an additional factor, the centrifugal force developed in the circling air, a force proportional directly to the square of the velocity of the air, and inversely to the radius of its path; its value is, of course, independent of latitude. It is known as the cyclostrophic component, and the wind that results from its addition to the geostrophic wind is the 'gradient wind' which actually blows (above the friction layer). In a cyclonic curvature the cyclostrophic component is directed against the barometric gradient, and reduces the velocity for any gradient, and in an anticyclonic the two forces act in the same direction and the wind is stronger. The cyclostrophic component must be largest in the violently revolving cyclones of the tropics, where the geostrophic component is small; in middle and high latitudes it is usually far outweighed by the geostrophic component.

In the friction layer the wind is slowed down as the surface is approached, and instead of blowing along the isobars it crosses them at an angle (Fig. 33), the size of which depends on the altitude and on the friction. Friction is greater on land than at sea, on land with forests or closely built areas than on bare open plains. Confirmation of this may be obtained from observation of the low clouds, which move from a point more or less to the right of the surface wind; the high clouds may be at a level where the gradient is not the same as below and their movement is not comparable.

A result of the difference between land and sea is a discontinuity along the shore, of velocity when the wind is at right angles to the coast, and of both velocity and direction when it blows obliquely; rising air-currents, sometimes marked by a line of cloud, are set up where the off-shore winds converge with winds of the same system which have travelled some distance over the sea and have a direction more nearly parallel to the isobars.

Turbulence

The wind is never steady either in direction or speed, but blows in gusts, and swings to either side of the mean direction; the trace of a self-recording instrument, or 'anemometer' (e.g. Fig. 61, p. 160) is not a regular line, but a ribbon which tends to increase in width with the speed of the wind and with the surface-friction, being much wider on land than at sea; stations with more obstructions on one side than on others show it in the greater gustiness in winds from the side with more friction, and at coastal stations the difference

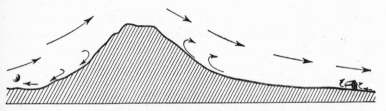

FIG. 35. Eddies set up by obstacles in an air-current

between winds from the land and the sea is prominent. The direction and force, as noted by observers and given in climatological tables, are estimates of the means of the variations over some minutes.

Gustiness and other irregularities are forms of turbulence, which may be described as the sum total of the eddies, vertical and horizontal, imposed on a moving body of air by friction with the surface over which it is moving, and by deflexions round obstacles such as buildings and trees (Fig. 35); instability due to heating at the base (thermal convection) may also be present and cause ascent, which adds its effect, a large one. Thus the air is churned in unceasing movement, as is often visible in the trail of smoke from a high factory chimney, rising and sinking irregularly in strong winds; the smoke from a ship's funnel at sea is much less disturbed. The stronger the wind, the rougher the surface over which it is blowing, and—an important factor—the more unstable the air, the more vigorous is the turbulence and the higher it extends. Even stable air, colder below than above, may be churned up in a strong wind, so that the lower layers become warmer, the higher colder; unstable air is subject to convection even in the absence of wind. An interesting case is recorded by G. I. Taylor from the ice-patrol ship *Scotia* south of Newfoundland in July 1913; a warm air-mass had reached the cold water of the Labrador current, and being cooled below as it blew over it, was in a condition of stability. But temperatures taken by means of kites showed the upward diffusion of the cold surface air; after a 6 days' journey of about 1,000 miles over a surface that became colder with distance the air had been cooled to 2,300 feet, turbulence having mixed it in spite of its stability.

Among the outstanding effects of turbulence and convection are the following: the increase in force of the wind and the slight veer in direction in the daytime owing to the replacement of the slow-moving surface air by the stronger wind aloft; the diffusion of vapour from the surface, where it originates, till it may reach altitudes with a low enough temperature to form cloud (the increased turbulence among hills is one cause of the lowering of the cloud-level there); the removal of dust and other suspensoids from the lower levels, where their concentration may reduce visibility seriously, to the higher layers where dilution through the mass of air in rapid movement renders them innocuous; the adiabatic cooling of the troposphere from the surface up, to attain the dry adiabatic lapse-rate as long as no condensation of vapour takes place, or the saturated adiabatic in the layers with condensation (see p. 71). Turbulence manifests itself for aircraft in bumpiness, which is nearly always present in some degree, and can be very unpleasant when vigorous convection is an additional cause of disturbance. The up-currents in cumulo-nimbus clouds are so violent as to be dangerous, but they have been used by glider pilots to gain height; the record altitude for a British glider, 14,170 feet, was thus attained over Dunstable on 1 July 1939; in the pilot's own words:

Once inside the cloud lift increased rapidly until the rate-of-climb indicator jammed at its maximum of 20 feet a second; . . . in 7½ minutes I climbed 10,000 feet, of which 3,000 feet were in one two-minute period. Then the air became rough, which, according to theory, marks a point near the top of the cloud where the ascending column slows down and commences to topple over and down on all sides like the spray of a fountain. German pilots have several times met with disaster in these regions of clouds, so I immediately straightened up . . . and flew out of the cloud through very wild air.

The eddies and down-draughts round large obstructions on the surface are dangerous owing to their low altitude, aircraft not having space to manœuvre into safety, and the neighbourhood of some hills and mountains has to be avoided with the wind in certain directions. On the other hand, windward slopes provide up-draughts of which gliders take advantage; gulls floating and soaring in onshore winds along coastal cliffs give beautiful evidence of the lift. The disturbance of the air-flow may extend high above the obstacle, even to three times the height in unstable air over mountains. Most turbulence originates on the surface and decreases rapidly with height, but the vigorous currents in cumulus clouds continue up to the greatest heights they reach, often the tropopause. And even in a cloudless sky violent and persistent bumpiness is sometimes encountered over considerable areas at altitudes between 20,000 and 40,000 feet.

Apart from the continual gusts described above as due to turbulence, anemograms show irregularities of another type known as squalls; these are increases in the wind-speed of longer duration, from some 5 minutes to an hour or more, which are not the result of turbulence but are of meteorological origin, being in many cases minor cold fronts. They start suddenly and die away gradually, and are associated with some change in wind direction, a fall in temperature, and sometimes an increase in cloud; the usual gustiness is superposed on the squalls.

CHAPTER XIV

DIURNAL VARIATION OF WIND VELOCITY.
SLOPE WINDS. LAND- AND SEA-BREEZES

Diurnal Variation

On lowlands the wind tends to be much weaker at night than in the day; calm nights are not uncommon, and in the tropics the nights are almost invariably calm, but a perfectly calm day is rare. At Batavia, 6° S., the mean velocity in January is less than 1 m.p.h. between 2100 and 0600, and increases to a maximum, 6 m.p.h., at 1400. As a general rule the wind freshens shortly after sunrise, strengthens to a maximum in the afternoon, and dies away again in the evening, but often with fluctuations near sunset. The explanation is that on clear nights the surface air is rapidly cooled and becomes stable and stagnant, unaffected by the wind aloft which blows over it; but if cooling is checked by cloud, or if the general wind is strong, the surface air continues to drift with the general current. After sunrise heating begins, in an hour or two convection and turbulence effect an interchange with the rapidly moving air above, and the calm of the night gives place to a breeze, the wind blowing stronger as long as the heating continues, and falling away again with the cool of evening. In the interior and east of the British Isles in summer the mean velocity in the afternoon is twice that in the night, but on the coasts the range is less, and hardly appreciable in winter:

MEAN WIND VELOCITY (m.p.h.)

		0100	1400
Kew	Jan.	8	10
	Jul.	5	10
Valencia	Jan.	15	16
	Jul.	9	13

Even the coasts of Greenland have a small tendency to an afternoon increase in summer. At Athens the mean velocity in winter ranges from 7 m.p.h. at 0400 to 11 m.p.h. at 1600, and in summer from 3 m.p.h. at 0400 to 15 m.p.h. at 1600.

At Helwan near Cairo the range is least in December (from 3 m.p.h. at 0800 to 8 m.p.h. at 1500) and largest in June (5 m.p.h. at 0600 to 16 m.p.h. at 2000). On the oceans, with their small range of temperature, the diurnal variation is inappreciable.

The increase in the velocity in the lower atmosphere by day must have its complement in a decrease in the higher levels, and vice versa at night. Fig. 36 shows this for Paris,

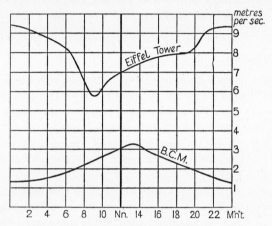

FIG. 36. The mean velocity of the wind in July on the top of the Eiffel Tower, Paris, and at the Bureau Central Météorologique, near the foot of the tower

the top of the Eiffel Tower, 990 feet above the surface, having a pronounced decrease from night to day. The curves are similar throughout the year, but the amplitude is much larger in summer; the wind is stronger at all hours at the higher station. In the free atmosphere 3,000 feet above the British Isles the velocity falls to a minimum about noon, and the direction backs from night to day; above that level the diurnal change dies out.

A consideration of the simple underlying causes will explain the variations. At sea the surface heating is slight, and the velocity changes little from day to night; in some regions the wind is stronger at night. On land a screen of cloud may prevent much change by checking both loss of heat from the surface with increase of air-density at night, and strong heating and active convection by day. Sometimes a clear calm night is followed by a cloudless hot day, and yet no wind springs up; the explanation may be the presence of anticyclonic conditions, in which convectional interchange merely replaces calm surface air by calm air from aloft. Conversely, the surface wind may be strong on a cold clear night if the upper wind is so strong that turbulence breaks up the denser surface layer and mixes it with the current above. But in long winter nights the surface air may be so cold that it remains calm and undisturbed even under a fresh upper wind.

Slope Winds

'Anabatic' and 'katabatic' winds are shallow local currents, mostly of small velocity. In contrast to the general winds which result from the gradients of extensive pressure-systems, they are the result of local heating and cooling of the ground, and the depth of air affected is not enough to modify the barometric pressure appreciably; they are most prominent in settled weather.

Anabatic, up-slope, winds are due to the heating of steep slopes by the sun, and blow from about 1000 till near sunset. On flat ground the diurnal heating is dissipated by normal convection currents, but where the topography favours, mainly in deep mountain valleys, a shallow surface layer moves up the slopes, and helps to form the strong valley-breeze which blows every day in the warm season up valleys of a large mountain-system, unless it is overridden by a general wind (p. 304).

Katabatic, down-slope, winds are much more common. The ground cools rapidly after sundown on a clear night, the air resting on it is chilled, and in the absence of a general wind, flows down any slope, even a slight one, as a gentle surface current, in places only a few feet deep, to spread over the low ground, and fill hollows to the brim with lakes of cold damp air (inversion of temperature, p. 42); such hollows may be formed unintentionally by man when his walls, or even thick screens of trees, act as dams across a valley bottom. Of hardly perceptible velocity in country of low relief, these winds can be strong on steep slopes, especially on a high plateau, and they are an important feature among mountains, where large areas of sloping ground at a high altitude lose heat rapidly at night and the cooled air gravitates into the bottoms; the tributary currents converge in the main valleys, where a strong, deep, and cold mountain-breeze blows regularly, unless a general wind counteracts it. It is well known in the Alps and similar systems, and in many valleys has a local name; houses and gardens avoid the lowest ground which is most exposed to it (Chap. XXXII).

Katabatic winds are prominent around ice-caps. They are very strong and persistent on the snow-slopes of Antarctica, the ice-cap of which develops a permanent anticyclonic system with outblowing winds which are strengthened by the katabatic effect; the south-easterlies of Antarctica and the Southern Ocean south of the polar circle are a definite element in the general circulation of the atmosphere (Chapter XV). Similar winds are well known in Greenland also, being a large factor in the possibility, not to mention the comfort, of sledge travel; they blow outward on all sides, strongest on the steep peripheral descent from the plateau, where sledges toil laboriously up against them. They are strongest at night, especially under clear skies, being largely dominated by the state of the weather; strong to a gale when reinforced by the general wind, they sweep cataracts of drift-ing snow, hundreds of feet deep, down from the interior. But these winds are comparatively shallow, and possibly, in the absence of a permanent anticyclone, do not form so large an element in the atmosphere as the winds from Antarctica.

Local topographical or thermal controls of the winds are prominent in many lands. Some of the more general cases have been described above; among minor ones, important, however, in their localities, are the following:—

A mountain range deflects the winds, which tend to blow round the ends rather than ascend bodily to cross it, the extent of the deflexion depending on the angle of approach and on the stability of the air.

Winds blow very strongly, and with some change in

direction, round a headland projecting into the sea, especially
if it is elevated and marks a change in the general trend of
a coastline; such a feature is the Cape Peninsula of South
Africa, where 'south-easters' are notably strong and persistent in summer. Another example is the north end of
Madagascar, where very strong winds swirl round the
obstacle the island presents to the SE. trade. It is possible
that the south of Greenland acts as a barrier in the westerly
winds and sets up great eddies which develop into depressions south-west of Iceland. Many straits are liable to strong
winds, due in part to this 'corner' effect, reinforced by the
lesser friction on the water, which strengthens the draught
through the strait.

Strong winds are a feature of hot deserts which are intensely heated on sunny days; if a mountain range encloses
such a desert the winds blowing in towards the focus of heat
take advantage of any ravine or gap, rushing through with
gale force in the day and dying away in the evening; the arid
plateaux of Iran and of the south-west of North America
contain many examples. Where these local winds reinforce
general winds of the same direction the result may be violent.

Land- and Sea-breezes

A widespread and interesting small-scale manifestation of
pressure differences and resulting winds, due directly to
differences of temperature, is seen in the mechanism of the
land- and sea-breezes on coasts. During the day the land
heats rapidly, the sea hardly at all, and pressure falls slightly
over the land; at night the opposite occurs; the resulting air
movements are described on p. 104. These breezes are not
appreciable more than 15 to 20 miles from the shore in most
places, weakening with distance. The upper, counter-cur-
rents are too diffuse to be prominent, but can be traced
by observations of the upper winds at suitable levels; the
plane separating the surface- and return-currents is usually at
2,000 to 4,000 feet, rather higher near the equator, lower
in the higher latitudes. Land- and sea-breezes blow nearly
directly across the coast-line, apart from the influence of any
general wind, being too shallow and local for the geostrophic
effect to be developed.

XIV LAND- AND SEA-BREEZES 119

The sea-breeze is most prominent where the diurnal heating of the land is strongest, and the general winds are too light to mask it. The cold water coasts (p. 121) are specially favourable in having an abnormally cool sea adjacent to a hot desert. The conditions are good in low latitudes, where a day without a sea-breeze is rare in any month, almost unknown in the dry season; they are a regular and important feature of the coasts of large lakes, as those of equatorial Africa, as well as of the ocean. Round the Mediterranean Sea they are regular, and in places strong, in summer. In higher latitudes they are so irregular, and usually so light when they do occur, that they pass unnoticed save by the trained observer, but their existence is recognizable in the records at some British stations, though they are overshadowed by the general winds, the shallow and light currents being lost to view in the deep and vigorous movements.

In lower latitudes a general wind, trade or monsoon, blowing onshore is reinforced by the sea-breeze during the day, and may attain great force in the afternoon; at night it is correspondingly weakened or neutralized by a well-developed land-breeze. On a coast backed by a mountain system with long and deep valleys, as in south Arabia, the land- and sea-breezes may be strongly reinforced by the mountain- and valley-winds. Where the general wind blows along the shore, as do the trades of the Indian Ocean on the coasts of East Africa, the sea-breeze and land-breeze components deflect it so that it comes in obliquely over the shore by day, and blows out obliquely at night.

The sea-breeze brings in cool ocean air, very welcome in hot lands (Fig. 17, p. 60), and vapour, and may be unpleasantly damp and a considerable factor in the afternoon clouds and heavy showers. On the other hand, where the land-breeze meets an on-shore general wind massive cloud and rain may be formed on the littoral in the night and early morning when the land-breeze is strongest; and for this reason on some tropical coasts the early morning is the rainiest part of the day in certain months, the afternoon being bright and sunny, in contrast to the usual tropical periodicity. In the East Indies the land-breezes from some of the large islands and peninsulas converge in the intervening channels, and cause massive cumulus cloud to build up at night on the warm water, with torrential showers and thunder. A similar

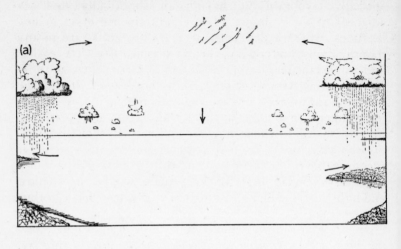

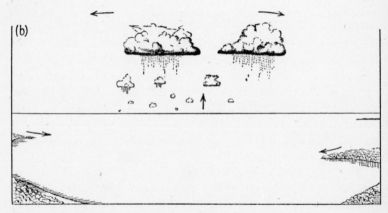

FIG. 37. Winds and clouds, Lake Victoria, East Africa, (a) in the day, (b) at night

process is to be seen over the great lakes in the tropics, very prominently over Lake Victoria (Fig. 37); at night the cool air from the surrounding land converges and rises on the warm lake, with the formation of towering cumulo-nimbus, thunder, and downpours of rain, and the storms may drift slowly north-west with the general wind, continuing active

over the north-west border of the lake till 1000 or 1100;
apart from this the shores have quiet weather and clear skies,
a marked contrast to the storms with their constant glows
and flashes of lightning on the lake below. The circulation
in the daytime reverses the picture; for the shallow lake-
breeze, charged with vapour, sets steadily on to the shores,
the lake being now a focus of descending air, with sky notably clear of cloud except for cirrus floating miles above the
surface. Meanwhile masses of cloud are swelling up to
great heights on the shores, where an afternoon rarely passes
without a violent thunderstorm, which continues into the
evening, flash after flash with little intermission.

Land- and sea-breezes are of considerable practical importance, as well as of theoretical interest. On tropical coasts
the cool, fresh air from the ocean gives a most welcome
check to the rapidly rising temperature; Europeans choose
sites for their houses that are fully exposed to the sea-breeze,
and windows are eagerly thrown open to admit it. In coastal
towns streets through which it blows are greatly to be pre-
ferred to the sheltered side-lanes. On some coasts the wind
blows so strongly in the afternoons that ships cannot leave
their berths, and boat-work is impossible; at Luderitz Bay,
on the cold-water coast of South-west Africa, the mean
velocity of the SW. wind in the afternoon in summer is about
30 m.p.h., and 35 m.p.h. is frequent.

CHAPTER XV

THE PRESSURE- AND WIND-SYSTEMS OF THE GLOBE

THE wind-systems control the climates of the globe, and are
themselves controlled by the great pressure-systems, whose
differences they are always striving to neutralize. An understanding of the pressure-distribution is essential for the study
of climate.

Fig. 38 is a diagrammatic sketch of the 'planetary'
arrangement that might be found on the globe if the surface
were homogeneous, all land or all water, and it is recognizable in the actual distribution of pressure in April and

October, in which months the disturbing effects of adjacent land and water on temperature are least (it is convenient to ignore their effects for the present in a first approach to the theory of the circulation of the atmosphere).

The pressure-systems owe their existence primarily to the differential heating of the globe by the sun. The equatorial low pressures are thus explained, but the explanation fails

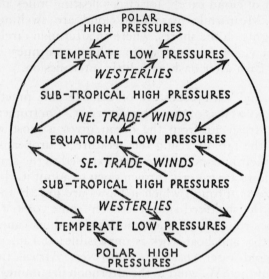

FIG. 38. Diagrammatic arrangement of pressure and winds on a rotating globe

outside the equatorial belt, for the lowest mean pressures are about 60° N. and S., and high pressures are found in the sub-tropics.

The heating of the atmosphere is at a maximum in the neighbourhood of the equator, where the air expands upward, and, as shown in Fig. 32 (p. 105), at levels above 12,500 feet pressure decreases poleward and the air moves down the gradient; this movement of the upper air must be considered further before the surface winds can be understood. In its poleward course the air is deflected more and more eastward by the earth's rotational deflexion, and a great circumpolar whirl of westerly winds is set up. In it a strong centrifugal force is developed, since its velocity is greater

than that of the globe below, and the air tends to be thrown
back towards the equator. The result is a piling up of the
air, and an increase of pressure, in the sub-tropics about 35°
N. and 30° S., between the thermal outflow from the equator
and the centrifugal, dynamic, return from higher latitudes.
Beyond these high-pressure belts pressure falls in the circumpolar whirls. The lowest pressures might be expected at the
poles, and it was long thought that the pressures there were
very low, but it is now known that the thermal influence is

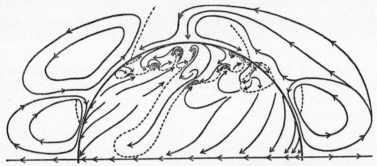

FIG. 39. Scheme of air circulation on a hemisphere (Bjerknes)

able to assert itself over the dynamic and produce a slight
increase of pressure. Some details are given on pp. 164–9.

The pressure belts swing 5° to 10°, north in the northern
summer and south in the southern summer, following the
seasonal temperature changes.

The winds considered so far have been those in the higher
atmosphere, not those on the surface. The surface winds
result from the differences of pressure which are themselves,
in part, the effect of the upper winds, as has been explained.
Fig. 39 shows the scheme of the general circulation according to Bjerknes, in plan and elevation (the vertical scale being
enormously exaggerated). The movements are simplest in
low latitudes, where they seem to form two closed systems,
one on each side of the equator; the air rises about the
equator, as is indicated by frequent cloud and rain, and
flows in the higher levels first to the west (as on the surface),
but soon turns poleward and eastward under the influence
of the earth's rotation, slowly losing heat by radiation on the

way. It descends again (very slowly, at a rate of probably some 400 feet a day) in the sub-tropical high-pressure systems, from which it returns equatorward on the surface as the trade-winds, completing the circuit; the upper, westerly, winds above the trades are commonly called the anti-trades or counter-trades.

For the highly complex westerlies no generalized picture can have much validity; Fig. 39 indicates a series of the cyclonic disturbances characteristic of temperate latitudes, with their variable winds and rainy areas, which are described in Part V; a section to indicate the air-movements in the disturbances is given on the right of the hemisphere, the broken lines being discontinuities.

It should be noted that both the sub-tropical and the temperate belts in the charts of mean isobars are generalizations of processions of smaller anticyclones and depressions respectively; through the gaps between these smaller anticyclones polar air can make its way and help to maintain the trades, and in the complicated air-movements of the depressions of the westerlies tropical air rises and goes poleward to help to feed the polar anticyclones; thus these belts are not continuous and impassable barriers in the general circulation but provide necessary passage for the air between low and high latitudes.

But the general circulation is by no means fully known, still less fully understood, and other representations have been suggested than that of Fig. 39.

On the actual earth the distribution of continents and oceans introduces great complications. The continents in middle and high latitudes are warmer in summer than the oceans and tend to have lower pressure, cooler in winter with a tendency to higher pressure. These local thermal influences are superposed on the diagrammatic scheme of Fig. 38, and the result may be represented, again diagrammatically, as in Fig. 40, based on Hettner, *Die Klimate der Erde*. The triangular shape of the land-mass represents roughly the actual land-masses of the globe.

In July the equatorial low-pressures are north of the equator. The most notable feature is the break in the sub-

tropical high pressures over the land in the summer hemisphere, which is hot enough to develop a low-pressure system
in spite of the planetary tendency to high pressure; the air
displaced from the hot continent tends to accumulate over
the sub-tropical oceans in large detached anticyclones. The
planetary belts of the south hemisphere are hardly disturbed. The winds of the north, the summer, hemisphere

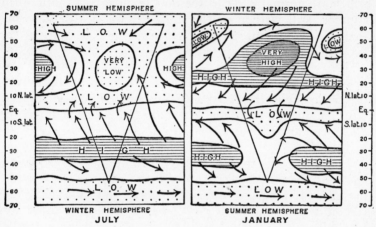

FIG. 40. Diagrammatic pressure and winds on a continent and surrounding oceans
(Hettner)

are very much modified. In particular the north-east trades
are no longer a belt round the globe, but blow only on the
east and south of the oceanic sub-tropical anticyclones; on
the south and south-east of the continent they are replaced
by monsoonal winds drawn in from the south, for the most
part a continuation of the south-east trade of the south hemisphere.

In January (right-hand diagram of Fig. 40) the severe
cold in the northern continent intensifies the sub-tropical
high pressures, which spread far north to cover the land and
form a cold anticyclone of little depth but great surface
intensity. The accumulation of air over the land leaves the
oceans with less, and their sub-tropical high pressures are
little more than narrow bridges between the continental
anticyclones. The temperate low-pressure systems over the
oceans have much lower pressures than in summer, and are

the scene of the vigorous cyclonic activity of the westerlies. The north-east trade blows strongly in an almost unbroken belt round the north hemisphere, being heavily reinforced by the continental anticyclone, which on its east side gives strong north-west winds, the winter monsoon of China and, to a less degree, of Labrador. In the south hemisphere the land is hot enough to draw the equatorial low-pressures, which are normally in this season a few degrees south of the equator, still farther south, and to develop a definite but shallow low-pressure system breaking the continuity of the sub-tropical high pressures.

The winds have the same modifications (though less prominently developed) as in the north hemisphere in July, the trades being replaced by monsoonal winds on the east coast; light winds, 'deflected trades', are drawn in to the equatorial low pressures.

Fig. 41 shows the generalized conditions over an ocean and its coasts more clearly, and Figs. 42–5 give the actual pressure- and wind-systems in winter and summer. The resemblance to the theoretical schemes described above will be evident.

CHAPTER XVI

THE MAJOR REGIONS OF PRESSURE AND WINDS

The Equatorial Belt

In this description the equator referred to is the equatorial trough, zone of confluence of the trades of the two hemispheres, which swings north and south with the sun, through about 10° of latitude in the Atlantic and Pacific oceans, farther in the North Indian Ocean and in the East and West Indies which are influenced by the adjacent continents, and much farther on the continents themselves. In July it is about 20° N. in north Africa, and north of the tropic in Asia; by January it has returned south to about 7° N. in the Guinea lands, 10° S. in the South Indian Ocean, and 20° S. in the southern continents.

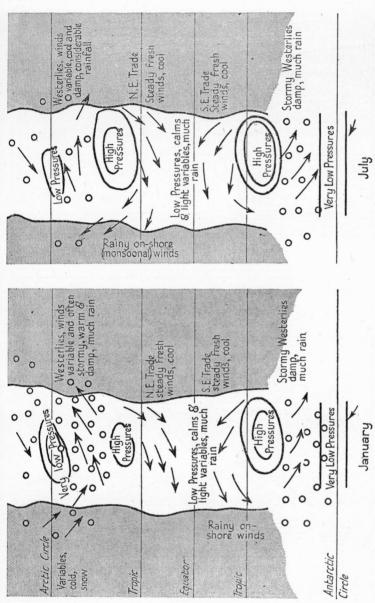

FIG. 41. Generalized pressure- and wind-systems over an ocean; the small circles indicate cyclonic activity

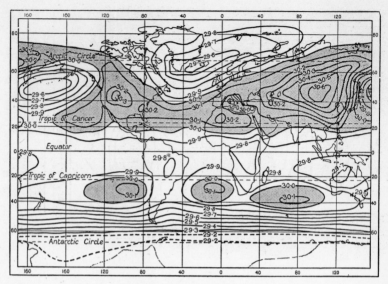

FIG. 42. Mean isobars, January

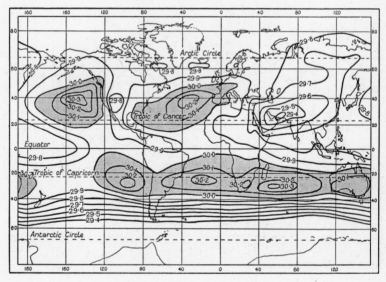

FIG. 43. Mean isobars, July

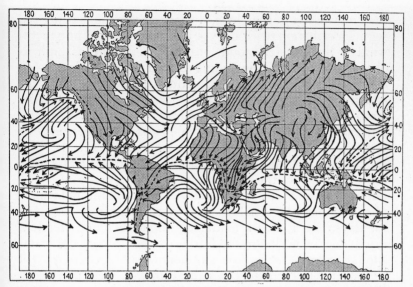

FIG. 44. Mean wind directions (stream lines) in January; the broken lines are fronts.
(Meteorological Office, London)

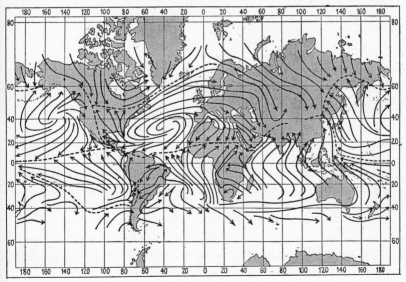

FIG. 45. Mean wind directions (stream lines) in July; the broken lines are fronts.
(Meteorological Office, London)

Barometric pressure is fairly low, and much more uniform than on the rest of the globe, the largest variations being the regular oscillation twice a day (Fig. 30, p. 102). The general wind is light easterly both on the surface and as high as observations extend, including the cirrus cloud level; but a definite westerly wind is sometimes found at high levels, and is usually associated with bad weather. On the coasts land- and sea-breezes are prominent every day. On land especially, thunderstorms, and in places tornadoes, may be very violent, with torrential rain and fierce squalls. But calms and light winds are normal, and the absence of a fresh breeze intensifies the enervating effect on Europeans of the hot vapour-laden air. The equatorial calms are the 'doldrums' of the sailors where sailing-ships were sometimes becalmed for days, and it was a matter of importance and frequent discussion in what longitude the passage of the doldrums should be made, shipmasters preferring a longer course if it would enable them to cross the calms at their narrowest. But calculations were often upset and days lost in the baffling airs and sultry weather; the duration of long voyages depended considerably on the ship's luck in this part of the voyage.

But equatorial weather is far from uniform (except in respect of temperature), and large variations arise from disturbances in the pressure-systems and winds; fairly definite types of disturbances are recognized though by no means fully understood. One type is expressed by the term inter-tropical front; in normal conditions the NE. and SE. trades are separated by a belt, 400 or 500 miles in width, with calms or light variables on the surface and a gentle drift from the east in the main atmosphere, skies half to three-quarters clouded and showers at intervals (Figs. 57 and 58, pp. 156, 157). But when the pressure-gradients round the sub-tropical anti-cyclones on the north and south are steeper than usual, the trades come in more strongly and converge more vigorously in a front, the 'inter-tropical front' or, in a wider sense, the 'inter-tropical convergence'. The front has very bad weather, fresh to strong and squally winds, dense clouds in several layers up to 30,000 or 40,000 feet, consisting of extensive sheets of alto-stratus with masses of very heavy and turbulent cumulo-nimbus, the bases of which coalesce into a uniformly overcast sky at times no more than a few hundred feet above the surface, heavy and often continuous rain reducing visibility to a hundred yards. With a width of 50 or 100 miles and a length, in a generally east-west direction, of some hundreds of miles, such fronts form an almost impenetrable barrier for aircraft; their intensity and position are variable.

Another source of disturbance is the arrival of surges of cool air from the westerlies; the polar current curves round the front of one of the sub-tropical anticyclones, and is carried with the trade into the equatorial trough, often giving a belt of cloud and rain at sea and on land in its passage.

A third type of broken weather, at any rate in some regions, is the frontal interaction in the cols between pairs of anticyclones travelling east in the sub-tropics (p. 124), the tropical air in the west of the leading system meeting air of a modified polar character in front of the approaching system; the frontal effect, however, is much damped even in the outer tropics, and only slight in the inner tropics, two thousand miles from the axis of the anticyclones.

On the continents frontal disturbances are more persistent in the rainy season (with which they are associated) and are reinforced by the general inflow of hot moist air and by convection in the hot hours; with increasing latitude the earth's rotational deflection is a significant factor. In some regions local meteorological peculiarities cause complications. Very violent thunderstorms, with squalls occasionally up to 100 m.p.h. and torrential rain, develop in the afternoons and may last far into the night.

In these low latitudes the frontal weather probably results in the main directly from the convergence of air-masses, the temperatures of which are nearly the same (in contrast to the temperature differences between the interacting air-masses in higher latitudes); but it must be noted that quite small differences of temperature are more effective in the hot equatorial atmosphere, since the associated differences of humidity are larger.

The Trades

The trades blow from NE. and E. in the north hemisphere, from SE. and E. in the south, between the sub-tropical high pressures of the horse latitudes and the equatorial trough. They continue as east winds to the west of the oceans, but in this later stage they are much modified, their temperature being higher and vapour-content greater, and they have been called the inter-tropical flow.

In the northern winter the north-east trade and its extensions sweep over an enormous extent of land and sea, the larger if the winter monsoons from north and north-west are included, which start in the east of Asia and North America about latitude 60° N., and are akin to the trades, though possessing some distinctive features. Apart from these the regular trade originates about 25° N. and becomes the 'deflected trade' on crossing the equator in the Indian and western Pacific oceans; but the winds do not change direction much unless they penetrate a considerable distance into the other hemisphere, since the earth's rotational deflexion is negligible within a few degrees of the line. The SE. trade is restricted at this season to the oceans, the sub-tropical high pressures being interrupted over the hot lands though less than in the north hemisphere in July. The indraught from the cool seas to the warm land changes the trade into a SW. wind along the west African coast from the Orange River to the Gulf of Guinea, steadiest and strongest in the hottest hours; it is cool and damp, and in the south often fog-laden, in marked contrast to the trade with its true SE. direction a few hundred miles seaward (see p. 279).

In the northern summer deep and extensive low-pressure systems cover the northern continents, and the trade blows only on the east and south-east of the sub-tropical anticyclones on the oceans. In the North Atlantic it is normally picked up by ships off Portugal, and carried as far south as Cape Verde. In the Pacific its range is between the parallels of 40° N. and 5° N. In the south hemisphere winter intensifies the high pressures on the continents, but large anticyclones persist over the oceans, and the SE. trade is continuous nearly round the globe from the tropic to beyond the equator; in the Indian and Pacific Oceans it continues far north as the south-west monsoon of south-east Asia. Similarly the SE. trade of the South Atlantic crosses the equator to become the south-west monsoon of the Guinea lands.

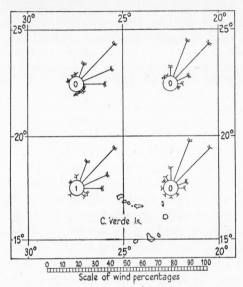

FIG. 46. Mean wind-roses for 5° squares in the NE. trade in July. The arrows fly with the wind and the number of barbs is the velocity on the Beaufort scale; the figures in the circles are the numbers of calms, light airs, and variable winds (U.S.A. Pilot Chart)

The trades on the oceans are the steadiest winds of the earth and in their central region in the South Atlantic they are almost constant in force and direction day and night throughout the year, with an average velocity of some 15 knots (Fig. 46). The mean directions (percentage frequencies) at St. Helena, in the heart of the trade of the South Atlantic, are:

	N.	NE.	E.	SE.	S.	SW.	Calm
Dec.–Feb.	—	—	3	56	39	2	—
Jun.–Aug.	—	1	4	47	37	4	6

The NE. trade of the North Atlantic is more variable, being strongest in spring with a mean velocity of about 14 knots, weakest in autumn, 10 knots.

The importance of the trades for navigation is indicated in Chapter XVII.

For four days we steamed south and east before the fresh trade breeze. The ocean was piled on end about us in white-crested ridges, flashing green on their sides, violet in the hollows. The sky was one unbroken sweep of crystalline ether, fading into neutral on the sea rim, while a glorious rush of pure keen air awoke weird music from every tight-strung shroud, and filled each cranny of the ship with life and freshness. And this is the weather of the NE. trade all the way from Cadiz Bay to Cape Verde. Now and then we crossed the course of a great four-masted clipper, storming down wind for Australia round the Cape under wide breadths of straining sail-cloth, with the ocean roaring apart beneath her swinging bows, and spouting high about the quarters as she tore through it at eleven knots. (Bindloss.)

No movements of the atmosphere are quite steady or uniform, and even the trades have their irregularities; occasionally they fail entirely over wide areas. Near the coasts they are subject to the daily alternation of the land- and sea-breezes, and the fringes of their domain have both regular seasonal changes and irregularities resulting from the temporary shifts of the pressure-systems. On land they are much less steady than on the oceans; the diurnal change of velocity usual in the tropics is strongly marked, the nights being calm and the wind reaching a maximum in the hottest hours and dying away towards sunset; the topography may cause variations in both direction and force. The seasonal change with the swing of the doldrums extends farther north and south on the lands than at sea, the trade being replaced by variable and usually light winds in the rainy season (less than half the year); the reversal to monsoon in summer in some regions is described later in this chapter.

Another irregularity in the trades is associated with the fact that the sub-tropical high pressures are not fixed, stationary systems, but consist of a procession of anticyclones moving with varying speed from west to east, and separated by troughs of lower pressure; in front of them the trade is much strengthened, and when a more than usually deep trough separates two anticyclones a surge of polar air from far beyond the polar circle, usually behind a vigorous depression in the westerlies, may be carried into the trade, causing the wind to strengthen and the temperature to fall somewhat in a belt of cloud and light rain which is carried onward to the equator, and even beyond in some oceans. But the most serious disturbance in the trades is the 'tropical cyclone', to which a later section is devoted.

Depth of the Trades

The trades are much shallower than the other great wind-system, the westerlies; their depth is very variable in time and place, but 5,000–10,000 feet may be taken as an average for the central areas; they are deeper near the sub-tropical high pressures where they originate, and also on the equatorial fringes. They are shallowest, at times 3,000 feet and in winter much less, in the east off the cold-water coasts, and deepen westward. Mauritius records 10,000 to 13,000 feet as an average for the SE. trade, with extremes of 3,000 and 20,000 feet; the NE. trade is about 12,000 feet deep at Teneriffe. Above the trade is a transitional layer of winds of irregular direction and velocity, and above it the anti-, or counter-, trade from a westerly point and of greater velocity.

Vertical Gradient of Temperature. Trade-Wind Inversion

The trades, in most of their extent, have certain characteristics in common in their vertical temperature gradient. Over the oceans in the lowest levels, up to about 2,000 feet, the lapse-rate is abnormally large, since the cool air is being rapidly warmed below by the ocean surface; the top of this moist, turbulent, layer is rendered visible by persistent soft fracto-cumulus cloud, so characteristic that it has received the name 'trade cumulus'. Above, the lapse-rate decreases abruptly, to approximately the saturated adiabatic up to the top of the true trade-wind, which is marked by a layer of strato-cumulus, often thick, under a large temperature inversion (of about 12° in the heart of the trade in the South Atlantic, less towards the equator, where it becomes imperceptible, more near the high pressures of the sub-tropics) at the base of the anti-trades. Off the cold-water coasts the surface air is so much chilled by the cool currents that very often the temperature increases upward from the surface itself; at other times a marked inversion is found in the layer from 2,000 to 5,000 feet, with a rise in temperature commonly of 7–15°.

On the continents the vertical gradient in the surface layers is much steeper, especially in the hot hours, than on the oceans, but the ascent of the dry continental air is checked by the decreased lapse-rate aloft, usually an actual inversion, before cloud can form, but fine dust is carried up

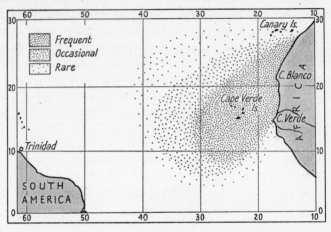

FIG. 47. Frequency of Saharan dust on the Atlantic (Schott)

from the ground. The sky remains almost cloudless in the trade-wind deserts, which indicate by their name the winds, dry, dusty, and very hot in summer, to which they owe their existence. Their most extensive area includes Arabia and the Sahara, and for 4 or 5 months in winter the trade continues south over the Guinea lands to the coast, and even beyond when its goal, the doldrums, is unusually far south. The contrast to the monsoon of summer has won for it a reputation and a distinctive name, the Harmattan (sometimes applied generally to the trade on land), but the distinction between the ocean trade and the land Harmattan is climatic rather than meteorological. The desert haze, consisting of minute sand-particles, is sometimes carried out over the ocean south-west and west of the Sahara far beyond the Cape Verde Islands; visibility is much reduced, even to less than 2 miles, and passing ships may be coated with

XVI

yellow sand. This occurs most frequently in winter, especially in February, and may last for days (Fig. 47).

That terrible wind that carries the Saharan dust a hundred miles to sea, not so much as a sand-storm, but as a mist or fog of dust as fine as flour, filling the eyes, the lungs, the pores of the skin, the nose and throat; getting into the locks of rifles, the works of watches and cameras, defiling water, food, and everything else; rendering life a burden and a curse. (P. C. Wren.)

Rain is almost unknown in the Guinea lands in the Harmattan months, and humidity may fall below 10 per cent. A thick dust-haze sometimes reduces the surface visibility to half a mile in the forenoon, but the range improves to a few miles in the afternoon; occasionally the haze is carried over the Gulf, to become a fog dense enough to hold up shipping. Most of the fine particles of which it consists are probably derived from the light, dusty soil in Bodele, south of the Tarso Mountains. A bad haze is associated with the arrival of a cold front from the Sahara, with many dust-devils:

The strong winds hinder the growth of seedlings by blowing along the surface sand, and by greatly increasing evaporation and transpiration they add to the difficulties of all plant life, but on the other hand they serve the plants by rolling their mobile seed-cases and attachments for great distances, and disseminating the species—a process which may occur on open sandy tracks in all climates, but notably in arid regions. They cause sand to swirl and pile up on the lee side of surface obstacles, stones, plants, so that living things which might otherwise obtain much-needed shelter from the plants are foiled, and some birds build their nests on the windward side, protecting them against the wind by constructing a barricade of small stones. (P. A. Buxton.)

A stronger wind than usual may do much damage to plants by both breaking twigs and removing so much sand that the rootstock is exposed to a depth of even a foot, repetition of which may kill the plant.

Tropical Cyclones

These are the most serious disturbances in (or usually, alongside) the trades, and are storms of great intensity with very low pressures, winds of extraordinary force revolving anti-clockwise in the north hemisphere, clockwise in the south, massive low cloud and torrential rain, but usually not much lightning. They are called hurricanes in the West Indies, typhoons in the China Seas, cyclones in the Indian Ocean. The following description of a violent hurricane (Figs. 48 and 49) which struck the coast of Florida on

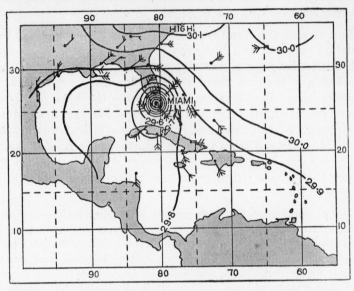

FIG. 48. A hurricane off Florida; synoptic chart, 0800, 18 Sept. 1926

18 September 1926 and devastated Miami illustrates their nature:

At noon it was realized that the centre of the storm was moving towards Miami. . . . In the evening the wind freshened, and by midnight it was blowing a full gale. Thereafter it steadily increased in violence until daylight, blowing in this first phase from the north and north-east. Estimates of a force of 110 to 120 miles an hour were made. Mere figures can convey no picture of the physical suffering and mental distress caused by the furious onslaught of the elements, wind and driving rain, wave and thunderbolt, amid the crashing of palms and firs, sputtering of telephones and vivid flashes from high-tension wires. Sign-boards and roof-tiles hurtled through the air, roofs were ripped off and wooden houses crumpled up like matchwood. . . . During the lull, which came as the centre of the storm moved over

the coast-line, many women and children were moved to safer dwellings
and some injured were brought to the hospitals. As most people did
not realise that a second phase was coming, the lull was not fully
utilized and many were caught wandering about the streets looking at
the damage. About 8 a.m. the wind came again with increased fury,
blowing now from the south and south-east, lashing into mountainous
seas the high tides of the equinoctial full-moon. Within the bay behind
the islands the wind drove the tide northwards to encounter the flood-
waters pouring down from the Everglades into the inlets of Miami

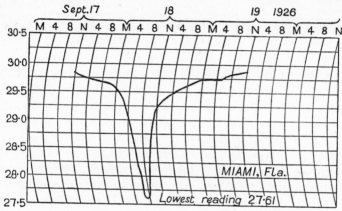

FIG. 49. Barogram during the hurricane at Miami

and Fort Lauderdale. Banked up in these inlets the waters spread
out through the city and suburbs, loosening foundations of houses and
roots of trees and palms. It was during this phase of the storm that
most of the casualties occurred. About half of those who met their
death were drowned. The remainder were caught in the collapse of
houses, or hit by flying debris as they ran to other shelter. (From *The
Times.*)

At least 114 lives were lost in the Miami district, and
the damage to buildings (exclusive of furnishings) was
estimated at £15,000,000.

Frequency of Tropical Cyclones. Tracks. Speed

The frequency varies much from year to year, and complete agreement is hardly possible on what degree of violence
entitles a storm to be classed as a cyclone, but the following
table gives a useful general picture:

FREQUENCY OF TROPICAL CYCLONES

	Average number per year	Percentage monthly frequency											
		Jan.	*Feb.*	*Mar.*	*Apr.*	*May*	*June*	*July*	*Aug.*	*Sept.*	*Oct.*	*Nov.*	*Dec.*
W. Indies . .	6	0	0	0	0	0	7	7	16	32	31	6	1
China Seas . .	22	4	2	2	3	5	6	15	16	19	15	9	5
Arabian Sea . .	2	4	0	0	5	11	25	7	0	4	22	18	4
Bay of Bengal .	10	0	0	0	2	5	11	18	19	15	15	10	5
S. Indian Ocean (Mauritius region) . .	6	21	29	20	9	3	0	0	0	0	1	4	13
S. Pacific (Fiji Is., Queensland) .	2	23	18	22	9	4	6	5	0	3	2	1	7

No two storms follow the same track or advance at the same speed. Most spring up in the neighbourhood of the eastern ends of the arrows shown in Fig. 50, and start on a westerly course, which many follow with a speed of advance of 10 to 15 knots till they die out; but variations in the tracks, and irregularities within the tracks themselves, are numerous. One striking form is parabolic, the storm re-curving from its early westerly course towards the north-east in the north hemisphere, the south-east in the south, into the westerlies, where it may degenerate into an extra-tropical depression; the speed of advance falls to less than 10 knots during the recurvature, and increases after it. Cyclones that pass inland lose their energy after leaving the coast, but if they reach the sea again they are restored to their previous vigour, as is the case in peninsular India.

Cyclones originate in definite regions on the oceans, where the trades from the two hemispheres, richly charged with vapour, are dying out and merging into the sultry equatorial calms (Fig. 50). The heat, moisture, and instability of the doldrums predispose to thermal depressions, but it is only beyond about 5° from the equator that the earth's rotational deflexion is adequate to set up the necessary whirl, which itself generates the centrifugal force to increase the violence of the storm, and cause the phenomenally low pressures, often below 920 mb. (887 mb. has been recorded). Cyclones are to be expected in late summer and autumn, when the doldrums are at their farthest from the equator, where rotational deflexion is considerable and the ocean temperature high. The meeting of the trades of the two hemispheres (one of them 'deflected') possibly tends to set up a revolving movement which assists the formation of the whirl. The South Atlantic is the only tropical ocean without cyclones, and it is noteworthy that the doldrums

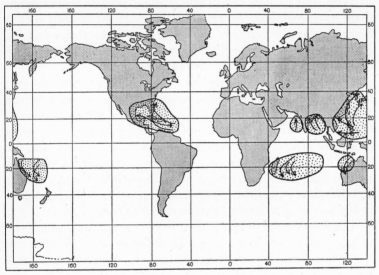

FIG. 50. The chief regions subject to tropical cyclones are stippled. The arrows show some of the usual storm tracks

never swing south of the equator there, nor does the NE. trade cross the line.

Probably some discontinuity of temperature, and, more effective, of humidity, is present in the surface air in the earliest stages, and according to some meteorologists a 'triple point', the meeting of three air-masses, is a favourable condition, but it seems unlikely that any front can persist in the wild whirl of a mature cyclone, which must presumably be maintained by other means. A surge of polar air in front of an advancing anticyclone in the sub-tropics (p. 131) seems to provide the start for many disturbances, and some observers incline to associate the origin with the inter-tropical front. It is difficult to set aside the old explanation of the enormous energy of the storm as being due to the liberation of latent heat in the massive clouds. An essential condition would seem to be such a distribution of pressure and winds (in respect of direction and velocity) in the atmosphere above the lower whirl that the air which rises is evacuated rapidly from the area.

The Zones of a Cyclone

Tropical cyclones have a much more circular arrangement than extra-tropical depressions, and it is convenient to describe them in terms of the outer and inner zones and the core or 'eye of the storm'. The autographic records in Fig. 51 illustrate the following description.

Premonitory signs may be observed even 700 or 800 miles in advance of a large cyclone—a day or more before the weather breaks. The barometer falls slowly, a long and rising swell swings across the ocean, recognizable a thousand miles from the centre; abundant cirrus, with haloes round the sun or moon, is followed by thickening middle cloud, typically alto-stratus, with patches of dark grey low cloud drifting across below it; lurid coppery-red, yellow, and green colours in the sky at sunrise and sunset are ominous.

The outer zone forms a ring between 100 and from 200 to 400 miles from the centre. In it the weather deteriorates fast; the barometer falls rapidly, the wind rises to gale force with a heavy, confused sea; the cloud thickens and lowers to dense nimbo-stratus, giving continuous rain (but usually no thunder), heaviest in the right front quadrant in the north hemisphere, left front in the south, to an observer looking in the direction in which the cyclone is moving.

The outer zone merges rather suddenly into an inner zone at some 50 to 200 miles from the centre according to the size of the system. The full fury of the storm is unloosed. The wind exceeds force 12 of the Beaufort scale, often attaining 150 m.p.h., as it blows almost in a circle round the core of the storm. The barometer falls very steeply to very low readings for the latitude; 886·8 mb. (26·19 inches), the lowest record for the globe at sea-level, was reported in a typhoon on the Pacific east of the Philippine Islands. The sky is full of cloud down almost to the surface, mist, spray, and rain fill the air, reducing visibility almost to nil; sea and swell

are dangerously high and confused. These tempestuous
conditions continue, ever wilder, right up to the inner edge

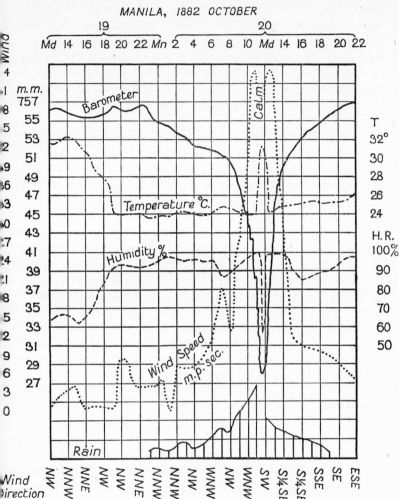

FIG. 51. Records at Manila, Philippine Islands, during a typhoon; the centre of the
storm passed over the station about noon on October 20

of this inner zone. Then, suddenly, they cease, and the
central calm succeeds.

The central calm is the core of the system, of varying
weather and diameter, averaging 10 to 20 miles across on the

surface and probably widening considerably upwards. An absolute calm is rare, but the wind falls well below gale force, and the sky clears enough for the sun or the stars to appear. The passage of this 'eye of the storm' may take from less than half an hour to over two hours. The calm ends as suddenly as it began, to be replaced by the inner zone again, now in the rear of the centre, with hurricane winds and weather similar to those already described. The outer zone follows, and then the clearing skies and fresh breezes mark the end of the cyclone.

Cyclones are essentially storms of the ocean, and in the days of sail, before the 'laws of storms' were understood, they were a most serious danger to ships; mechanical power and wireless warnings have greatly diminished the risk. Cyclones decrease in intensity if they pass over land, but small islands and coasts within their area suffer terribly both from the violence of the winds and the onslaught of the waves—the more so nowadays with the advancing standard of life and the building of more elaborate settlements. Trees are uprooted, crops washed out or buried, buildings and factories damaged, roads, railways, and embankments carried away. Hundreds of people may be killed; and the after-effects of the storm are frequently even more serious, when water-supply and drainage works are destroyed, and typhoid and other diseases break out and spread with alarming rapidity in the stricken community.

Monsoons

Derived from the Arabic word for season, 'monsoon' is applied to wind-systems which are reversed from winter to summer by the change in the pressure-distribution due to the heating of a land-mass, forming a mighty annual respiration of the continents; summer is definitely the damp, cloudy, rainy season. They are characteristic of the east of the continents within the tropics, but are prominent also outside, as in east Asia to 60° N. The seasonal change of pressure in Asia is so large that its effect appears in most of the rest of the globe, where pressure is higher in the northern summer than the northern winter. The following table shows the extent of the reversal of the winds in north China:

PLATE 2

Cirrus

Light cumulus clouds, with alto-cumulus above

WIND DIRECTION, MEAN PERCENTAGE FREQUENCIES

GULF OF PE-CHIH-LI

	N.	NE.	E.	SE.	S.	SW.	W.	NW.	Calm
Jan.	25	6	5	4	8	13	11	23	5
Jul.	6	7	11	19	26	12	4	7	7

Most monsoonal air-masses are not very deep.

In winter the continental winds are notably strong and regular in north and central China, where the cataract of air from the cold anticyclone pours over the rim of the plateau; the proximity of the deserts makes the winds dry and dusty as well as cold. Their directions are imposed by the position of the high-pressure system which controls them, NW. in north China, N. in central China, working round to NE. in the south of India. The bold feature-lines of the south of the continent introduce modifications. In particular the plains of north India are sheltered by their mountain wall from the cold but shallow monsoon of the interior. Instead they have a light drift from north-west which merges into the monsoon current in the south of India; probably it is fed by air sub-siding from the high pressures above, which belong to the normal, dynamic, high pressures of the latitude and are distinct from the cold anticyclone of Siberia, prominent on the charts but a comparatively shallow, surface feature. The winter monsoon ends in the equatorial trough about lati-tude 10° S. (Fig. 44).

Though fairly constant in comparison with many of the other great wind-systems, the monsoon is liable to interrup-tion by cyclonic disturbances. The interruptions are least in evidence in the north of China, but occasional snowstorms there, and the not infrequent dust-laden gales, are associated with passing irregularities of pressure. Central China has frequent depressions, shallow systems (many of them origi-nating, probably, as 'lee depressions' under the mountain ranges which lie athwart the path of the NW. winds), which travel east, with southerly winds in front; these, coming from the sea, are damp and warm, but the intensity of the polar current is more noticeable physiologically.

Small depressions appear in the north-west of India. The charts (Fig. 52) show that they come from the Mediterranean over Persia and Afghanistan and travel slowly towards Bengal. Though of no great intensity and having only light winds, they are important as giving appreciable precipitation

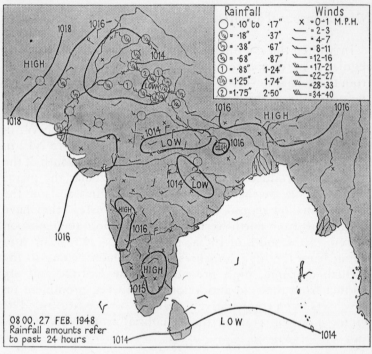

Fig. 52. Synoptic chart showing a cold-season disturbance in the north-west of India. (From the Indian Daily Weather Report by courtesy of the India Met. Dept.)

(0·5 to 2 inches in January) over a considerable area, and making possible the cultivation of wheat. Their passage is marked by a change in wind and weather from the usual clear skies and light breezes of the cold weather season.

The winter monsoon lasts from October to March. In April a shallow depression is forming over Asia, and it deepens under the fierce heat of summer. The equatorial trough sweeps slowly with the sun to its most northerly position—the G. of Cambay (avoiding the Indus valley), the Plains of India, Burma, China, south Japan, its inter-tropical front becoming more active in its course; tropical cyclones of full intensity form on it as it passes over the Bay and the Arabian Sea (p. 140). The arrival of the front marks the onset of the monsoon, with its strong squally SW. winds (a continuation of the SE. trade from the South Indian

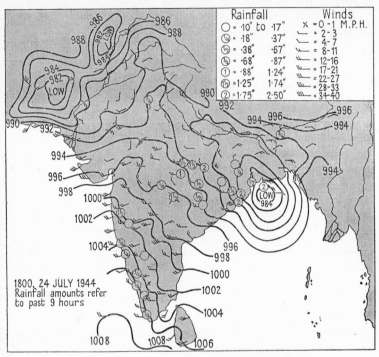

FIG. 53. Synoptic chart, showing a depression advancing up the Ganges Valley during the south-west monsoon. (Reproduced from the Indian Daily Weather Report by courtesy of the India Meteorological Department)

Ocean), heavy seas, skies overcast with massive cloud, torrential downpours, saturated air; the sudden change from the long weeks of heat and drought is a climatic event of the greatest importance. The 'burst of the monsoon' is at about the same date each year, at Bombay on 5 June, in Bengal 15 June, the Punjab 1 July. The SW. winds which sweep into the area behind the front are saturated after their long ocean passage, and orographic rainfall is extremely heavy on the escarpments and the lofty ranges which enclose the Indian area; most of the general rain falls in shallow depressions which form on the inter-tropical front and advance westward from the head of the Bay (Fig. 53); thermal depressions also contribute. The rains vary greatly from year to year according to the activity of the front, breaks in the rains being long and frequent in dry years.

Two main currents may be distinguished in the monsoon, the main south-west current which meets the western Ghats

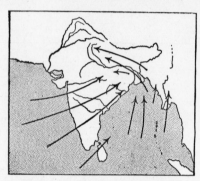

FIG. 54. The main currents of the south-west monsoon

almost at right angles, and the current from the south in the Bay which proceeds up the Ganges (Fig. 54); the two converge in the inter-tropical front in the north of India. The Himalayas limit the monsoon on the north, and by preventing any inflow from the north strengthen the winds on the south. The monsoon continues till mid-September, and then the equatorial trough retreats south, giving tropical cyclones over the seas in October and November, and heavy rain (the heaviest of the year) in the south-east of the peninsula.

The summer monsoon of China is more composite, consisting of air-masses from the Indian Ocean, the Australia–East Indies region, and the South and North Pacific Oceans. The general wind is south-easterly, much weaker than the winter monsoon (in contrast to the case in India). The south-east winds set in gradually in April and continue till September, blowing from the warm ocean to the heated interior. They are laden with moisture, and the weather is hot, sultry, rainy and unhealthy. Most of the rain may be

classed as frontal, falling where the advancing south-
easterlies meet the cooler and drier continental air.

No other region has such strongly developed monsoons
as south-east Asia. The south and south-east of North
America has a distinct monsoonal tendency, but not a complete reversal of the wind; at Charleston the prevailing wind
is NW. in January, S. in July, at New Orleans N. in January,
SE. in July, but the winds are more variable than in east
Asia. The southern continents have damp winds from the
sea on the east coasts in summer, but the land areas outside
the tropics are too small to develop large winter anticyclones
and systems of outblowing winds.

The Westerlies

The westerlies are the winds of the wide belts between the
sub-tropical high pressures and the polar anticyclones; their
areas, and the intensity of their weather, especially in the
north hemisphere, vary with the seasons. They contain the
semi-permanent low pressures of temperate latitudes, the unbroken girdle of the Forties and Fifties in the south, the
Icelandic and Aleutian systems in the north hemisphere, and
the winds and weather are dominated by the numerous
pressure-systems, most of low pressure, travelling from west
to east. The prevailing winds are westerly equatorwards of
the polar circles (an approximate boundary), and the name
westerlies may be conveniently applied to the whole, though
easterly winds prevail farther poleward.

The sub-tropical high pressures on the oceans normally
give fine weather, clear skies, and light winds, but even in
summer stormy interludes occur, and in winter the westerlies
often make inroads, so that the climate is of the Mediterranean type as in the Azores and Madeira (but the Canaries
lie well within the north-east trade in summer). Similarly in
the North Pacific, the Hawaiian Islands have almost constant
trade-winds in summer but a considerable proportion of
westerlies in winter, and as a result more than twice as much
rain in winter as in summer; in June to September the
trade blows day after day almost without interruption,

but in December, January, and February only on one day in two.

Between latitude 40° N. (35° S.) and the polar circles—which make convenient though only very approximate general boundaries—the westerlies prevail all the year.

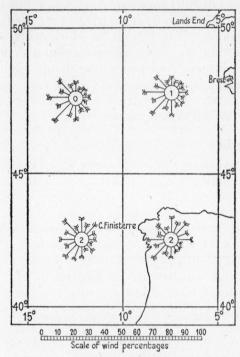

FIG. 55. Mean wind-roses for 5° squares in the Westerlies in January. Symbols as in Fig. 46, p. 133 (U.S.A. Pilot Chart)

They deserve attention both for their meteorological interest, and from the fact that they embrace those parts of the earth where the highest civilizations have developed, including the most advanced parts of Europe and North America. The prevailing winds are south-westerly in the north hemisphere, north-westerly in the south hemisphere. Unlike the trades, the winds are very variable in force and direction, and sometimes for weeks together may be easterly (Fig. 55); in the severe winter of 1947 in Britain the winds were from an easterly point from 22 January till 22 February without intermission—probably the longest spell of easterlies on record in the country, and in England also during all August and the first few days of September of the same year. The mean annual directions (percentage frequencies) in the Scilly Islands are:

N.	11	S.	12
NE.	9	SW.	14
E.	12	W.	**17**
SE.	8	NW.	15

Calm 2

These zones are the scene of an almost constant procession of high- and low-pressure systems (generally the latter with their many fronts), moving from west to east (Fig. 56), and the sequence of winds and weather depends on position in relation to them; their characteristics are described in Part V.

The westerlies of the south hemisphere cover a belt of nearly uniform width between 35° and 60° S., the Roaring Forties as the sailors have significantly named it, on the almost unbroken Southern Ocean, a wild tract where gale follows gale with little interruption, the wind veering and backing under the sway of the depressions. The skies are overcast with low clouds drifting rapidly, rain and snow are frequent, the air is damp, raw, and cold, owing to the cold water that spreads from Antarctica; icebergs come far north, not seldom reaching 40° S. in the South Atlantic, and ice has come within sight of Cape Agulhas. Even large ships do not face the westerlies of the Roaring Forties if they can avoid it. A westward passage round Cape Horn is a wild experience in the mountainous seas and head winds. Antarctic expeditions find the voyage from New Zealand to the Ross Sea no bad preparation for the hardships that await them when they land. The Roaring Forties are stormy all the year round, with little difference between summer and winter, and the great expanse of ocean has but minor variations from place to place.

In the north hemisphere the conditions are more complex

owing to the alternation of oceans and continents, the latter
with high mountain ranges and vast plateaux, and the oceans
themselves add variety since they have the warmest and the
coldest currents (relatively to the environment) of the globe.
The seasonal change of wind and weather is also prominent;
in winter the North Atlantic certainly equals, and probably
exceeds, in storminess all other oceans, but in summer the
weather is much less boisterous than in the Roaring Forties.
Ships have a special load-line for winter voyages in the North
Atlantic, more freeboard being insisted upon.

Having crossed the Pacific the westerlies reach the
American coast, with its mountains range behind range as
a defence for the interior, but they surmount the obstacle
and continue across the continent. In the intense cold of
the continental winter pressure is higher than on the ocean,
but the depressions maintain their energy and characteristics.
Anticyclones frequently build up in the west of the continent
and join in the procession to the east. The passage of
cyclones and anticyclones sets in motion the great floods of
cold air, 'cold waves' which surge forward from the frozen
north-west to the Gulf of Mexico (p. 67), and the warm
waves from the south. The cyclone tracks from both west
and south converge in the neighbourhood of the Great Lakes
and the St. Lawrence, those in the east tending to follow the
discontinuity of temperature along the Gulf Stream (Fig. 114,
p. 346). Hence the south-east of Canada and the north-east
of the United States have as much precipitation, most of it
in the form of snow, in winter, when cyclonic activity is at a
maximum, as in summer, when onshore winds are frequent
owing to the heating of the land-mass. The interior of the
continent is too remote from the ocean, and the air is too cold,
for the winter precipitation, all of it snow, to be heavy. The
windward slopes of the western mountains have abundant
rain and snow, but the deep valleys get little.

It should be noted that although the mean isobars for the
winter months indicate a large anticyclone in the interior of
North America, the region has great cyclonic activity, and the
daily synoptic charts usually show one or more depressions
crossing the continent. The pressure in them is higher than
when they are on the ocean; not the absolute pressure, how-

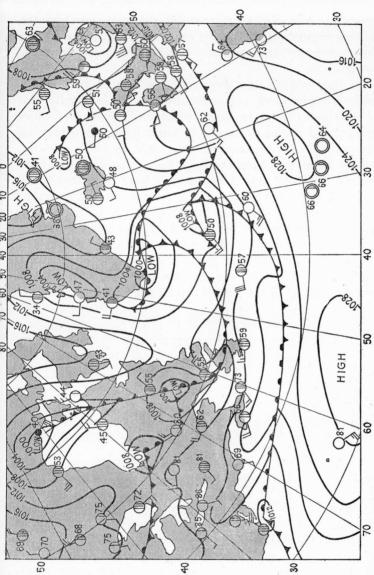

FIG. 56. Synoptic chart 0000 G.M.T. (approx.), 7 Aug. 1947, showing the irregularities of pressure and the conflicting air-masses of the westerlies, in contrast with the steady conditions in the sub-tropics. For meaning of symbols see Fig. 22, p. 64

ever, but the gradient determines the weather. The absolute pressure is increased by the cold of the continental winter, and this region which appears on maps of mean isobars for winter as anticyclonic is really subject to vigorous cyclonic disturbances.

On the Atlantic the westerlies, dominated by the Icelandic low pressures, become more stormy, especially near the meeting of the warm Gulf Stream and the cold Labrador current, and round the south of Greenland. In winter depression follows depression, with rare intervals of anticyclonic calm, and even the large liners that work the ferry between England and America may have to reduce speed for days together when bound westward, and suffer much damage. Smaller ships are battered by the gales till they become unmanageable, and when help does arrive it calls for the ablest seamanship to effect a rescue in the wild seas. The data[1] for the British Isles give some idea of the frequency of gales (force 8 or above of the Beaufort scale, velocity more than 38 m.p.h.) in the east of the North Atlantic:

MEAN NUMBER OF GALES

	J	F	M	A	M	J	J	A	S	O	N	D	Year
North-west Ireland	7	5	4	2	1	1	1	1	3	4	6	6	41
Bristol Channel	5	5	4	2	1	1	1	2	2	4	5	6	38
East England	2	2	2	1	1	0	0	1	1	2	3	3	18

Western Europe, with no mountain barriers, is fully exposed on the west, and moreover, the Mediterranean, the Black Sea, and the Caspian on the south, the Baltic and the White Sea on the north, invite the westerlies far into Eurasia.

The North Atlantic narrows towards the north-east, but offers a wide passage between Norway and Greenland into the Arctic Ocean. The Gulf Stream, after sweeping northwards off the American coast, sends vast volumes of drift water across the ocean towards Europe; much of it passes

---

[1] *The Weather of the British Coasts.* Meteorological Office, H.M.S.O., 1918.

between Norway and Iceland, continues east round the north
of Norway, and has an appreciable warming influence even
on Novaya Zemlya and the south of Spitzbergen. The warm
water offers a favourable path for depressions, most of which
indeed, instead of entering Eurasia, skirt the land-mass;
west and north Europe, however, come under the influence
of their fronts, and though primary depressions tend to avoid
the land, many secondaries cross the British Isles and enter
west and central Europe (Fig. 111, p. 343); the lowest
pressure recorded in the British Isles, 925·5 mb. (27·33 in.)
on 26 Jan. 1884 in Perthshire, was in a primary depression.
East Europe and central and north Asia are dominated by
the winter anticyclone which feeds outblowing winds—the
north-west monsoon of China, the north-east monsoon of
the North Indian Ocean, the piercing north-east winds of the
steppes of Trans-Caspia and Anatolia, and the north-west
winds of Iraq; although very stable, it is invaded at times by
disturbances from the westerlies.

The westerlies of the Pacific find no warm sea-passage
round the north of Canada, the way being blocked by the
westward extension of Alaska, and this may be one factor in
causing them to cross the continent; certainly the interior
of North America is subject to more frequent and intense
cyclonic activity than the interior of Eurasia. But, in the
east of Asia at any rate, depressions are frequent, travelling
from Siberia or Central Asia across China, and forming over
China itself; they give strong winds with most unpleasant
dust-storms, and some snow in winter. Their intensity
increases as they reach the Pacific, where they develop into
the ordinary stormy cyclones of the westerlies which have
been mentioned already.

It is only in the westerlies that the sharply contrasted
tropical and polar air-masses (p. 62) meet and conflict, and
and in doing so give rise to the wave disturbances which may
develop into depressions, with bad weather, cloud, rain,
strong winds, and gales (Chap. XXXVI). The contrasts in
the temperature and humidity of the air-masses are greatest
in winter, which is consequently the stormiest season. The
lines, or rather belts, of most frequent meeting of air-masses,

resulting in the formation of depressions, are known as 'polar fronts', which are usually present, despite wide variations in prominence and in position in each season as well as from season to season (Figs. 57 and 58).

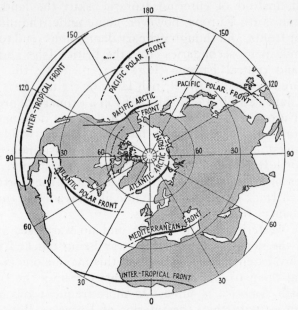

FIG. 57. Normal frontal zones, winter (Petterssen: *Introduction to Meteorology.* McGraw-Hill Publishing Company, London and New York)

The Mediterranean Regions

The Mediterranean Sea and its surrounding coasts, the littoral of California, Chile between latitudes 30° and 37° S., the south-west of the Cape Province of South Africa round Cape Town, small areas of Western Australia round Perth, and the Spencer Gulf district of South Australia, are of meteorological interest as being transitional, dominated in summer by the trades or similar winds from a polar quarter and anticyclonic in type, but in winter by the westerlies. The change is one not merely of wind direction, but also of the whole face of the weather.

In the case of the Mediterranean the topography introduces peculiarities which deserve mention. In summer the general winds in the middle and east of the region are fairly

steady, blowing between the North Atlantic anticyclone and
the low-pressure system of south Asia and north Africa; they
are moderate to strong, and gale force is not infrequent, for the
Mediterranean is by no means a calm sea; on land the

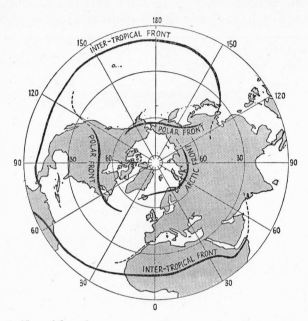

FIG. 58. Normal frontal zones, summer (Petterssen: *Introduction to Meteorology*.
McGraw-Hill Publishing Company, London and New York)

vigorous air movement in the open spaces is valuable in
tempering the midday heat, which can be almost Saharan in
places sheltered from the wind; land- and sea-breezes blow
regularly on the coasts (so that the wind directions at coast
stations are not representative of the region), and the cool
of the sea-breeze is a welcome relief, though its humidity is
less pleasant; its range inland, however, is 10 or 15 miles.

In winter the Mediterranean may be classed with the
westerlies, but it is really a separate area in view of many
local peculiarities; the relatively warm and humid atmosphere tends to develop low pressures, bounded on the
north by the high pressures of central Europe, on the south
by those of north Africa; a semi-permanent 'Mediterranean

front' forms the divide. The general circulation is anti-clockwise, with prevailing SW. and W. winds on the south coasts, N. and NE. winds on the north, but as in the true westerlies, speed and direction are variable, under the control of frontal depressions moving from west to east (Fig. 59, also Fig. 113, p. 345), and strong winds and bad weather are

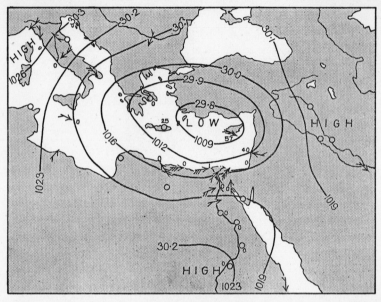

FIG. 59. A depression in the east of the Mediterranean; synoptic chart, 0800, 10 January 1926. The small figures give the rainfall in mm. during the 24 hours 10–11 January

frequent. The wind-roses in Fig. 60 show the change from summer to winter, and the contrast between the steady north-westerlies of summer and the northerlies and variables of winter in the eastern basin; in the western basin the change is from prevailing NW. and W. in winter to E. and NE. in summer. The seasonal change is most marked in the south, for on the north coasts the winds blow from a northerly point in both winter and summer, but are more variable in winter.

Local Winds

Many districts are liable to visitations at irregular intervals by winds of marked individuality. There may be warm or

cold air-masses in a more than usually intense form associated with the pressure-systems of the westerlies, but in
many cases the local topography plays a prominent part.
They are most prominent in middle latitudes of the north
hemisphere into which both cold and warm winds can penetrate under favourable pressure distributions; inside the

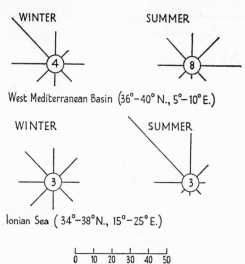

WINTER   SUMMER

West Mediterranean Basin (36°–40° N., 5°–10° E.)

WINTER   SUMMER

Ionian Sea (34°–38°N., 15°–25° E.)

0   10   20   30   40   50

Scale of percentages of all observations, measured from
the circumferences of the circles. The figures in the
circles are the number of calms (i.e. winds of less than 1 m.p.h.)

FIG. 60. Mean wind-roses for the Mediterranean Sea

tropical and polar zones temperatures are too uniform to
give rise to great abnormalities.

Hot Winds

To consider first the hot winds, the tropical air in front of
a Mediterranean depression may be derived from a source-
region far to the south in the deserts of north Africa or south
Arabia, which are hot even in winter; it appears as a very
hot, dry, and dusty wind, so prominent that it has received
local names, of which sirocco is the most general; in Lower
Egypt it is the khamsin (Fig. 61). It sets in when the
appropriate gradient is established, and blows for hours, or
even days, till the trough passes and polar air replaces it;

the sequence of sirocco, trough, and polar air progresses from the west along the Mediterranean. If the sirocco reaches the middle or north of the sea it is still unpleasantly warm, and enervating too, for in its passage over the sea the warm air is charged with moisture, and the hot and dry sirocco of the south becomes warm, moist, and depressing,

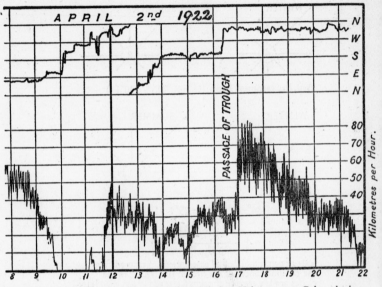

FIG. 61. Velocity and direction of the wind at Helwan, near Cairo, during a Khamsin, 1130–1700

ready to yield torrential downpours of rain when forced to rise over mountains; the Dalmatian coast has the highest rainfall in continental Europe (183 inches at Crkvice). Sirocco winds are most prominent in spring, depressions being active, and the deserts already very hot, so that the winds from them appear as scorching blasts on the coasts of the Mediterranean, which are still cool.

Similar hot winds ('Santa Ana') are well known in California, which occupies the corresponding climatic position in the New World; they blow from the hot deserts east of the Sierra Nevada, and acquire additional heat by descent.

The 'heat wave', which at times prostrates the inhabitants

PLATE 3

Alto-stratus cloud

Strato-cumulus cloud

of the Atlantic states of America in summer, consists of the
tropical air in front of a depression, but it originates not
in a hot desert but over the tropical Gulf of Mexico, and
may travel for hundreds of miles over the hot waters of
the Gulf Stream, becoming extremely moist. The high
humidity rather than any excessive heat—for the thermometer rarely rises above 100°, and often not above 90°
—is the cause of the heat-stroke which afflicts many city-
dwellers.

Cold Winds

The polar air which constitutes the well-known cold winds
behind a Mediterranean depression is derived from the
interior of Europe, and at times from higher latitudes, even
from the Arctic; in its southward advance it meets the
obstacle of the Alps and is deflected, to the west to pass down
the Rhone corridor, and to the east into the Danube lands,
and so reaches the Mediterranean, sweeping down, sometimes with extreme violence, through the gaps in the ranges
that shelter most of the coasts (see p. 53). More local supplies of cold air may be available, in the cold, often snow-
covered, Massif Central and Alpine region of France, and
the bleak limestone plateaux pitted with dolines in the
Dinaric Alps. The cold winds blow in all seasons, but they
are most prominent in the winter half-year.

Necessary conditions are evidently (a) a reservoir of very
cold air in the hinterland, and (b) a slope to the coast, but
the descent must not exceed about 2,000 feet or the inevit-
able adiabatic heating will give the air perceptible warmth;
with a lesser descent the temperature is still notably low on
the Mediterranean coasts that normally enjoy more genial
airs. The best known of these cold winds are the Mistral
of the north-west, notably round the mouths of the Rhone,
the Bora of the north-east Adriatic, and the Vardarac of
Macedonia.

The mistral is associated with high pressures in central
Europe and beyond, and a depression on the Gulf of Genoa;
the Rhone corridor provides a funnel down which the mistral
rages wildly; Marseilles has recorded temperatures well
below freezing-point, down to 11°. The wind is squally as

well as of gale-force, and even railway carriages have been blown over; houses are built without doors or windows in their north walls, and market-gardens require wind-breaks of reeds or trees, set some 30 or 40 yards apart athwart the wind. Though the sky is usually clear and the sun bright, it is well-nigh impossible to protect oneself from the dry, piercing blasts. The mistral may continue for a few hours or as long as some days without intermission. Its violence at sea has given the Gulf of Lions its name and reputation. In the winter of 1808 Lord Collingwood, his flag flying in H.M.S. *Ocean*, was blockading Toulon, and in one of these gales the three-decker was almost lost:

> At that moment the *Ocean* was struck by a very heavy sea, which threw her nearly on her beam-ends, so much so that several of our men called out 'The Admiral's gone down!' But in a few seconds I had the pleasure to see her right again. We understood afterwards that the blow completely disabled her, and that nearly all the bolts of her iron knees were broken. It was the most awfully terrific scene I ever beheld. Lord Collingwood told Admiral Thornborough a short time after that he thought the top-sides were actually parting from the lower frame of the ship.... This happened in December and we must have been about the middle of the Gulf of Lions, with the wind at north-west.

While the lower Rhone valley is exposed to the rigours of the mistral, the west coast of Italy may be suffering the discomforts of damp, sultry heat brought by the sirocco in front of the same depression.

The bora of the north Adriatic is sometimes a continuation of an extensive polar current which has been deflected into the Danube lands and advances over the lower, northern, Dinaric Alps to the Adriatic, and even reaches peninsular Italy as a strong and gusty wind of low, though not notably low, temperature. A more violent variety is the local bora of Trieste and its immediate neighbourhood; it is fed in part from the dolines and other depressions in the limestone uplands 20 or 30 miles inland, which are often filled with intensely cold air in winter, and it descends through a gap behind the town in most furious gusts which do much damage; it is colder than the mistral, and a reading of 9° has been recorded at Trieste. Some boras are anticyclonic, with

dry, though cold, air, and bright sunny skies above the
driving, white-capped waves of the blue sea; some are
cyclonic, cloudy and gloomy, controlled by an Adriatic depression; this latter, cyclonic, type may continue across the
breadth of the Adriatic, but the anticyclonic usually loses its
distinctive features after leaving the coast.

Another local wind of small range, the maestrale, a
frequent scourge of Genoa, is derived from the lake of cold
air over Lombardy in winter. It sweeps down through a
depression in the Ligurian Apennines, blowing with gale
force, mostly in the early morning, over the harbour, but
only below about 2,000 feet, for it is quite independent of
the higher currents.

The cold waves of North America are comparable, being
essentially associated with the rear of depressions travelling
eastward, but unlike the Mediterranean winds their prominence is rather due to the absence of mountain-barriers, the
flood of polar air sweeping south unhindered from the north
of Canada and often bringing disastrously low temperatures
even to the Gulf of Mexico. In its place of origin the air
may be far below zero, and it warms as it moves south, but
it may still be below 32° on the shores of the Gulf, and do
serious damage to the sub-tropical crops. The cold wave is
displaced eastward with the depression, and the eastern
states usually receive warning of its approach.

In the south hemisphere the land-masses of temperate
latitudes are not large enough to have such reservoirs of cold
air in winter as feed the cold winds of the north hemisphere, but the southerly burster of the New South Wales
littoral belongs to the same class. A V-shaped trough of low
pressure crosses the region from west to east, the V pointing
north. In front of it hot northerly winds (known as brick-
fielders) carry heat and dust from the arid interior, like the
sirocco of the Mediterranean. With the passage of the
trough the wind suddenly changes and blows very strong
from the south—the southerly burster—and it appears
cold by contrast, although, as it comes from the ocean, its
temperature is well above freezing-point. The suddenness
of the wind-change, and the violence of the polar current

are due to the topography, the mountains rising steeply not far from the coast. The hot Zonda and the succeeding cold Pampero of the Plate estuary are similar.

The Polar Zones

Antarctica. The poleward gradient from the subtropical high pressures continues steep through the Roaring Forties nearly to the Antarctic circle, in the neighbourhood of which the trough of remarkably low pressure (with appreciable regional differences) encircles the globe. Some annual means, based on very inadequate records, in the north, in the middle, and in the south of the trough are 998·7 mb. (29·49 in.) at Macquarie Island, 54° S., 986·5 mb. (29·13 in.) on the coast of Queen Mary Land, near the Antarctic Circle, 990·8 mb. (29·26 in.) on Ross Island (77° S.). The gradient varies seasonally; between Australia and Antarctica it is probably least in the summer of the south hemisphere. It was formerly thought that pressure continued to decrease all the way to the south pole in the circumpolar whirl (p. 122), but exploration has corrected this view. Antarctica is a vast plateau, nearly twice the area of Australia, much of it more than 8,000 feet above sea-level, and the whole covered by a thick ice-cap; it lies fairly symmetrically about the pole. Most of the interior is still unknown, but the central expanses seem to be not a dome but an elevated irregular basin, the rim of which projects in places as mountain ridges reaching 15,000 feet west of the Ross Sea, and over 12,000 feet south-east of the Weddell Sea. The ice-cap itself, according to the German Antarctic Expedition of 1939, rises to 15,000 feet in latitude 80° on the meridian of Greenwich. The pole, at about 9,000 feet, would thus be bounded by much higher elevations on at any rate two sides. Since the altitude and slope of these huge snowfields exert a major control on the winds and temperatures, meteorological research awaits further topographical knowledge.

The ice-cap must be intensely cold in winter, and even at midsummer the snow and ice prevent the temperature rising above freezing-point. The local thermal influence outweighs the dynamical force exerted by the general circulation of the atmosphere, to develop an anticyclone over the continent, probably a shallow system in the cold surface layers, with a depth of not more than a few thousand feet, but enough to reverse the barometric gradient of the westerlies and to feed a system of outblowing winds. All expeditions have reported S. and SE. winds as soon as the belt of lowest pressure near the polar circle has been passed,

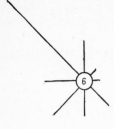

S. Orkneys

C. Evans

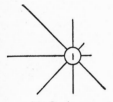

Mt. Erebus smoke

FIG. 62. Mean annual wind directions. The lines, read towards the centres, are proportional to the frequencies. The figures at the centres are the percentages of calms and variable winds

and on his last journey to the pole Scott recorded S., SSE., or SSW. winds in 73 per cent. of his observations. The anticyclonic outflow is strengthened, and locally intensified to violent gales, by the tendency of the cold air to flow down even the slightest slopes of the ice-cap as a katabatic wind; such was probably the cause of the remarkably violent and continuous gales from SE. experienced by Mawson in 1913 in Adelie Land, an inhospitable waste which he has named the 'Home of the Blizzard'; the mean annual wind-speed during his stay was 43 miles an hour.

Above the surface anticyclone is presumably the centre of the general circumpolar low pressures, with a slight inward movement of air from WNW. This movement seems to be shown by the smoke-drift of Mount Erebus, a volcano

13,000 feet high on Ross Island, which is a useful wind-vane
for its level; the direction is the opposite of that of the surface
winds at Cape Evans at the foot of the mountain (Fig. 62).
The inflowing winds aloft feed the descending currents on
the ice-cap. For contrast Fig. 62 also shows the winds in the
South Orkneys, in the westerlies.

The southerly winds on the surface are, of course, liable
to variations. Blizzards are only too well known to explorers,
and during the stay of the British Antarctic Expedition at
Cape Evans they were raging for almost a quarter of the
time, the wind rising to gale force, with furious gusts of over
50 miles an hour. Part of the snow falls from the clouds,
but much is swept up from the surface—which is always
covered with dry, powdery snow-crystals. Blizzards are
clearly due to a steepening of the barometric gradient, but
probably not to depressions of the ordinary type. Such depressions are frequent enough in the westerlies, and sometimes their poleward sectors sweep the coasts of Antarctica,
but Simpson,[1] on Scott's expedition, failed to find evidence
that their influence extends any distance inland, or that
blizzards are connected with them. According to him
'surges' of pressure move outwards from the pole, and where
the topography is suitable steep barometric gradients may
be set up, giving strong winds. Previously the surface air has
been so much chilled, and is therefore so dense, that on a flat
surface it remains stagnant under a strong temperature inversion which may persist for some time, the winds set up by
the barometric gradient blowing high overhead. But if the
wind becomes strong enough under the influence of the
pressure surges, turbulence works down into the underlying
strata, their calm comes to an abrupt end with sudden gusts,
and the full force of the storm is developed sometimes within an hour or two, and continues to rage for a few hours or
even days. The snowfall is largely due to the ascent of the
air over the denser surface strata. This theory would explain
the abrupt and often large rise in temperature immediately
the blizzard starts, the very cold surface-air being replaced
by air at the normal temperature. It has been stated that the
temperature falls when blizzards start, but instrumental

[1] Simpson, G. C., *Scott's Polar Journey and the Weather.*

records disprove this, the apparent fall being a physiological effect of the rapid movement of the air past the body.

There are difficulties in applying this theory to all blizzards, though it seems to explain adequately the facts observed on and near the Great Ice Barrier. Elsewhere other causes may be in operation; possibly in most regions the blizzard is a locally intensified katabatic wind. It is a striking fact, supporting Simpson's theory, that in the Ross Sea quadrant there is usually either a calm or a high wind, light winds being rare.

The Arctic Region. The Arctic is a more complex region than the Antarctic. The polar basin itself is a deep ocean, entirely ice-covered in winter, and with but little open water in summer. It is nearly surrounded by Eurasia, Canada with its large, closely-set archipelago, the great ice-covered plateau of Greenland as large as India, and Spitzbergen and the islands on the east towards Cape Chelyuskin. The only wide entry is between Greenland and Scandinavia. The Arctic circle passes through the north of Siberia and Canada and the south of Greenland, enclosing large areas of tundra land within the polar zone.

In winter the north-east of Siberia, the north of Canada, and the interior of Greenland are the coldest tracts on the globe. The ice-covered Arctic basin is certainly cold during the winter, though considerably less cold than the surrounding lands, and the available data indicate that a belt of high pressure crosses the basin on the Bering Strait side of the pole, connecting the Asiatic and American anticyclones by pressures not so high as on the continents, but very much higher than in the Icelandic and Aleutian low-pressure systems on the oceans on either side; it has been termed the 'Arctic wind-divide' in relation to these systems, into which it sends north-east winds. The pack-ice is drifted slowly by wind and current from east to west. Trusting to this, Nansen let the *Fram* be frozen in north-west of the New Siberian Islands, and for three years the ship was carried on a generally direct course, in spite of many temporary digressions and even reversals, towards the north of Greenland, finally reaching open water north of Spitzbergen; the westward

drift was more rapid in winter than summer. The middle of
the Arctic is probably fairly calm in winter, with clear skies,
rarely troubled by high winds; the ice develops a surface
layer of cold, dense air, and there are no katabatic winds to
create disturbances. But on the outskirts, over against the
warm waters and low pressures of the Icelandic and Aleutian
regions, the winds are strong and often boisterous under the
control of the depressions of the westerlies.

In summer pressure appears to be fairly uniform. The
anticyclones of the adjacent continents have disappeared,
and the polar basin probably has slightly higher mean pressure than both the lands and the oceans which bound it, with
a weak gradient for outflowing winds. The partial break-up
of the ice allows the temperature to rise in July to about
freezing-point, and this is not cold enough to maintain very
high pressures.

Greenland. It was long maintained, in particular by
Hobbs,[1] that the ice-cap of Greenland bears an extensive anticyclone, almost permanent throughout the year, developed
by the intense cold, a system so stable that no depression
could penetrate it from the surrounding seas; the skies might
be expected to be cloudless, the air calm. But the experience
of parties who have spent both summer and winter on the
middle of the ice-cap in recent decades gives a different
picture. The observers at Eismitte (latitude 71° N., altitude
10,000 feet, near the middle of the ice-cap) had much
evidence of the passage of depressions from the west—
strong southerly winds, rising at times to gale force, overcast skies, blizzards of snow (simultaneously heavy rain fell
on the lower slopes up to 6,000 feet), conditions typical of
warm sectors; cold sectors are apparently too shallow to
reach the interior. The wind was usually moderate to strong,
even in the absence of a depression, only one observation in
fifty giving less than 2·5 m.p.h., and the mean cloud was
6/10, all in painful contrast to the calms and cloudless
skies expected. The surface winds are katabatic, very sensitive to slope in their force and direction; they blow
outward with a tendency to take up a clockwise direction,

[1] Hobbs, W. H., *Glacial Anticyclones*, New York, 1926.

and near the coasts they follow closely the fiords and other features.

Thus Greenland differs from Antarctica in climate as in position, being at a distance from the pole, and surrounded by seas with strong cyclonic activity. The cold of the ice-cap certainly tends to maintain an anticyclone, and the winds, largely katabatic, blow outward, but the anticyclone seems to be liable to invasion by depressions from the stormy neighbourhood.

The meteorology of the poles is not of great human importance, for few inhabitants or travellers frequent them. But the Arctic region is crossed by the shortest routes between Europe and Asia and North America, and they may be followed by regular air-services, for which detailed weather observations and investigations will be needed. At present the importance of the meteorology is chiefly indirect; currents of cold air blow southward into the low pressures of temperate latitudes, and there meet warm and moist tropical air-masses, their interaction giving birth to the cyclones and anticyclones for which the westerlies are notorious. In this or other ways polar conditions influence the daily and seasonal weather of the temperate zones, and help in its study, and more success in forecasting, might be derived from the establishment of an adequate number of reporting stations. The atmospheric pressure in the polar zones is an important element, and it seems to be controlled in part by the amount of ice present, ice tending to maintain high, open water lower, pressure; a knowledge of the amount and position of the ice is very desirable, both by reason of the immediate and the more remote effects, for a large field of ice can only melt slowly, since it surrounds itself with cold, fresh melt-water which floats on the saline water of the sea. A detailed knowledge of the surface drifts might facilitate the forecasting of the arrival of ice and cold water, and might give an indication of the weather of coming seasons. It is not impossible that some control of the seasonal weather in the temperate zone is exerted less directly also by the varying ice-cover of the polar seas.

CHAPTER XVII

SAILING-SHIP TRACKS

A GOOD knowledge of the wind-systems was essential to navigation in the days of sail; high-powered steamships can afford to ignore them in shaping their courses, choosing the

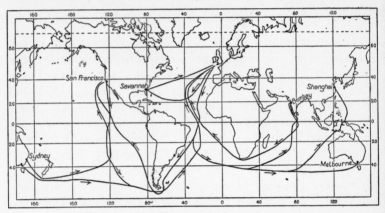

FIG. 63. Recommended tracks for sailing ships, December–February

shortest passage from point to point, but aircraft are now again demanding information on both the mean directions and velocities, and the day-to-day variations, of the winds on the surface and in the upper levels.

The tracks followed by sailing-ships (Fig. 63) with the object of profiting from the prevailing winds even at the cost of an increase in distance, are an interesting illustration of the surface winds. Ships bound from the United Kingdom to Australia usually sight Madeira and the Cape Verde Islands, and endeavour to cross the line between 25° and 28° W., where the doldrums are narrowest, and pick up the SE. trade as soon as possible. They then stand to the south-west in the strong and steady winds, and approach the Brazilian coast near Pernambuco; losing the trade about 20° S. they work southward and eastward in light variables, mostly northerly, and well before reaching Tristan da Cunha they are in the westerlies, and make their easting between the fortieth and forty-fifth parallels; farther south gales, heavy seas, and, at times, ice are formidable obstacles. On the homeward voyage they still sail eastward, south of New Zealand, and carry the prevailing westerlies to Cape Horn;

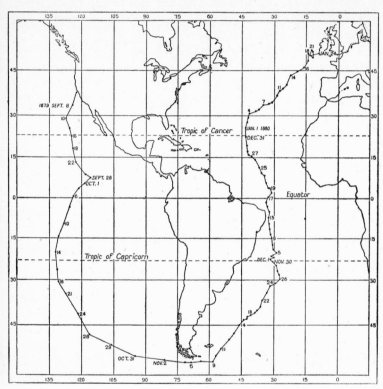

FIG. 64. Track of the barque *Scottish Hero* from San Francisco to the United Kingdom

gales are almost continuous, and may blow with terrific force, and raise seas and swells exceeding 70 feet in height. After rounding Cape Horn better weather is found, but off the River Plate pamperos may be met. Beyond the south-east trade the north-east trade is entered near the equator, and the ship takes a north-westerly course till she reaches the westerlies, which carry her to the Channel.

Ships bound to China follow the same route as those for Australia until they reach the meridian of 80° E., when they

stand to the north-east to pick up the SE. trade. During the
SW. monsoon they proceed by the Sunda Strait direct up the
China Sea, but in the NE. monsoon they keep south-east of
the Malay Archipelago, passing Timor and the north-west
of New Guinea, and then well to the east of the Philippines,
working to the eastward in the variable winds before standing
to the north-west in the monsoon.

The voyage from the United Kingdom to ports on the
west coast of South or North America involved a westward
passage round Cape Horn, with strong head winds and very
severe weather.

The outward and homeward tracks between the United
Kingdom and Savannah indicate the advantage derived from
the prevailing winds of the North Atlantic.

Fig. 64 shows an actual voyage as pricked off from day
to day.

PART III

THE VAPOUR IN THE ATMOSPHERE AND ITS CONDENSATION. RAIN. CLOUD. SUNSHINE. VISIBILITY

CHAPTER XVIII

RAIN AND ITS MEASUREMENT

IT is unnecessary to state in detail how our daily life, work, and pleasures are controlled by the weather, and especially by the rain. Our water-supply depends on it, and even in England, which is not a dry land, a few weeks of drought brings the fact clearly to notice, for springs and wells fail, and the land dries out. Not only our drink but our food is at its mercy; crops can grow only where the rainfall is adequate or artificial irrigation can be supplied, the rainfall of distant areas being directed to the dry lands. In the three years 1926–8 it is estimated that a prolonged drought caused the death of 10,000,000 sheep in Queensland; a deficiency is especially destructive in semi-arid lands, which have barely enough in good years for the stock which optimistic farmers put on them, and for the expected crops. Widespread famines are liable to afflict India and China. On the other hand an excess of rain works even greater havoc over re-stricted areas, which are flooded by rivers breaking their embankments. The floods of China are notorious; in the summer monsoon the Yangtze may rise 100 feet above its lowest winter level. The Hwang Ho is specially dangerous, having built up its lower course high above the level of the plain, through which it flows on an embankment; in September 1925 it burst its banks, over 2,500 persons were drowned, and the survivors were in perhaps a worse case since the river spread debris over their cultivated lands and ruined the crops, so that death by famine awaited them after their escape from the flood.

Not only must the rain be adequate, but it must fall in the right season for the crop. In some regions it falls in the hot

season and the combination of heat and moisture is conducive to a vigorous growth; with high temperatures and
heavy rains all the year round growth will be luxuriant,
as seen in the exuberance of the rain forests of low latitudes.
In other lands the rain falls in the cool season, and the hot
summer is rainless. For plant life, and also in other relations,
20 inches of rain with the temperature at 70° provides
far less moisture than the same amount with the temperature at 50°.

The regularity of the rainfall from year to year is evidently
an important consideration, and it shows wide variations
from place to place (p. 195). The kind of rain is another
factor to be taken into account; rain may fall in heavy downpours, often sporadic thunderstorms of short duration in
small areas, the intervening country having none, as in the
example described on page 244. Or 'general' rain may
affect a wide area either at the same time or consecutively
as the rain-belt advances, the rate of fall being much less
than in thunderstorms. This is the ordinary type in the
British Isles and other lands with a similar climate, and it
may be called frontal, being associated with the fronts of
depressions. In some lands the usual precipitation is a light
drizzle.

The number of rainy days is significant, a rain-day
being commonly regarded as a day on which at least 0·01
inch, or 0·1 mm., of rain is registered; a higher limit is
adopted in many tropical lands in which 0·01 inch is inappreciable.

The Measurement of Rain

The amount of rain is the depth in inches or mm. of the
resulting layer of water, on the assumption that all remains on
a flat surface, without loss by run-off, percolation, or evaporation. The rain-gauge indicates it by collecting the rain in a
suitable receptacle and storing it till it can be measured,
usually once a day. The instrument is placed in an open
situation well away from the shelter of trees or other objects,
but not so exposed that eddies round the gauge in strong
winds prevent some of the rain (or snow, which is still more

at the mercy of the wind) from entering, or that winds blowing up a steep slope carry the precipitation right over it. Where possible it should be on turf to avoid splashings from the ground adding to the catch. The rim is 1 foot above the ground at British stations, but in some countries higher and discrepancies may result; a series of measurements in north Germany showed that a gauge 1 metre high catches on the average about 8 per cent. less rain in winter, 3 per cent. less in summer, than a gauge 1 foot high. At the Radcliffe Observatory, Oxford, a gauge on the tower, 112 feet high, caught on the average 30 per cent. less rain in the year than the standard gauge on the adjacent ground. Many patterns of self-recording gauges are used, which register automatically on a revolving drum, thus showing the time of beginning and ending, and the rate of fall.

A rain-gauge cannot be used in ships at sea, and no method has been devised to obtain even approximate measurements; the amounts shown in Fig. 69 (p. 198) are estimates based on various considerations.

CHAPTER XIX

WATER VAPOUR. ABSOLUTE AND RELATIVE HUMIDITY. DEW-POINT

The nitrogen, oxygen, carbon dioxide, and other gases of the atmosphere, the proportions of which remain almost constant, are of less meteorological significance by present knowledge, but the water vapour, being very variable in amount, is of obvious immediate importance, since the precipitation, and to a small extent the atmospheric pressure also, depend on it. It decreases rapidly upwards, partly because its source is the water on the surface of the earth, and partly because the possible amount decreases with the air temperature; about half is in the lowest 8,000 feet, and the mean vapour-content at 4,000 feet is only one-tenth of the mean near sea-level. The capacity increases, at a rapidly increasing rate, with the temperature, as is shown in Fig. 65.

At any temperature and pressure vapour can be present in unit volume up to a certain fixed amount, and the air is saturated if it contains all that amount—a state which is frequent in the troposphere. Absolutely dry air, on the other hand, is never found in nature, but the vapour may be so scanty as to be very difficult to measure, as is the case in the stratosphere. The vapour actually present at any time

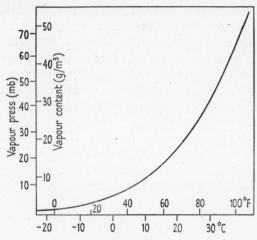

FIG. 65. Curve of water vapour capacity

is the 'vapour-density' or 'absolute humidity', which is expressed numerically as the mass of vapour in unit volume, or more commonly and conveniently in meteorology, as the 'vapour-pressure', that is the pressure the vapour would exert if measured alone without the many other constituents of the atmosphere which provide most of the total pressure which the barometer records. In England on a summer afternoon the vapour-pressure is about 15 mb. (0·45 inch), in a winter night about 5 mb. (0·15 inch). At Calcutta the mean is about 34 mb. (1 inch) in July during the hot moist monsoon, and about 15 mb. (0·45 inch) in January. The lowest records have been obtained in the polar regions in winter; during the drift of the *Fram* in the Arctic the pressure in January was about 0·3 mb. (0·007 inch) throughout the 24 hours. At Helwan near Cairo, representative of the

PLATE 4

Cumulus clouds over the land on each side of the Strait of Dover

Sahara, the monthly mean ranges from 8 mb. (0·25 inch) in February to 17 mb. (0·5 inch) in August. It is usually highest when the temperature is highest, since the tendency is towards saturation and warm air can contain more vapour than cool, but one of the lowest readings at Helwan, 1 mb. (0·03 inch), was taken on 8 May 1918 at 1400 when the wind was south and the atmosphere abnormally dry though hot. At Athens the mean is lowest, 7 mb. (0·2 inch), in January, highest, 17 mb. (0·5 inch), in July.

The vapour-pressure is highest in the humid tropics, where the broad rivers, wet ground, and dense foliage are always pouring vapour into the sluggish air, and keeping it almost saturated. It is least in the great anticyclone that covers Asia in winter, in which the intensely cold air contains far less than even its possible vapour-content owing to distance from the oceans, and to some extent subsidence of the air. Between these extremes it is not possible to enunciate any regular relationship with latitude. The air in the Sahara in the scorching heat and drought of summer may contain more vapour than the obviously damp air of a dull winter day in England, since it is so hot that even when its relative humidity is low—and our sensation of damp or dry depends largely on the relative humidity—it may still hold much vapour. Apart from weather irregularities, the absolute humidity is greater by day than by night, but the relative humidity is greater at night.

The vapour-pressure is not changed except by the addition or removal of vapour. A change of temperature does not affect it unless the air is cooled below its dew-point and moisture is deposited. It is different with the relative humidity which depends as much on the temperature as on the amount of vapour. Relative humidity is the percentage of the possible amount of vapour that is actually present; thus, if air at 60° contains 9 grammes in a cubic metre, its relative humidity is 68 per cent., since the saturated vapour-content is 13·3 grammes. Saturated air at 40° contains 6·6 g./m.^{3}, and the vapour-pressure remains the same however much the air

is heated; but the relative humidity decreases rapidly with
increasing temperature, being

at 40° . . 100%	70° . . 35 %
50° . . 70 „	80° . . 26 „
60° . . 50 „	90° . . 19 „

The relative humidity is normally above 90 per cent. everywhere in the night and early morning, and falls rapidly with
the rising temperature in the day, to 5 per cent. or less in the
hot deserts in summer; even in the humid tropics (lowlands)
midday values down to 60 per cent. in the dry season, 70
per cent. in the rains, are not uncommon. For some purposes a statement of absolute humidity is preferable, for
others a statement of relative humidity. The matter is
considered from the physiological standpoint in Chapter
XXVII.

Determination of Humidity. Dew-point

A very significant figure, especially in synoptic meteorology, is the 'dew-point'. If air which is not saturated is
cooled, a temperature is reached at which the vapour present
is all that it can normally contain, and this is the dew-point.
It may be determined as follows. A small vessel of thin
polished metal, containing a volatile liquid such as ether, is
placed in the air to be tested, and a current of air is passed
over the liquid so as to evaporate it rapidly and thus cool it.
After a few moments the polished exterior will become dim
with the deposit of moisture from the air in contact with the
cold surface; the temperature of the surface when the deposit
begins is the dew-point. In practice wet- and dry-bulb
thermometers are more convenient; two ordinary mercury
thermometers of the same size and form are exposed side by
side, the bulb of one being covered with muslin kept wet
by a wick from a small vessel of water. The evaporation
cools the muslin according to its rate, and the depression
of the wet-bulb in relation to the dry indicates the humidity;
the necessary tables have been calculated giving the vapour-
pressure, relative humidity, and dew-point, the following
being an extract:

Dry-bulb (°F.)	Depression of the wet-bulb (°F.)																
	0·5			1·0			2·0			5·0			10·0			15·0		
	a	b	c	a	b	c	a	b	c	a	b	c	a	b	c	a	b	c
20	3·2	92	16	2·9	84	14	2·4	68	10	0·8	21							
30	5·3	94	29	4·9	88	27	4·3	77	23	2·4	43	10						
40	8·0	95	39	7·6	91	38	6·9	82	35	4·7	56	26	1·6	19				
50	11·8	96	49	11·4	93	48	10·5	86	46	8·0	65	39	4·0	32		0·2	2	
60	17·1	97	59	16·6	94	58	15·6	88	56	12·5	71	50	7·8	44	38	3·5	20	
70	24·4	97	69	23·8	95	68	22·5	90	67	18·9	75	62	13·2	53	52	8·1	32	39
80	34·2	97	79	33·4	96	79	31·9	91	77	27·4	79	73	20·6	59	64	14·4	41	54
90	47·2	98	89	46·2	96	89	44·3	92	87	38·9	81	83	30·5	63	76	23·0	48	68

a is the vapour-pressure in mb., *b* the relative humidity, *c* the dew-point.

Almost all statements of humidity and dew-point are based on readings of dry- and wet-bulb thermometers interpreted by such a table.

If the atmosphere is cooled below dew-point the excess vapour is condensed in the form of minute drops of water or crystals of ice, so minute at first that they float as fog or cloud. The important case of supersaturation is mentioned below. If the droplets coalesce to form large drops (a process not altogether easy to understand) they fall to earth as rain; probably nearly all rain-drops grow from crystals of ice. Many familiar instances illustrate the process of condensation; a glass of cold spring water placed in the hot air of a summer afternoon is soon dimmed with a film of droplets, in favourable conditions so copious that drops of water trickle down; in winter when a spell of cold gives way to warm damp weather the walls of houses are still cold, and the warm air condenses so much water on them as to be a source of discomfort.

More water is derived from the cooling of saturated warm air than cool. Saturated air at 80° contains 25·3 g./m.³, at 60° 13·3 g./m.³, so that cooling from 80° to 60° gives a condensation of 12·0 g./m.³ But a further cooling of 20° gives only 6·7 g./m.³ since saturated air at 40° contains 6·6 g./m.³.

Pure air can be cooled far below its dew-point without condensation of its vapour. But very much supersaturation is unusual in the lower layers of the atmosphere, for if hygroscopic nuclei are present, condensation takes place on them even before the air is saturated, and such nuclei are abundant throughout the lower troposphere; most of them are minute crystals of sea-salt left floating in the atmosphere after the evaporation of fine spray and carried even into the middle of the continents by the winds, and minute liquid particles, compounds of sulphur or nitrogen with oxygen derived from the combustion of fuels in factories and houses. Condensation on salt begins when the relative humidity rises to about 75 per cent., long before saturation, the crystal becoming a minute droplet of saline water, which continues to grow as long as the necessary concentration of vapour is maintained.

CHAPTER XX

CLOUD FORMS

THE main types of clouds are described first, and the next chapter gives a short account of the processes of their formation; this order is convenient though it involves some repetition.

Clouds are of great variety, but classification is possible and useful, according to height, into:

High cloud ('cirro-'), including cirrus, cirro-cumulus, and cirro-stratus, usual level 20,000–30,000 feet and up to 50,000 feet near the equator.

Middle (or medium) cloud ('alto-'), alto-cumulus and alto-stratus, usual level 7,000–20,000 feet.

Low cloud, stratus, nimbo-stratus, strato-cumulus, cumulus, and cumulo-nimbus with tops up to cirrus level.

Clouds of the same type are higher in summer than in winter, in the tropics than in higher latitudes.

A major distinction in structure and form is between 'stratus' cloud, in sheets of no great thickness but often of large and unbroken horizontal extent, and heaped or 'cumulus' clouds, which rise to great heights relatively to their horizontal extent, the vapour in the rising currents condensing in rounded masses separated by blue sky; 'cirrus', fibrous clouds of delicate, almost transparent, texture, consisting mostly of minute crystals of ice, occur only at great heights. The lower clouds may be wind-torn and ragged, and are then distinguished by the prefix fracto-, e.g. fracto-cumulus. Only the main cloud types are mentioned here, without the numerous subdivisions that are recognized.

Clouds are constituents of almost every scene, and most are features of beauty and interest; the cloudless skies of arid lands soon pall by their monotony. They are manifestations of the processes going on in the atmosphere, and their movement gives useful information on the direction and velocity of the winds at their levels. All cloud forms are to be seen in most parts of the world, but with different frequency and development. The sky often contains clouds of many forms (the higher sometimes derived from those below), moving with different directions and speeds—an indication of the complexity of the movements of the atmosphere.

High Clouds

Cirrus (Plate 2, facing p. 144) is a fine-weather cloud, too high and tenuous to give rain, and so thin that it appears white, without shadows. In its most beautiful forms it is fibrous and feathery, often hooked in shape. The upper part seems to consist largely of supercooled droplets of water, the rest almost entirely of crystals of ice, which are formed either by sublimation or by the freezing of water in the top of the cloud, grow rapidly at the expense of the neighbouring droplets, and fall, as it were in cascades; in passing through air-currents of different velocities they are drawn out into the characteristic trails resembling curls of hair (whence the name cirrus).[1]

Cirro-stratus is a very thin amorphous layer at a similar high level, appearing only as a milkiness of the sky; haloes of the sun or moon, with a radius of about $22°$, are to be seen in it, and occasionally mock-suns and other optical phenomena.

Cirro-cumulus consists of small white cloudlets, separate but usually grouped closely in large sheets or waves; it is outstanding for delicacy of form and colour.

[1] Ludlam, F. H., *The forms of ice-clouds*, Q.J.R. Met. Soc., 1948.

Cirrus is common in the equatorial belt, moving slowly from the east. In the westerlies it is a forerunner of depressions, drifting fast 500 miles and more in front of the centre; after the cirrus comes cirro-stratus with its haloes, thickening and lowering into alto-stratus. This sequence is a useful sign of the approach of bad weather (Chapter XXXV).

Mention may be made here of the curious 'mother-of-pearl' clouds, floating high above the cirrus level, at about 15 miles, which have been reported from Scandinavia, and seem to indicate occasional vertical movements in the stratosphere, and of another variety, 'luminous night clouds', still rarer, at 50 miles, quite removed from our 'weather' atmosphere, which may not consist of water or ice; little is known of their composition or significance.

Middle Clouds

Alto-stratus (Plate 3, facing p. 160) has been named above as succeeding cirro-stratus in the pre-cyclonic sequence. In its thinner forms it can be recognized by the 'watery' sun or moon visible through it, but this stage soon passes into a thicker, too thick for even a watery sun to be seen. The cloud itself is an almost amorphous grey sheet, dull and uninteresting. Common in all regions, it gives large amounts of steady persistent rain, at times remarkably heavy, not only in the westerlies but notably in the inter-tropical front where it is much in evidence.

Alto-cumulus (Plate 2) is a beautiful cloud form, of small rounded cloudlets, white with light-grey shadows, floating high aloft, often grouped in wave-like lines; an edging of rainbow colours ('irisation') is an added feature of beauty, more often seen in the tropics and at high altitudes than in the westerlies. The cumulus form suggests a certain instability in the atmosphere at its level, and may indicate disturbed conditions; the cloud is frequent on the outskirts of the inter-tropical front, and near the cold fronts of depressions of higher latitudes. A more turbulent variety, alto-cumulus castellatus, so called from its turreted form, is the expression of greater vertical development, and often foretells thunder within 12 hours.

Low Clouds

Cumulus (Plate 2) is the most beautiful form of low cloud; the rounded cauliflower-like heads are usually to be seen in the afternoon sky. They may result from the condensation of the vapour in the air that rises from heated ground, and are fine-weather clouds giving little rain, usually none except in cases of abnormally vigorous ascent of very humid air; they build up in the warmest hours of the day over the lands, but are not so common over the oceans, and we can often fix a distant coast by the cumulus over it long before the land appears above the horizon (Plate 4, facing p. 176). Cumulus dies away as the heat of the day fails, and flattens to stratus in the evening, coloured brilliantly by the setting sun. It must be reckoned as 'low cloud' since it originates in the surface layers and the base is low (2–4,000 ft. in middle latitudes), but the summits may be at 15,000 feet or higher, even without the extreme vertical development of cumulo-nimbus; this latter, the most spectacular of clouds, is described on page 188.

Stratus is the least impressive of the main types of cloud. Its essential feature, common to all varieties, is its layer form and more or less uniform thickness over large areas, so that it appears amorphous from below, with little variation in its dull greys covering the sky from horizon to horizon. One simple form results from loss of heat by radiation at night from a layer of vapour or of solid or liquid particles in the atmosphere a few hundred, or thousand, feet above the ground in stable air, the cloud-sheet forming when dew-point is reached, and extending till morning when the heat of the sun dissipates it. The flattening-out of cumulus into stratus on calm clear evenings has been mentioned above.

Stratiform cloud may also be formed by mixing at the junction of superposed air-masses of different humidities; such cloud is not usually thick enough to give rain. A more rainy type results from elevation when extensive masses of damp air slowly converge. And very often in the depressions of the westerlies great sheets are formed by the gradual ascent of tropical air up the sloping plane of the warm front. In strong winds the layer is more broken and confused, and

is called nimbo-stratus, though that term is strictly applicable
only when rain is falling from the cloud.

Strato-cumulus (Plate 3) usually results from turbulence
in cool damp air, the whole mass being churned and cooling
at the dry adiabatic lapse-rate up to the level where condensation starts; this widespread elevation of the air over an
extensive area is in marked contrast to the localized, cellular,
ascent which results in cumulus. The turbulent air must be
in fairly rapid movement horizontally (otherwise turbulence
would not be set up), and consequently the cloud layer tends
to assume a widely wave-like form, made visible by lighter
and deeper shades of grey. It forms most readily in stable
air, for instability conduces rather to cumuliform development, and for this reason it is commoner in winter than in
summer; it (and stratus) are often present in anticyclones.
In the heat of summer it is likely to break up in the daytime
into cumulus owing to convection from the warm surface, but
a less degree of instability may merely tend to increase the
existing turbulence, and intensify the formation of strato-
cumulus.

Stratus and strato-cumulus often mark the base of an
inversion, temperature rising abruptly in the clear air above
the cloud; the transition from the hazy bumpy air below
to the damp grey cloud itself, and then to the dry, bright,
transparent, smooth atmosphere above the dazzlingly white
billows of its upper surface is impressive.

Strato-cumulus is one of the commonest types, and may
overspread the whole sky for days and even weeks together
in the westerlies, the persistent gloom constituting a depressing feature of the climate. It and stratus are the usual
forms on mountains, frequently present even when the lowlands are clear, and when the lowlands are clouded much
thicker on the mountains, the base being lower on the
windward slopes and the top higher; the whole mountain
may be hidden, to the great danger of aircraft, though the
cloud base is well above the surface over the low ground.
A humid current forced over a mountain barrier condenses
its vapour after a few hundred feet of ascent, to envelop the
heights and pour down the lee slopes in a beautiful white

PLATE 5

Eddy cloud in an Alpine valley: Umhausen, Ötztal

curtain or cascade, which, however, dissolves before it can descend far.

Two minor but very common types formed by turbulence among mountains are interesting. One is the beautiful 'banner-cloud' that trails to leeward of a lofty mountain summit, sometimes in an otherwise clear sky, remaining stationary and attached to the mountain like a flag to its flagstaff in spite of the wind which rushes past (Plate 1, Frontispiece). In the eddy behind the mountain obstacle the air ascends and the vapour is condensed to appear as the banner-cloud; the droplets are soon evaporated and disappear in the main current, but new ones take their place as long as the eddy persists. The other is a result of eddy movements in mountain valleys, seen in the bands of cloud that hang along the mountain sides in bad weather (Plate 5, facing p. 184). Air-currents are deflected, vertically and horizontally, by the irregularities of the topography, and in its ascent the vapour-laden air condenses wisps of cloud which are usually to be seen when the weather is unsettled. They are quite local and have no connexion with the main mass of cloud high above.

Amount of Cloud. Diurnal Variation

As a rule the afternoon with its strong convection is the cloudiest, the night and early morning the least cloudy period. This is most prominent in the tropics, for example at Trincomalee, Ceylon, where the mean cloud-amount (in tenths of the sky covered) in January is:

at 0000	2	0600	3	1200	4	1800	4
0200	2	0800	3	1400	5	2000	2
0400	2	1000	4	1600	5	2200	2

The other months show a similar but smaller variation. The same tendency appears in summer in temperate lands; for example at Potsdam the July means are:

at 0000	5	0600	7	1200	7	1800	6
0200	6	0800	7	1400	7	2000	6
0400	7	1000	7	1600	7	2200	5

The night is less cloudy than the day, the minimum being at 2300, but clearly the cloud-forming processes are not restricted to the day hours.

In fine weather the morning may be quite cloudless, but clouds collect as the day warms, and by afternoon the sky is almost overcast; the clouds dissolve in the evening. In bad weather the diurnal control is masked by the general conditions, and consequently it is not so prominent in the mean values as it is noticeable on certain days. An absolutely cloudless day is rare except in the trade-wind deserts. Elsewhere cloud appears towards midday if not before, especially in humid climates. If the sky remains clear, the reason may be exceptional cold on the surface, unusual dryness of the air, or the presence of an inversion or a small lapse-rate of temperature, with resulting stability of the atmosphere up to such a level that the ascending air does not cool to its dewpoint before ascent is stopped.

But this type of diurnal variation is not universal. An interesting exception is found on some tropical coasts, where the cloudiest hours are before sunrise owing to the landbreeze meeting a general on-shore or along-shore humid air current; this occurs on many coasts in south-east Asia in months when the monsoon is on-shore, and also on the coast of Nigeria, and of East Africa (p. 119). On most seas the diurnal variation in cloud-amount is small, with a tendency to a night maximum, which is strongly developed in some regions. On land in clear calm weather low stratus may form at night at some level where radiation is active, to dissolve again in the morning sunshine, as in the Egyptian Sahara where stratus and strato-cumulus are often abundant in the early hours in summer; but in winter the afternoons are more cloudy than the mornings. In London the cloudiest hours in winter are from 0700 to 0900, but the 'cloud' often consists in part of thick haze or fog at no great height above the surface.

CHAPTER XXI

PROCESSES OF CONDENSATION. PRECIPITATION

CLOUD is formed when the air at some height above the surface is cooled sufficiently below its dew-point to condense its vapour. If condensation continues the particles coalesce into drops, or crystals of ice, large enough to fall as precipitation unless they are evaporated in their descent. The processes leading to condensation will now be described. Though in most cases one definite process is dominant, nearly always several are involved in some degree.

It should be noted that 'precipitation' includes not only rain, snow, and hail, but also the 'occult' forms, dew, hoarfrost, and rime, which result from condensation on the surface. These latter forms are treated in Chapter XXIII.

Radiation

Direct radiation from pure air is very slow and almost negligible as a cause of cooling, but suspended dust or water particles are efficient radiators which may cool the adjacent air below its dew-point at night, with the formation of stratiform cloud, rarely, however, enough to give rain. But in one case heavy rain may occur, when the tops of lofty cumulus clouds lose heat so fast at night as to give a steep lapse-rate between their level and the surface, where the air, blanketed by the heavy clouds, remains warm, and vigorous convectional overturning results. This is probably a usual factor in late evening and night thunderstorms in tropical lands, and in the night rain, often heavy, on tropical seas (where more rain falls by night than by day).

Ascent

The most general and effective cause of cooling is ascent. The temperature and condensation conditions in ascending air are described in Chapter VIII.

Causes of Ascent

Thermal convection is perhaps the most general cause of the ascent of air; since the air is heated from the surface, instability is a normal condition in the day-time, ascent often manifesting itself by the shimmering of the atmosphere, and by the formation of cumulus clouds a few thousand feet up. They are prominent all the world over, but mostly on hot lowlands and in the warm season (unless the air is unusually dry, or its ascent is checked by an inversion).

Condensation begins at a uniform level, shown by the flat

bases of the clouds over large areas. The convectional over-turning between the surface and the cooler air above is effected in up-currents arranged like the cells of a honey-comb, the cooler air descending in less definitely localized currents, so that the cloud forms individual heads separated by blue sky.

The extra vertical development required for rain or thunder-showers occurs chiefly in the following circum-stances, (*a*) when the lower air is abnormally hot and damp, as is the case almost every afternoon in the humid tropics; (*b*) when a polar air-mass crosses a warm sea, the surface air becoming damp and warm, and vigorous convection forms showery cumulus; if the polar maritime air crosses a warm land, the additional heating from the surface intensifies the vertical development, giving heavy showers in the after-noons; the 'April showers' of the British Isles are often of this origin; (*c*) when cool air undercuts warm and damp at the cold front of a depression heavy and lofty cumulus clouds build up, and may coalesce into a menacing, dark, turbulent rain-belt which advances across the sky.

In its finest development cumulus becomes cumulo-nimbus, mighty upswellings of vapour which may attain a height of 6 miles (even 8 or 9 miles near the equator), the upper parts putting out horizontal protuberances or anvil-like extensions, and sometimes thinning out above in a filmy or fibrous tangle of cirrus (Plate 6, facing p. 192). All cumu-lus cloud has updraughts, which are very violent and irregular in these great cumulo-nimbus masses, often attaining speeds of well over 30 m.p.h. in the tropics; hence such clouds are dangerous for aircraft, and their neighbourhood is avoided if possible; the compensating down-currents outside the cloud are not so sharply localized, and may be hardly notice-able. These clouds are always liable to give heavy showers of rain or hail, and thunder, with a pronounced afternoon and evening maximum but in some regions continuing far into the night. Their surpassing size and height, and their innu-merable rounded cloudlets showing every contrast of light and shadow, and at times ominous shades of red, copper, and purple, make them, particularly in their gigantic forms of the humid tropics, the most magnificent spectacle in the skies.

Convection plays an important part in the formation of all types of rain in the tropics, and is a large factor in the summer rainfall of continental climates in higher latitudes.

Mountain Barriers

The barrier presented to an air-stream by mountains is another, and very effective, cause of ascent of the air and heavy rain. Such precipitation is termed orographic rain, and it results not merely from the direct, straightforward, ascent of air over the barrier, but from several other tendencies which already exist and are intensified by the mountains. It must be noted that only air which is unstable, absolutely or conditionally, rises easily over a range; stable air prefers to make its way round an obstacle. Rain may fall on the hills when the lowlands have none, and when it rains on the lowlands it almost always rains more heavily on the hills. The rate of increase with altitude varies too much with the atmospheric and topographical conditions to admit of any general statement.

In some mountain-systems the configuration assists ascent, helping to drive a large volume of air upward, as in the Khasi Hills of Assam, where the funnel-like topography acts in this way, giving Cherrapunji, at the end of the funnel, the record rainfall total of the earth (p. 214). In the westerlies the greater part of the orographic rainfall is received from the warm sectors of depressions (p. 330), which do not give much rain on the lower ground; they contain a great depth of warm tropical air, almost saturated after a long ocean passage from lower latitudes, and when the air, sometimes potentially unstable, is forced up over the mountain barrier, copious condensation results throughout its depth. Warm-front rainfall is also increased by a mountain range, for the cold air in advance of the front is trapped by the obstacle, and provides a good gliding slope for the warm air. Rainfall at cold fronts and in polar air is also increased, but its duration is short, so that the orographic addition is not large. Other factors conducing to orographic rainfall are the valley-breezes of the warm hours, which carry their stores of vapour to the summits, to condense in massive clouds which often give afternoon showers with thunder. The

general turbulence of all air-streams is greatly magnified in
the broken relief of mountains and may rise to over twice the
height of a range, with consequent increase of cloud and rain.

Orographic influences account for the heaviest rainfalls
of the globe. A striking example is the Western Ghats of
India, rising to over 4,000 feet for long distances full in the
path of the south-west monsoon after it has swept over
thousands of miles of tropical seas and become saturated
with vapour. In the four months June to September the
monsoon gives 71 inches of rain at Bombay, and more than
200 inches on the top of the Ghats; descending to the
plateau of the Deccan it gives not more than 15 inches in
many places. In July parts of the west slopes have more than
50 inches, while only 0.5 inch is received on the east. The
windward slopes have rainfall far in excess of the needs of
agriculture while the east suffers from serious drought, and
an irrigation system in the south of India effects a useful
redistribution; the River Periyar, which rises on the west
slopes of the Cardamom Hills and formerly carried its over-
abundant waters to the Arabian Sea, has been dammed at an
altitude of 3,000 feet to form a large reservoir, and a tunnel
$1\frac{1}{4}$ miles long leads the water to the arid lands east of the
watershed where the need is urgent. The excessive rain on
the west was itself the cause of almost insuperable difficulties
in the construction of the works, for the embankments were
more than once carried away by rains of as much as 3 inches
in a few hours, and the floods swept all before them. Malaria
and other diseases fostered by the moist climate were ram-
pant, and the maintenance of an adequate labour supply was
a task hardly less formidable than the engineering of the
works to harness the refractory river. But determination
triumphed, and the undertaking was completed in 1895;
the system irrigates 176,000 acres in southern Madras
which were formerly liable to famine, and is very successful
financially.

The western highlands of the British Isles are favourably
placed for a copious rainfall—exceeding 200 inches a year
in places. They lie in the path of the depressions of the
westerlies, and the vapour-capacity of the air is the higher

over the warm North Atlantic Drift which washes the shores. R. L. Stevenson gives a graphic description of a frequent type of weather in the Scottish Highlands:

For the best part of the three nights we travelled on eerie mountains and among the well-heads of wild rivers; often buried in mist, almost continually blown and rained upon, and not once cheered by any glimpse of sunshine. By day, we lay and slept in the drenching heather, by night, incessantly clambered upon break-neck hills and among rude crags. We often wandered; we were often so involved in fog, that we must lie quiet till it lightened. . . . This was a dreadful time, rendered the more dreadful by the gloom of the weather and the country, . . . the rain driving sharp in my face or running down my back in icy trickles, the mist enfolding us as in a gloomy chamber—or, perhaps, if the wind blew, falling suddenly apart and showing us the gulf of some dark valley where the streams were crying loud. The sound of an infinite number of rivers came up from all round. In this steady rain the springs of the mountain were broken up; every glen gushed water like a cistern; every stream was in high spate, and had filled and overflowed its channel.

In lee of the western mountains the totals decrease rapidly, to less than 25 inches in the east, but even such minor uplands as the Chiltern Hills have about 5 inches more than the neighbouring plains. Scandinavia, British Columbia, the south-west of South America and of New Zealand, have similar conditions, the mountains standing out as clearly on the rainfall as on the topographical map. The precipitation on these mountains of middle and high latitudes is probably a good deal more than the records show, since much of it is driving snow, only a part of which enters the gauges and remains to be measured. Even the massifs of the Ahaggar, Air, and Tibesti in the arid wastes of the Sahara have enough rain to maintain perennial streams and nourish vegetation.

Where the rain is due to the ascent of strong winds the largest totals are not on the actual ridges, but a little to leeward; thus in Snowdonia, North Wales, the largest records are round Llyn Lydau, a mile east of the top of Snowdon, which had 247 inches in 1909, the highest record of the British Isles; and in the Lake District of Cumberland considerably more rain falls at Styehead Pass than on the neighbouring summits of about 3,000 feet. Some of the rain is carried beyond the summit line by the strong winds;

other factors are the vigorous eddies in lee of the ranges, rendered visible in the 'banner clouds' of many mountains (p. 185), and the forced ascent of the air far above the summits, to attain its greatest height not above, but well beyond them. As a result the low ground on the weather side of a range may have less rain than a district at the same altitude on the leeward side. The Cape Peninsula of South Africa

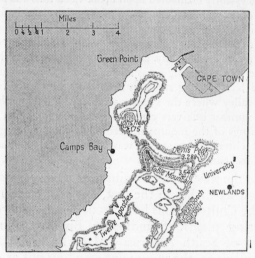

FIG. 66. Table Mountain and district

provides a good example; Camps Bay, altitude 100 feet, on the west of the Table Mountain plateau (the weather side for the rain-bearing winds) has a mean annual total of only 24 inches, while Newlands, at about the same altitude on the leeward, eastern, side, has 60 inches, and claims the highest record for 24 hours in the Cape Peninsula (6·7 inches, 9 August 1948); both stations are 1½ miles from the edge of the plateau (Fig. 66).

It is particularly frontal, cyclonic, rain which shows a pronounced increase with altitude; convectional rain is usually heavier on the plains. Hence the orographic excess is greater in winter than in summer on the western seaboards in the westerlies, in which almost all the winter rain is cyclonic with strong winds and bad weather (Fig. 67). In Great Britain intense downpours of 0·75 inch in half an hour, or

PLATE 6

Cumulo-nimbus cloud on the equator

1 inch in 1 hour, or, rarely, as much as 2 inches in half an
hour, or 2·5 inches in 1 hour, nearly all occur in the dry
Midlands and east in the warmest months, not in the moun-

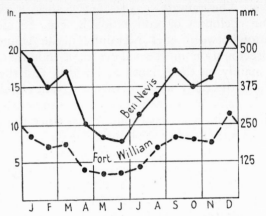

FIG. 67. Mean monthly precipitation at Fort William (alt. 171 ft.)
and Ben Nevis (4,406 ft.)

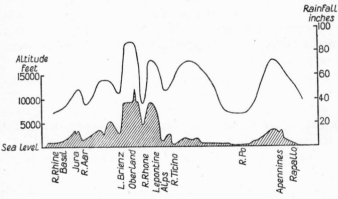

FIG. 68. Mean annual precipitation (upper line) and topography in the Alpine
region. The Apennines owe their heavy precipitation to the proximity of the
Mediterranean. The upper Rhone Valley (2,500 ft.) has little more than the Po
plains (250 ft.)

tains. But the mountains provide most very high totals over
longer periods, a week or more, e.g. 57 inches on Snowdon
in the month of October 1909, 50 inches at Styehead Pass,
Cumberland, in January 1872. In the tropics the increase
with altitude is far greater in the rains than in the dry season.

The area of low rainfall to leeward of a mountain system is sometimes called the rain-shadow; Alberta is in the rain shadow of the Rockies, Sweden in that of the Norwegian Highlands. The rain that falls in the shadow is mostly frontal (or cyclonic) or convectional. Fig. 68 shows the close relation between relief and rainfall in the Alpine region.

The precipitation in the valleys of a mountain system depends mainly on their depth and width, and their trend in relation to the rainy winds. A narrow valley, only a mile or two wide, lying athwart the rainy winds may receive even more rain than its windward mountains, since the lee eddy may have its largest effect at about the distance of the valley bottom from the summits. But a valley or depression 5 miles or more wide, trending with the rainy winds, will probably show a rain-shadow effect with appreciably less rain than the bounding mountains; such are the Engadine, the Valais (upper Rhone), the Maurienne, and indeed almost all the larger valleys in the Alps, with annual means in places less than 25 inches between ranges with over 100 inches; and many of the main valleys east of the watershed of Norway, the precipitation of which, falling to below 15 inches, stands in marked contrast to the 100 inches and more of the western slopes of the fjelde.

Mountain ranges are obvious, visible barriers; but the atmosphere contains invisible barriers, formed of cooler, denser air lying across the path of the less dense currents, and they play a notable part in the depressions of the westerlies, in which air-masses of different origin and density are brought into contact. Some details are given in Chapter XXXV.

Turbulence

Ascent by turbulence forms sheets of cloud, mostly strato-cumulus, not usually massive enough for rain unless rein-forced by other processes, but active turbulence in damp unstable air may give drizzle or light rain, the more so if the added effect of ascent of the air up even a gentle slope is present. The heavy rainfall of the Niger delta and similar low tropical shores results in part from the increased turbu-lence over the forests.

Convergence

Convergence of air-streams necessarily involves ascent—hence a tendency to cloud and rain, often drizzle, in all low-pressure systems. In the case of in-blowing monsoons convergence must occur, but it is probably of little general influence compared with the other rain-producing processes. Divergence, on the other hand, involves descent to feed the diverging currents, with consequent adiabatic heating and drying, and this is a main immediate cause of the clear dry air of anticyclones, both the travelling anticyclones of the westerlies, and, on a larger and more important scale, the sub-tropical high-pressure systems.

Vortical Ascent

Vortical ascent in revolving storms, tornadoes and tropical cyclones, is vigorous enough to form an extensive area of dense cloud and torrential rain, the high temperature and humidity conducing to intense condensation; the ascent in depressions of the westerlies, however, is frontal, not vortical.

Variability of Rainfall

Rainfall is variable from year to year. The variability may be expressed as a percentage of the normal by taking the mean of the excess above and the deficit below the normal (ignoring signs) for as many years or months as possible. Such figures (annual) are:

	%
British Isles (as a whole)	11
Central and Western Europe	13
Moscow	13
Rome	15
California	26
India: Assam and E. Bengal	5
Allahabad	23
Punjab	13
N.W. Provinces	23
Sind	37
Entebbe, Uganda	12
Onslow, Western Australia	50
Charlotte Water, Northern Territory, Australia	57

It is useful, though somewhat lengthy, to state, with the mean rainfall, the mode, the median value, and the quartiles (the interquartile range being the amount of variation of the rainfall of half the years or months of the period of records).

As a rule the most arid climates are the most variable. The shorter the period considered the greater is the variability, greater for a season than for the year, for a month than for a season. It is useful to know not only the mean but the absolute highest and absolute lowest rainfalls that have been recorded, provided that the records are of adequate duration, not less than 30 years. The following tables give these figures for each month for Oxford:

Highest rainfall (in.) recorded, 1815–1948

Jan.	5·5	Apr.	4·4	July	7·2	Oct.	7·4
Feb.	4·7	May	5·5	Aug.	5·2	Nov.	7·3
Mar.	5·3	June	7·6	Sept.	6·0	Dec.	5·6

Year 40·7

Lowest rainfall recorded, 1815–1948

Jan.	0·21	Apr.	0·02	July	0·03	Oct.	0·41
Feb.	0·01	May	0·14	Aug.	0·08	Nov.	0·19
Mar.	0·06	June	0·07	Sept.	0·10	Dec.	0·19

Year 14·9

Mean rainfall, 1815–1945

Jan.	2·1	Apr.	1·8	July	2·5	Oct.	**2·7**
Feb.	1·6	May	1·9	Aug.	2·3	Nov.	2·3
Mar.	*1·6*	June	2·1	Sept.	2·3	Dec.	2·2

Year 25·5

Extreme annual rainfalls for other zones are:

	Lat.	Mean annual rainfall (inches)	Highest rainfall recorded in a year	Lowest rainfall recorded in a year
Malden Island (1890–1919)	4° S.	29	94	4
Lagos	6° N.	72	115	40
Manila (1887–1930) . .	15° N.	81	154	41
Brisbane (1840–1930) .	27° S.	45	88	16
Beaufort West (Cape Prov.) (1931–41) . . .	32° S.	8	20	3
Athens (1857–1930) . .	38° N.	15	33	5
Paris (1851–1930) . .	49° N.	23	33	11
New York (1826–1930) .	41° N.	42	60	29
Victoria, B.C. (1881–1930) .	48° N.	31	51	17
Winnipeg (1885–1930) .	50° N.	20	27	14

To consider shorter periods, the lowlands of the south of England seem to be liable to receive as much as 10 inches in 24 hours; among the highest records are 9·6 inches at Bruton, Somerset, on 28 June 1917, and 9·4 inches near Cannington, Somerset, on 19 August 1924. These excessive falls of short duration are generally, though not always, sudden downpours in thunderstorms; they are very rare and only a small area is affected by any one storm (Fig. 89, p. 245). The highest record for a day at Berlin is 6·6 inches. In the mountains facing the westerlies heavy rain of long duration is common in the warm sectors and warm fronts of depressions, but intense falls of short duration are much less frequent than in the lowlands.

In the humid tropics larger totals are to be expected. Twelve inches in 24 hours is not uncommon in tropical lowlands, and 15 inches on mountains; over 40 inches has fallen in north-east India. The heaviest rainfall recorded anywhere in 24 hours was 46 inches at Baguio (4,800 feet) in the Philippine Islands during a typhoon in July 1911; the total in 4 days on this occasion was 88 inches. Manila in the same group has a daily fall exceeding 4 inches 2 or 3 times in most years, and more than 8 inches was recorded 12 times in 54 years; the highest record for a day was 13 inches.

The climatologist is concerned primarily with the amount and the conditions of precipitation. These must not be confused with the available water present on and in the ground, which depends on many topographical, botanical, and geological factors as well as meteorological; even a desert tract may contain sub-surface moisture in quantity sufficient for much vegetation, derived not from local rain but from rain that fell hundreds of miles away a long time previously.

The distribution of precipitation is conveniently shown by isohyets, lines (on the principle of isotherms) separating areas with more from those with less than the amount the line indicates; they may be drawn to show mean values for the year or any part of it—such are Figs. 69, 70, and 71 for the globe—or the actual precipitation in any period. Unlike isotherms, isohyets cannot be reduced to sea-level; they

Ch.

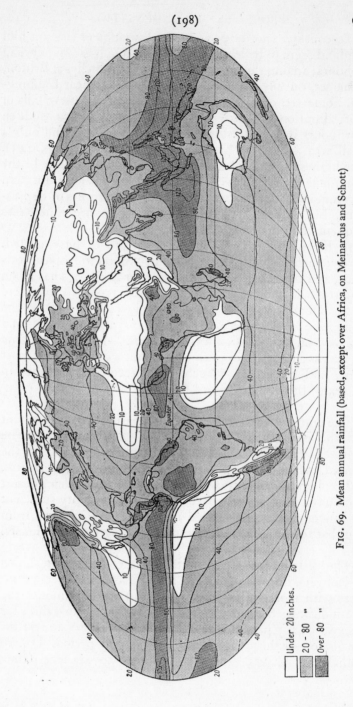

FIG. 69. Mean annual rainfall (based, except over Africa, on Meinardus and Schott)

Under 20 inches.

20 - 80 "

Over 80 "

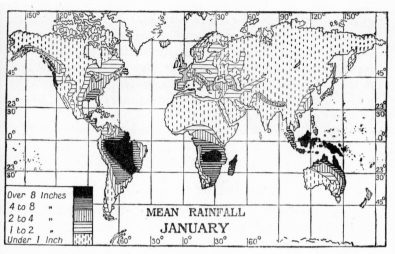

FIG. 70

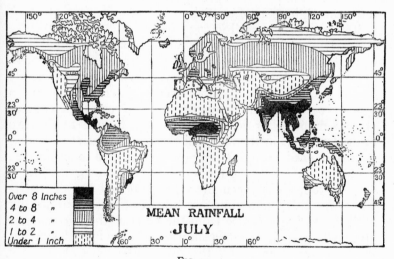

FIG. 71

must show the actual rainfall, which may differ greatly within small distances even in flat country, and the network of stations is rarely close enough, at any rate in mountains, to give 'fine definition', so that the details of the picture depend largely on the skill and, it may be, the imagination of the climatologist, using all his knowledge of topography and winds; they can be seriously inaccurate or incomplete in a region of varied relief.

CHAPTER XXII

MAJOR RAINFALL REGIONS

BEFORE describing the regions it will be convenient to indicate the main régimes of rainfall on the earth. Régime denotes the seasonal distribution, and it can be expressed graphically by plotting the monthly rainfall (e.g. Fig. 73, p. 205). The régime is similar over wide areas though the amount of rain may vary greatly, and the boundary between different régimes is often sharp.

The chief régimes (Fig. 72) are:

(a) Equatorial; most of the rain is probably frontal, associated with the convergence of the trades from the two hemispheres, but a strong convectional effect is nearly always present, alone or, more usually, in combination with other processes. The convergence belt crosses the equator about a month after the overhead sun, and tends to give two rainfall maxima in the year, but the dry seasons are not long or pronounced enough to dry out the ground to any depth. This is not the only régime found in the equatorial belt.

(b) Tropical, between the equatorial belt and the trade-wind deserts. The régime is of the same type as in (a), but with increasing distance from the equator the two maxima approach, to coalesce into a single maximum in high summer in the outer tropics. Of the two dry seasons of (a), one becomes shorter, the other longer, and most of the tropics has a long season of such marked drought that plant life has to be specially adapted to resist it. Thus we may generalize that the equator is bounded by belts, roughly between latitudes 5° and 12°, where the two maxima are within one half-year, separated merely by a month or two of less rain, the other half-year being almost rainless; and outside this, to about lat. 16° in N. Africa, the year is divided into a short rainy season and a long dry season with no rain at all. The greater the distance from the equator the shorter is the

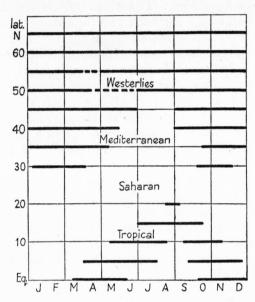

FIG. 72. Generalized rainy seasons (shown by thick lines) in the north hemisphere

rainy and the longer the dry season, till the former disappears in the trade-wind deserts.

(c) Monsoonal, with a pronounced maximum in summer; the contrast between summer with its floods and the long dry winter is more marked than in (b), from which this type is distinguished chiefly in that its seasons are dominated by the prominent reversal of the winds. It occurs both inside and outside the tropics, most extensively on the east of continents.

(d) The oceanic régime of the westerlies; rain, mostly cyclonic or frontal, all the year round, with a maximum in autumn or winter and a minimum in spring.

(e) The continental régime of the westerlies, with most rain in summer. A subdivision is the steppe type, with its maximum in spring and early summer (in spring and winter in some regions, including Turkestan and Iraq).

(*f*) The 'Mediterranean' régime, on the west of the land-masses between the westerlies and the trade-wind deserts. The rainy season is winter, and 3 or 4 summer months are almost or quite rainless. The winter rain is associated with the westerlies, which encroach with the swing of the pressure belts. Around the Mediterranean Sea the distribution of land and sea introduces some modifications into the régime, the northern half of the area having two maxima, in autumn and spring. The dry, hot, and sunny summer is everywhere characteristic, and on the south-east coasts rain is all but unknown from May to September inclusive. At Alexandria in the 35 years 1888–1922 no rain fell in July; it rained only once in June, twice in August, five times in September.

The length of the season or seasons with adequate precipitation is a major control of the luxuriance and the duration of plant growth, particularly in hot lands where the ground dries out rapidly in the dry months of strong evaporation. The even spacing of the two rainy seasons in some equatorial regions has the more value in that it tends to keep the ground moist most of the year.

The Equatorial Belt (Inner Tropics)

This is one of the very rainy belts of the globe, with totals exceeding 80 inches over large areas. The converging trades from the two hemispheres are highly charged with vapour, and the damp ground, swamp or forest, pours additional vapour into the air, which is hot, moist, often calm as in a hot-house, and enervating for whites. Apart from the orographical rain common to all regions, the precipitation is largely frontal, at the meeting of the two trades, and may continue with little interruption for a day or more, day and night, as a steady downpour like the cyclonic rain of the westerlies but much heavier. Rainy and cloudy spells may alternate with dry and sunny. The rain always tends to be of the instability type, even if only as a modification of a more fundamental process, for the damp air, resting on the hot ground, is unstable, and towards midday convection

becomes active to great heights, the higher owing to the
elevation of the tropopause in the tropics. Towering masses
of cumulus and cumulo-nimbus cloud swell upward, a
magnificent spectacle of dazzling white in the blue sky when
viewed from the side, but dark and ominous from beneath,
to give heavy downpours, often with thunder and violent
gusts of wind up to 80 m.p.h. in the afternoon and evening.
The rain cools the air, and by early night the clouds have
dissolved, except a few from which cascades of lightning
continue to flash, and the stars shine brilliantly from the
clear sky. But few are the nights in the humid tropical lands
without the frequent flicker of distant lightning, visible to
the passing sailor far out at sea. Towards dawn shallow fog
may cover low wet ground and forests, to be dissipated by
the sun before 0830. Such is a common sequence in equatorial lands, and Bates[1] gives a description for Brazil:

The heat increased rapidly towards 2 o'clock (92° and 93° F.), by
which time every voice of bird or mammal was hushed; only in the
trees was heard at intervals the harsh whirr of a cicada. The leaves,
which were so moist and fresh in early morning, now became lax and
drooping, the flowers shed their petals. . . . On most days in June and
July a heavy shower would fall sometime in the afternoon, producing
a most welcome coolness. The approach of the rain-clouds was after
a uniform fashion very interesting to observe. First, the cool sea-
breeze, which commenced to blow about 10 o'clock, and which had
increased in force with the increasing power of the sun, would flag
and finally die away. The heat and electric tension of the atmosphere
would then become almost insupportable. Languor and uneasiness
would seize on every one, even the denizens of the forest betraying it
by their motions. White clouds would appear in the east and gather
into cumuli, with an increasing blackness along their lower portions.
The whole eastern horizon would become almost suddenly black, and
this would spread upwards, the sun at length becoming obscured.
Then the rush of a mighty wind is heard in the forest, swaying the
tree-tops; a vivid flash of lightning bursts forth, then a crash of thunder,
and down streams the deluging rain. Such storms soon cease, leaving
bluish-black motionless clouds until night. Meantime all nature is
refreshed; but heaps of flower petals and leaves are seen under the
trees. Towards evening life revives again, and the ringing uproar is
resumed from bush and tree. The following morning the sun again

[1] Bates, H. W., *The Naturalist on the River Amazon*, chap. II.

rises in a cloudless sky, and so the cycle is completed, spring, summer, and autumn, as it were, in one tropical day. . . With the day and night always of equal length, the atmospheric disturbances of each day neutralizing themselves before each succeeding morn; with the sun in its course proceeding midway across the sky, and the daily temperature the same within two or three degrees throughout the year—how grand in its perfect equilibrium and simplicity is the march of Nature under the equator!

It is evident that in this cycle of weather the main control is diurnal, not cyclonic as in temperate latitudes. But there are variations depending on position and season, since local convection is not the only control. Batavia, Java, gets 57 per cent. of its rain between the hours 1400 and 2200 in the dry season (July to September), only 31 per cent. between the same hours in the rains (January and February); the lowlands in the east of the same island get 80 per cent. between 1200 and 1800 in the rains, but in the dry season they get most, 64 per cent. of the whole, at night between 2200 and 0800. The highlands of Kenya have most of their rain between sunset and sunrise, often with a secondary maximum in the early afternoon. At sea the rainiest period is the night, as is illustrated by the records from a small islet in the open Java Sea between Batavia and Borneo which has 45 per cent. between 0200 and 0800, only 16 per cent. between 1400 and 2000.

The rain falls much more heavily than in higher latitudes; Mahé, Seychelles, altitude 15 feet, latitude 4·6° S., has a mean total of 16·9 inches in January, falling on 16 days, so that the mean on a rainy day is 1·1 inch; Half-Assini on the Gold Coast has 25·8 inches in June on 15 days, a mean of 1·7 inches a rainy day, about ten times that of south England. Braak gives a similar comparison between Batavia, Java, with 72 inches a year, falling in 357 hours, and Potsdam, north Germany, with 23 inches a year in 657 hours; heavy tropical rains are not usually associated with a notably cloudy or sunless climate.

The equatorial belt contains in its vast area many modifications of the régime described above. In general the east coasts of continents, facing the trades strengthened by a monsoonal tendency, have more rain and longer rainy seasons than west coasts. The windward slopes of elevated ground are notably rainy, and some mountains facing strong and steady winds from a hot ocean have enormous totals; the south-west of Cameroon Mt., with on-shore SW. winds most of the year, has 412 inches even near sea-level, and very much more on the higher slopes; the rainiest months

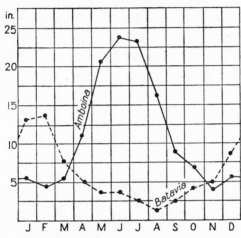

FIG. 73. Mean monthly rainfall

are June to October, when the monsoonal in-draught is strongest. Another peculiarity in West and Central Africa is the torrential rainfall in tornadoes, violent line-squalls often with thunder, at the beginning and end of the rains; the heaviest rain is in the heat of the day, but tornadoes may occur in the night as well as the day hours.

In the East Indies the amount and distribution of the rain, in respect of both season and locality, are particularly complicated. The archipelago lies between south-east Asia and Australia, full in the track of the two monsoons, E. and SE. from May to September, N. and NW. in the rest of the year; all the islands are mountainous, and the ranges trend in manifold directions. The general rainfall is heavy, over 100 inches a year, for the air comes hot and humid from the surrounding seas. No season is rainless, but most districts have one pronounced rainy season and a relatively dry season. The rains fall from on-shore winds, in the west monsoon on west- and north-facing shores, in the east monsoon on east- and south-facing shores; neighbouring districts may have their rains in different months. Thus Batavia, on the north coast of Java, has a strong maximum in January

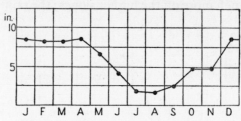

Fig. 74. Mean monthly rainfall, Manáos

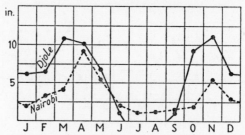

Fig. 75. Mean monthly rainfall

and February when the NW. winds are at their height; but Amboina, in the same latitude on the south coast of the island of Ceram, is comparatively dry at that time and has a very pronounced maximum in June and July, the season of SE. winds (Fig. 73).

Equatorial South America shows striking contrasts, the south of the gulf of Guayaquil on the west coast having less than 10 inches a year, the mouth of the Amazon over 80 inches, and the Montaña, with east winds rising up the slopes of the Andes, still more; in the Amazon basin the southern summer is the rainy season, without the double maximum that is sometimes considered typical of the zone (Fig. 74). The Congo basin, on the other side of the Atlantic, has two prominent maxima (Fig. 75, Djole), and the totals are smaller, most not greatly exceeding 60 inches a year owing to the position in lee of the plateau of East Africa. That plateau itself has remarkably small totals, mostly between 30 and 40 inches, but falling to 10 inches in the east Rift valley, and part of the low east coast is poor scrub with less than 15 inches; but the régime is normal, with a pronounced double maximum in April and November (Fig. 75, Nairobi). The equatorial plateau of Ecuador also has a small rainfall in spite of its altitude of over 9,000 feet,

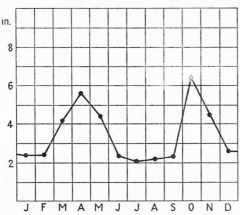

FIG. 76. Mean monthly rainfall, Bogotá

for it is shadowed by the continuous ranges of the Andes on each side; Quito, on the equator, has a single maximum, in April, but the rain is adequate from September till May. Bogotá, latitude 5° N., on the eastern Cordillera, has a well-marked double maximum (Fig. 76).

The rainfalls of the many island groups in the Pacific differ greatly in amount and season. Jaluit, Marshall Islands, 6° N., has the high total of 163 inches, with 336 rainy days, the rainiest months being May, June, and July, each with over 16 inches, and the driest, February, with 9 inches. Nauru, almost on the equator, has 75 inches well distributed over the year, with most in December, 10 inches, least in March, 4 inches.

The equatorial zone is by no means exempt from variability of rainfall from year to year, a standing menace to agriculture in the regions with medium and small means,

and the more liable to cause failure owing to the high
evaporation in hot lands. Malden Island, 4° S., 154·5° W.,
has remarkable variability for its position in the midst of the
expanse of the equatorial Pacific, the annual total having
ranged from 4 inches to 94 inches in 30 years; possibly the
explanation is the fact that the island is washed at irregular
intervals by varying currents, warmer and cooler, in the

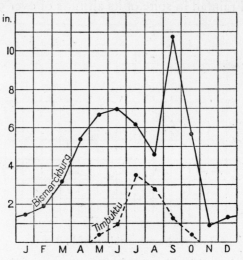

FIG. 77. Mean monthly rainfall in the outer tropics at Bismarckburg
(lat. 8° N.) and Timbuktu (18° N.)

adjacent ocean. Apia, Samoa Islands, 14° S., had 59·6 inches
in January 1939, only 3·3 inches in January 1940, the mean
for the month being 17·9 inches. In Labuan, Borneo, the
February total has ranged from 30·3 inches to nothing.

The Outer Tropics

The equatorial rains move north in the northern summer,
south in the southern summer, returning to the equator
shortly after the equinoxes. The type is the same everywhere; Fig. 77 illustrates the two régimes described on
p. 200. Though the annual total decreases, and the rainy
season becomes shorter with distance from the equator,
the amounts in the rainiest months are similar throughout the
humid tropics except at their limits (in the absence of local

PLATE 7

A dust storm (haboob) sweeping over Khartoum and the Nile

influences). The rainy season, summer, is a hot season with the sun passing overhead, though the hottest weeks are just before, not during, the rains; it is a time of luxuriant plant growth, in strong contrast to the winter when the land is brown and arid.

The Trades

The trades are dry winds, which originate for the most part in the high pressures of the horse latitudes where the air is slowly subsiding. The ascent of the air heated by a hot land-surface will usually be checked at some few thousand feet by the inversion of temperature characteristic of the trades, before condensation of the water vapour which may be abundant can take place; this is a main factor in the aridity. In their passage towards the equator the trades are reaching warmer latitudes, and this dries them still more. They are almost free from the irregularities of pressure and weather which are responsible for most of the rainfall of the westerlies, being among the steadiest winds on the globe. Most of the hot deserts owe their aridity to them, notably the Sahara which is under the north-east trade throughout the year. The desert coasts of South-west Africa and Chile are dominated by the south-east trade, the more arid under the lee of elevated land. Even at sea the trade-wind regions have little rain, except in tropical cyclones (p. 137), where 10 inches may fall in a single storm.

The delightful weather of the trades in the earlier part of their ocean passage is famous. The air is fresh and pure, cool and invigorating. The sun shines brilliantly from a blue sky brightened by light clouds, and white-crested rollers swing across the transparent ultramarine ocean. The relative humidity of the surface air between the Canaries and Cape Verde is about 70 per cent., and evaporation is active so that the sea-surface is more saline than the normal. But the trades are absorbing vapour wherever possible in their passage over the sea or a land covered with vegetation, and although the humidity remains below saturation the vapour-content is high, and ascent may give very heavy rain where a mountain range confronts them after they have crossed a wide ocean; the rainfall in many cases is heaviest in winter, the season of strongest wind. The NE. trade of the Pacific meets such a barrier in the Hawaian Islands, whose volcanic mountains rise steeply to 13,000 feet; in the island of Kauai a high cliff of Mount Waialeale (5,075 feet), facing north-east, forces the trade to rise almost vertically, and the rain is heavy and continuous, the daily mean being over 1 inch and the annual 460 inches, among the highest on the globe. But the leeward coast of the island, 15 miles south-west, has 20 inches, and the south-west of West Maui, another island in the same group, only 8 inches. Most of the high islands of the South Seas show a similar contrast. Apia, Samoa Islands, has 118 inches, falling on 218 days, and Utumapu in the same group 131 inches on 193 days. The peaks of these islands hardly ever put off their cowl of cloud. Even in the middle of the Sahara the mountains receive some precipitation, are snow-capped in winter and have perennial streams.

Most of the elevated east coasts in the tropics get heavy rainfall from the prevailing on-shore trades, with the maximum in the hot season, when convection is active and the heating of the land tends to produce a monsoonal effect. West coasts have much less, and in many parts are arid. The east coast of Africa south of the equator has more than 40 inches a year, but most of the west coast less than 10 inches, and some hundreds of miles in South-west Africa are barren desert, practically rainless. South America and Australia show similar differences between east and west coasts.

The hot deserts are notable not only for their scanty totals, the variability is equally striking. Years may pass without a drop of rain, and reports of 5 years of drought in the very dry tracts seem to be well authenticated. Some of the reptiles and insects of the desert live without drinking at all, many have no other liquid than droplets of dew. But the instability caused by abnormally excessive heating of the sand, or by the arrival of a cool upper current, sometimes gives extremely heavy falls, usually of short duration. At Helwan, 12 miles south of Cairo, the annual mean is 1·5 inches. But this figure conveys an inadequate idea of the conditions. 'A mean annual rainfall of 37 mm. seems almost negligible, but the yearly fall results from only a few storms which are often severe. Thus from 1904 to 1924 the total rainfall was 780 mm., nearly a quarter of which fell in 7 single storms.'[1] In one severe storm on 19–21 April 1909 1·8 inches was registered; torrents swept down the wadis, and much damage was done to buildings and crops. This storm was cyclonic and travelled up from the south, making its way to Syria. Hogarth records similar visitations in the desert of Arabia: 'I myself have been witness of such a flood. It lasted about 4 hours, and the result was to lay silt 5 feet deep over the whole plain on which I was living.' Baghdad has recorded as little as 2·0 inches and as much as 17·3 inches in a year; Roeburn, Western Australia, had 0·1 inch in one year, 42·0 inches in another. At Doorbaji, in the desert of Sind where the mean annual rainfall is 5 inches, on one occasion 34 inches fell in 2 days.

Owing to their uncertainty and violence these rains cannot be turned to account, and most of the water is lost by rapid run-off; but a certain amount sinks and helps to maintain the underground supplies, which are brought to the surface here and there by artesian and other wells and by plants. To roads, railways, bridges, irrigation systems, and other public works the floods may do much damage in their short life. The wadis, generally quite dry, are filled in a very short time with a rushing torrent of muddy water which makes its way to a great distance from its place of origin. In the French Sahara army regulations forbid troops to camp overnight in dry wadis, a tempting site owing to the shelter of the high and steep banks, for in the past camps have been washed away by floods which swept down suddenly from deluges in distant parts of the basin.

Dust, not rain, is the great discomfort of life in arid lands. Except on still nights the air is full of fine particles which percolate through the finest chinks into houses and even closed boxes. Dust lies thick on every shelf, covers furniture, settles on food, and is inhaled with the air we breathe; many natives cover their mouths and nostrils with mufflers. It is present in all degrees of intensity, according to the nature of the ground and the strength of the wind, sometimes blown

[1] Sutton, *The Climate of Helwan.*

in light clouds along the surface, at other times whirled up
in dust-devils, usually less than 500 feet high, but at
times 1,000 feet or more, and of small diameter often only
15 feet; the winds may be violent enough to raise and carry
away heavy articles, and the slender writhing columns almost
resemble tornadoes as they move over the desert with the
general wind. Worst of all, dust is carried up to great
heights, and is thick enough to darken the sky in bad dust-
storms. These may be 5,000 feet high, or more in Meso-
potamia and the Plains of India in April and May, and in the
Sudan where they are called haboobs (Plate 7, facing p. 208).

Thus the trades have the distinction of providing over
enormous areas the smallest but most variable rainfall of the
globe, and also, in very small areas, some of the largest totals.

Monsoons

The rainfall is among the heaviest (over extensive areas)
on the globe and nearly all falls in 4 or 5 months; consequently the downpours during the rainy season are more
copious than even the high annual totals might indicate.
The winter months are almost or quite dry (Fig. 78, Alla-
habad). Bombay has a mean of 76 inches in the four months
June to September, and only 0·2 in the four December to
March. The seasonal contrast is impressive and as important for plants and animals as the contrast between winter
and summer temperatures in higher latitudes. The whole
life of the monsoon lands, which are essentially agricultural,
is based on the seasonal rhythm, and any serious departure
from the normal may lead to great distress and even widespread famine. Unfortunately both the duration and the
amount of the rain are very variable, especially in India
and China; the crops may fail through drought, or the
rain may be so excessive that the rivers burst their banks
and the floods destroy crops and drown the people by thousands.

The association of heavy rain with the heat of high summer
fosters riotous luxuriance of plant life; rice, the characteristic
and very prolific crop, supports a very dense population,
and these lands are the most densely peopled of the globe
outside industrial Europe and North America.

The summer winds contain very rich stores of vapour after their long passage over warm oceans—several thousand miles in the case of the monsoons of south-east Asia and west Africa. The massive condensation in the monsoon shows itself in the fact that in July the atmosphere over India between 7,000 and 30,000 feet above sea-level, in which most of it occurs, has a mean lapse-rate of temperature of only 3·0° in 1,000 feet, while the layer above, between 30,000 and 50,000 feet, has 4·5°. Condensation results from

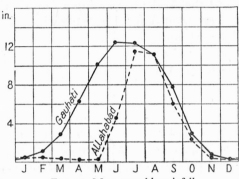

FIG. 78. Mean monthly rainfall

many processes; in the monsoon of south-east Asia the rain-fall is largely in the intertropical front at the convergence of the warm and damp monsoon and the dry continental air; convection, active over the heated land, is another fruitful source; shallow depressions, of merely local thermal origin, give long steady downpours and thunderstorms; tropical cyclones increase the totals of the late summer months. Orographic influence is specially prominent in India and south-east Asia. India may be regarded as a compartment bounded by practically continuous mountain ranges 6,000 feet and more high on the north, west, and east; but on the south it lies open to the sea, and receives the great mass of air that has crossed the South and North Indian Oceans.[1] None of this air can leave the area without rising at least 6,000 feet, and the ascent is a primary cause of the general rainfall. In addition there is the local effect of mountain ranges, which stand out so unmistakably on the rainfall map

[1] Simpson, Sir G. C., 'The South-West Monsoon', *Q.J.R. Met. Soc.*, 1921.

that it is unnecessary to refer to them in detail (Fig. 71, p. 199). The complement of the heavy rains of the mountains is the rain-shadow in their lee; while the coastal strip and the windward slopes of the Western Ghats receive more than 100 inches of rain a year, the total drops abruptly beyond to less than 20 inches. The most striking orographic effect is in the Khasi Hills of Assam, a range rising to about 5,000 feet which runs west from the Arakan Range; the plain narrows in from the south-west to the junction of the Khasi Hills and the Arakans forming a funnel widely open to the south-west monsoon. The narrowing of the funnel causes rapid ascent, and the rainfall is the heavier owing to the floods of warm water which cover the lowlands and pour vapour into the air. Cherrapunji, 4,455 feet above the sea on the south slopes of the Khasi Hills, receives during the monsoon months June to September a mean of no less than 318 inches, and 41 inches has been recorded in a single day; the average fall on a rain-day in June and July is 4 inches. Shillong, on the same range at a rather greater altitude but on the northward, leeward, slope, gets only 55 inches in the same months.

In China, too, the influence of relief must be considerable, for the winds from the sea are confronted by the eastern edge of the interior plateau and the ranges that buttress it; but the rainfall is heaviest in the east near the sea, and especially in the south-east where the temperature is highest. Similarly in the north of Australia the monsoonal rain is heaviest near the coast, especially on the mountains of north-east Queensland, and decreases rapidly towards the arid interior. Monsoonal influences contribute to the rainfall of the Guinea lands of West Africa, but here the lower latitude introduces other factors.

The periodicity is very pronounced, notably in the Asiatic monsoon; in India about 85 per cent. of the rain falls in the summer monsoon, and in north China as much as 90 per cent. in the five months May to September. The monsoon effects an abrupt transformation of the face of nature. During the previous months the land has lain dry and hard as a paved road, parched and dusty, with hardly a green blade of grass or a leaf to be seen; and for many weary weeks before the rains begin the air is dry, the heat intense, the sky cloudless, though grey with heat and haze rather than blue. The rivers, except those fed by melting snow and glaciers, are mere trickles of water, meandering through wide banks of sand on the floor of a channel altogether disproportionate to the volume of the stream. But once the rains start all is changed. Massive dark clouds cover the sky. The land is saturated and large areas are flooded by the torrential down-

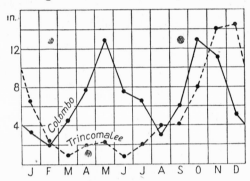

FIG. 79. Mean monthly rainfall

pours. Vegetation springs into life and the landscape is clothed in green. The air is as unpleasantly moist as it had previously been uncomfortably dry; wood swells and doors and windows jam, leather becomes mouldy and paper damp and limp. The river-beds, which in the dry season seemed survivals from some past epoch, justify their great width, which indeed proves all too little to contain the swollen floods of rushing muddy water. Tree-trunks, debris of all kinds, light and heavy, is carried down, and bridges have to be built to resist not only the terrific force of the rushing river but also the impacts of the floating projectiles. The highest floods are in the middle and at the end of the monsoon, for the heavy rains at the beginning are absorbed by the empty channels and reservoirs, the thirsty land, and the riot of vegetation.

To consider monsoonal rainfall in more detail, Ceylon is in such low latitudes (6°–10° N.) that in most of it the

rainfall is equatorial, modified by the monsoons; but the east
and north coastal plain and the eastern slopes of the central
highlands have a well marked monsoonal régime, the rainy
monsoon being the NE., not the SW. (Trincomalee, Fig. 79).
The west and south coasts have rain in every month, with
two strong maxima round May and October (Colombo,
Fig. 79), an equatorial rather than monsoonal type. The
monsoonal effect comes out strongly in the highlands

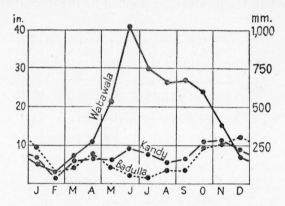

FIG. 80. Mean monthly rainfall in the highlands of Ceylon

(Fig. 80); Watawala, 3,259 feet on the west slope, facing
the SW. monsoon, has its maximum in the months of its
dominance, and the eastern slopes (Badulla, 2,195 feet)
have theirs during the NE. monsoon; Kandy, 1,611 feet in
the middle of the highlands, has a more uniform rainfall,
with maxima in October–December and June–July, and
February alone has less than 5 inches—a combination of the
equatorial and the SW. monsoonal types, the total being
increased by the altitude. The coast of Annam, the west
coast of Hondo (Japan), and the eastern islands of the
Philippine group, like east Ceylon, get most rain from the
winter monsoon.

Assam (Fig. 78, Gauhati), a humid, mountain-girt land,
has considerable rain from local thunderstorms in April,
May, and June, and the arrival of the monsoon intensifies it.
The early rains are valuable in lengthening the growing
season for the tea-plants. The Punjab and north-west of

Pakistan (Fig. 81) have two maxima; that of summer is by far the more prominent, but the secondary maximum in January and February is of interest both theoretically and practically (see p. 146).

In China the rainy season is May to October. The heavy rains begin in the south in April, and advance towards the

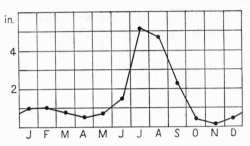

FIG. 81. Mean monthly rainfall, Lahore

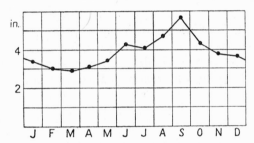

FIG. 82. Mean monthly rainfall, Galveston

north, reaching the Yangtze valley (where the early monsoon months are specially warm and damp, with heavy low cloud and persistent rain) in May, and Manchuria in July. The weather within the monsoonal air-mass itself is hot and cloudy, but more pleasant, and the rainfall less, than in the frontal zone. Typhoons (p. 140) are responsible for much of the heavy rain of late summer in the China Seas and their islands, and on the coasts of south China.

North America has only a much-modified monsoon, in respect of rainfall as well as of winds. In the south-east of the United States August and July are the rainiest months, but rain is abundant throughout the year (Fig. 82). The

warm waters of the Gulf of Mexico and the Gulf Stream
which bathe the shores favour cyclonic activity in winter
even more than in summer, and the winter rainfall is heavy
in spite of the cold in the interior. The hurricanes of late
summer add to the totals.

The Westerlies

These zones lie poleward of the horse latitudes; they have
damp air and moderate rainfall, ranging, however, from very
heavy on windward mountains to small amounts in rain-
shadows and interiors of continents.

The westerlies always tend to be saturated since they blow
from warmer to colder latitudes, and their passage over wide
oceans which are abnormally warm for the latitude provides
abundant vapour. If they blew as a steady current they might
be expected to bring warm damp air, overcast skies, and constant light rain, the opposite of the trade-wind conditions;
but, far from being a steady current, they consist of a turbulent procession of irregularities of pressure, most of them
low-pressure systems of various forms, but some anticyclones,
giving winds very variable in force and direction, and
notoriously changeable weather. Instead of a constant light
rainfall fairly heavy rains alternate with finer and drier days.
The rainfall is frontal and on the oceans is heaviest in
autumn and winter, when depressions are most numerous and
active. An advancing depression carries its weather with it,
modified continually by changes in its own form and intensity, and in the associated air-masses, whose origin, and
therefore temperature and humidity, are necessarily different
in the different parts of the system's course. The structure
and the rainfall of depressions are treated in Chapter XXXV.
The precipitation is very variable, light in some depressions,
copious in others; it may be of short duration, or last for
several days with few breaks if the system moves sluggishly
or erratically, or if it has secondaries, a fruitful source of bad
weather. Spells of 30 consecutive rainy days are not unknown. Thunderstorms and orographic influences add to
the variability; some account of the former is given in
Chapter XXV and of the latter in Chapter XXI. Mean
values are of limited significance.

Although cyclonic activity is at a maximum in the winter half-year the rainfall is more copious in the summer over the lands except on the west coasts, since the higher temperature, and therefore greater vapour-content of the air, in the warmer months, together with the instability due to the strong surface heating, more than compensate for the lesser cyclonic activity. Moreover, the higher temperature is conducive to lower air-pressure, which facilitates the entry of depressions. It was in summer (June 1903) that one of the heaviest and most persistent cyclonic rains within living memory occurred

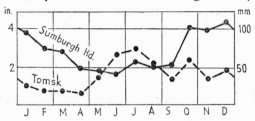

FIG. 83. Mean monthly precipitation

in south England (Fig. 120, p. 357); August 1912 was another summer month which gave notably large totals over much of England. On both these occasions the rain was of a cyclonic type, without thunderstorms.

A predominance of autumn and winter rain generally indicates that a climate is oceanic, and its absence that it is continental; transitional climates have two maxima, that of autumn and winter being the major peak in the more oceanic, that of summer in the more continental climates.

The régime in the westerlies on the ocean, unaffected by land influences, is illustrated by Sumburgh Head, Shetland Islands, full in the stormiest tract (Fig. 83):

SUMBURGH HEAD (altitude 112 ft.)

	Mean rainfall (in.)	Mean number of rain-days		Mean rainfall (in.)	Mean number of rain-days
January .	3·9	27	August .	3·1	20
February .	3·0	22	September .	3·2	20
March .	2·9	25	October .	4·1	25
April .	2·0	19	November .	4·0	24
May .	1·9	18	December .	4·4	27
June .	1·7	15			
July .	2·3	18	Year .	36·7	260

The strict oceanic régime prevails only on the ocean and a narrow belt on the windward coasts. Even in the east of England continental influences begin to appear:

LONDON, CAMDEN SQUARE (altitude 110 ft.)

	Mean rainfall (inches)	Mean number of rain-days			Mean rainfall (inches)	Mean number of rain-days
January	1·9	15	August .	.	2·2	14
February	1·7	14	September	.	1·8	12
March .	1·8	13	October	.	2·6	15
April .	1·5	13	November	.	2·4	14
May	1·8	13	December	.	2·4	16
June .	2·0	12				
July .	2·4	13	Year .	.	24·5	164

The rainiest month is October, and the rainiest seasons autumn and summer. Spring has least rain, as on the ocean, but winter almost as little; the summer half-year has more than the winter half, and an interesting feature is the heavy rain in July, almost as heavy as in October. In the interior of Europe continental features are intensified; at Munich June and July are the rainiest months, February the driest; summer is the rainiest season, and the summer half-year has more than twice as much rain as the winter half; Munich is within the influence of the westerlies, but the continental cold reduces the winter precipitation, and the instability rains and frequent thunderstorms of hot summer days swell the summer records. In Hungary the proportion of the rain on days with thunderstorms is:

43% in May   51% in July
51% ,, June   49% ,, Aug.

In the lowlands of England more than half the summer rain is, at least partly, of the instability type, and at Oxford 28 per cent. of the rain in June, 32 per cent. in July, falls on days on which thunder is heard. The summer maximum is due to the heaviness of the rain rather than to the number of rainy days; thus Moscow has 18 rain-days in December, only 13 each in May, June, and July, but the rainfall of July is 2·8 inches, of December only 1·5 inches.

The continental régime (Tomsk, Fig. 83) covers most of the interior of Europe except the Mediterranean lands, most of Siberia, most of Canada, and much of the United States, but only small areas in the south hemisphere. No season is rainless, and even where winter has least rain the rainy days may be as numerous as in summer. With the low temperatures and damp air, in many regions winter may appear wetter than summer, despite the records of the rain-gauge. In England February has been named 'fill-dyke', but its mean precipitation is in some places less than in any other month; yet in view of the damp chilly air and the water-logged condition of the land the name is not inapt. Even in abnormally wet summers, with a rainfall twice the mean, evaporation is more vigorous than in winter, and it is noticeable that floods are usually of shorter duration and the land soon recovers, but in spite of this the weather may be so wet as to be ruinous for agriculture. The only season that has definitely less rain than the others is spring, and its smaller rainfall is associated with strong dry winds and bright skies. In the continental interiors the winter cold is intense, the air dry physiologically, and the sky often clear; almost all the precipitation falls as snow, and the clear dry air makes the keen frost much more pleasant than the damp warmth near the coasts where the temperature may be well above 32°.

Mediterranean Regions

In the Mediterranean region, including both the Mediterranean Sea and its coasts, the rainy season is the winter half-year (Fig. 123, p. 367), and a similar régime prevails in the corresponding regions on the west coasts of the other continents in sub-tropical latitudes—California, central Chile, the south-west of the Cape Province of South Africa, and the south-west of Western Australia. The rainfall is associated with the westerlies as in north-west Europe, and is cyclonic in type, but the duration is less, the sky is less cloudy, and the sunshine much more abundant, although the amount of rain associated with any one depression may be larger. Thus while the mean rainfall in November at Oxford is 2·3 inches, falling on 16 days, Nice, on the French Riviera, has 5 inches on only 8 days. Most of the Mediterranean region has about 90 rain-days a year, north-west

Europe about 180. At Athens the mean duration of rain on a rain-day is only 1·9 hours, at Paris 3·9 hours.

Very heavy downpours characterize the mountains which surround the Mediterranean, and they are not uncommon on the lower ground, most of which may get 6 inches in a day, though rarely. Perpignan has had over 4 inches in a day 10 times in 50 years; in October 1876 14 inches fell within 63 hours. At such times the water-courses, which in summer are wide expanses of gravel and sand, dry and white in the dazzling sunshine save where dotted with dark oleander bushes, soon fill with roaring torrents of muddy water that flood the country and do serious damage. Similarly in Greece, Athens, with an annual mean of 15 inches, had 4·5 inches on 10 November 1912, and downpours, though seldom of that intensity, are almost as frequent as light steady rain. Much havoc is sometimes worked in Algeria; in the 6 days 24–9 November 1927 even the low plain of the Sig had 14 inches, and 17 inches and more fell in the neighbouring mountains, about 80 per cent. of the mean for the year. Crops were ruined, houses destroyed, and many persons drowned. These storms are largely responsible for sweeping the limestone mountains bare of soil. The district north-east of Damascus, Syria, had a similar experience in October 1937.

Thus the Mediterranean regions tend to be distinguished from the zone of the westerlies by the heaviness of the showers and the quick return of clear skies, a result, possibly, of the close juxtaposition of the damp air over the sea and the cold dry air of the continents. As a depression passes on eastward a flood of clear dry polar air sweeps down in rear of it, and the weather is fine again.

Summer, the season of the trades or similar winds, has little rain even on windward coasts, but the dry season is shorter than the rainy in most of the Mediterranean. Pressure irregularities sometimes disturb the weather in the west, where in most years every month, even in high summer, has some rain though very little; the south and east of the Mediterranean have three or more almost rainless

months. The dry season is longer in the other regions with
a Mediterranean type of climate. The régime is in general
simple—a steady rise from the dry summer to a maximum
in mid-winter, and a steady fall again to summer (Fig. 84,
Cape Town); the north-west of the Mediterranean Sea
(Fig. 84, Barcelona) is peculiar in having two maxima, in

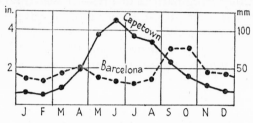

FIG. 84. Mean monthly precipitation

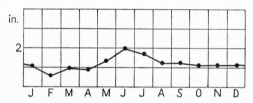

FIG. 85. Mean monthly precipitation, Orenburg

autumn and spring, separated by a much drier mid-winter.
Further information will be found in Chapter XL.

The Steppes

The steppe lands including south-east Russia, Turan,
Anatolia and other plateaux round the Mediterranean, and
the western plains of North America have a modification of
the continental westerlies régime in that most rain falls in
spring and early summer, and late summer is drier (Fig. 85).
The prevailing winds in the Old World steppes are N. and
NE., and as they come from the arid interior of Asia the
rainfall is scanty. But Mediterranean depressions, active and
advancing far inland in spring, conduce to precipitation, and
another favouring factor is the instability of the atmosphere,
for insolation is rapidly increasing and warming the ground

while the higher atmosphere is still cold, and convection during the hot hours of the day gives instability showers. In high summer the ground is hotter, but so also is the higher atmosphere, and convection is less active; moreover, a definite air-movement, controlled by the low-pressures of south Asia, is established, and local differences of temperature and minor irregularities of pressure which favoured the convectional showers of the earlier months have less chance to develop.

The early-summer rain maintains the prevailing vegetation of grass, which requires moisture especially in the early growing season. The rainfall of high summer is less valuable for water-supply than the amount might indicate owing to the heat, for the surface of the hot ground is baked so hard that much of the rain is lost by rapid run-off or by evaporation. In winter most of the scanty precipitation is snow, and the fierce NE. winds that sweep over the bleak open plains blow it away. These cold dry winds are in themselves hostile to tree growth; grass is the natural vegetation. The steppe type of rainfall has a wide extension over the great wheat lands of the south of Canada and the north of the United States. It is limited in the south hemisphere by the absence of large land-masses in middle latitudes.

The Polar Regions

The conditions are simpler in the south hemisphere than the north, for almost the whole area inside the polar circle is occupied by Antarctica, an ice- and snow-covered plateau. It is intensely cold in winter; even in the warmest month the mean temperature is below freezing-point on the coasts, and much below on the high snowfields of the interior. Rain is very rare; the precipitation is snow, and at the low temperature it consists of hard, fine, sharp spicules of ice. But the origin of precipitation of any kind is a problem, since the continent is covered by an anticyclone, apparently very constant in position (p. 164). However, the facts that huge tabular great glaciers move outwards from the interior and that icebergs are constantly being calved from the edges of the ice-sheet indicate that the precipitation must be in excess of the very appreciable loss by evaporation; the annual mean on

PLATE 8

The Thames in high flood near Weybridge, 3 January 1928: the result of heavy rain and melting snow, patches of which are seen on the right

the low coasts was estimated by Kidson to be equal to about 4 in. of rain.

Various theories have been advanced. Hobbs[1] points out that the intense cold is the result of vigorous radiation from the snow surface; the air descends in the anticyclone, and carries down vapour derived from the cirrus clouds, which on contact with the cold snow is condensed in fine ice-crystals, or as hoar-frost. This deposit is slow but continuous, and the total amount may be considerable, but it is difficult to believe that it accounts for all the precipitation; many of the cases of surface mists and drifts of ice-spicules which have been observed are capable of other explanations, and condensation of this kind seems inadequate to explain the thick snow of blizzards. Moreover, the middle of an anticyclone is a region of calms; but this process could provide much snow only by rapid renewal of the air in contact with the surface, and strong winds rather than calms would be needed.

Simpson[2] advances another theory, explaining the precipitation by the forced ascent in blizzards of air which advances over the more slowly moving or stationary layers in front. Though in its descent in the polar anticyclone the air is warmed and dried, it loses so much heat by contact with the very cold snow-surface that the additional cooling resulting from an ascent of 1 or 2 km. suffices to bring it below its dew-point. This can easily occur in blizzards, and it produces the thick snow that fills the air. If this is the complete explanation of the precipitation in Antarctica, blizzards must be frequent in the interior, a point on which there is not much evidence; they are certainly frequent near the coasts.

The north polar zone is a more complex region. The central tract is ocean, but the peripheral zone includes considerable areas of America, Eurasia, and Greenland. Greenland resembles Antarctica, but although the ice-cap is covered normally by a shallow anticyclone it is frequently invaded by depressions from the surrounding seas, and most of the precipitation is cyclonic and orographic, all of it snow on

[1] Hobbs, W. H., *Glacial Anticyclones*, New York, 1926.
[2] Simpson, C. G., *British Antarctic Expedition: Meteorology.*

the ice-cap but much of it rain in summer on the lower slopes and the coasts. At Eismitte, in the middle of the ice-cap, precipitation occurred on 56 per cent. of the days in the year of observation, 1930–1; direct measurement of the driving snow was not possible, but a mean total equivalent to 12 inches of rain a year was deduced from the stratification of the snowfield, most of the contribution appearing to consist of snow, but some of rime and drift snow; the greater part fell in winter, and was supplied by the warm sectors of depressions crossing Greenland.

Arctic Canada and Eurasia, including the Barren Grounds and some of the forest belt, get most of their precipitation in summer and autumn, when the temperature is above freezing-point; most is rain with occasional wet snow. Some fine dry powdery snow falls in winter, but the strong winds prevent it lying deep; the annual mean is not much more than 10 inches, if as much. Even on the warmer Atlantic Drift between Greenland and Norway the annual total, judged from the records of island stations, is only about 15 inches, most falling in autumn, least in spring. The middle of the Arctic probably has scanty precipitation; in winter the sky is fairly clear, and the precipitation consists of fine dry spicules of snow; summer tends to be damp and cheerless, with frequent fog and only light rain, sleet, or snow.

CHAPTER XXIII

FROZEN PRECIPITATION

Snow

SNOW is a source of many difficulties for man, but it also serves a useful part in the heat- and water-economy of the ground in middle and high latitudes. A heavy snowstorm in a region unaccustomed to such visitations quickly demonstrates how much our communications by land, sea, and air are at its mercy. Driven by a strong wind it forms the dreaded blizzard, in which the bewildered wayfarer may lose his way and perish from exposure, and thousands of cattle

and sheep are buried in deep drifts and suffocated. On the
other hand, in many lands the winter snow-cover is welcomed
as giving the means of sledge-transport and logging. And
in cold countries snow is a valuable blanket for the ground
against the keen frost, favouring tree growth, for example in
the northern forests while the bare steppes remain treeless. It
is an excellent reflector of light, and gives a welcome addition
to the illumination in the winters of high latitudes. The melt
water in spring soaks slowly into the ground, replenishing
the supply against the likelihood of failing in the hot dry
summer. But it may cause disastrous floods when melting is
rapid (Plate 8, facing p. 224), and Russia suffers from them
every spring; in 1926

the Volga broke its banks, spreading destruction for miles on each side
of its normal bed along the whole of its course of 2,000 odd miles,
from the Valdai Hills to the Caspian Sea. For a month the floods
continued, and town after town was inundated. Some 10,000 villages
were swamped, even the roofs of houses being in many cases sub-
merged. . . . Nizhny-Novgorod was under water, the level of the
Volga had risen to 46 ft. above the normal, and the width of the stream
was over 20 miles. (*The Times.*)

Losses to farmers in Great Britain in spring 1947, caused
mainly by floods after the rapid melting of deep and widespread snow, were estimated at £20,000,000.

Rivers such as the Tigris (Fig. 86) that drain snow-
covered mountains increase in volume when the snow begins
to melt; the rivers of the Alps have a similar rise in late
spring, but the melted snow from the many glaciers maintains the high level of the rivers throughout the warm
months (the Rhone, Fig. 86); many irrigation systems are
fed from them.

Snow consists of vapour condensed at a temperature
below 32°; the minute crystals unite into beautiful white
flakes as much as an inch across; but at very low temperatures they remain separate and float in the air as a haze of
glittering spicules. The atmosphere through which it falls
must be below, or at any rate little above, freezing-point, or
the flakes will melt. Twelve inches of snow, melted without
loss by evaporation, give approximately 1 inch of water, but
there is much variation according to the nature of the snow;

of the very dry, light, and powdery type, as when freshly fallen in Antarctica, 30 inches may be required to make 1 inch of water. At the other extreme snow merges into sleet, wet and compact, so that 4 inches or less suffices. The older the snow the more compact it becomes; the transparent ice of glaciers shows the result of long-continued compression

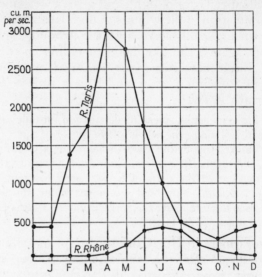

FIG. 86. Mean monthly flow of the Tigris at Baghdad (Willcocks), and of the Rhone at Porte-du-Sex, Valais (Parde)

and the percolation of water; the usual expressions of snowfall in terms of the equivalent rain are merely approximate. It is not easy to measure the real depth of the snow itself, for even on a flat surface it varies through drifting, and it is almost impossible to recognize where deepening has taken place in an expanse of smooth snow. However, a good approximation may be obtained if the mean of the depths at several points is taken. It is desirable to record the depth in the drifts, a matter of great practical importance, but it depends on the interaction of the wind and the details of the topography. Measurements of snow by an ordinary rain-gauge are unreliable.

A useful addition to a statement of the total snowfall, expressed either as depth of snow or as the equivalent

amount of rain, is some indication of the mean dates of the
first and last appreciable snowfalls, and of the duration of the
snow-cover; this last can best express not the total number of
days on which the ground is snow-covered, but the period
with snow on the ground for continuous spells long enough
to be of practical significance in the region concerned, about
5 days in lands with snowy winters, 2 days where snow is
infrequent as in the British Isles; but unfortunately such
data are not generally available.

Regional Distribution of Snowfall

Snow, even perpetually lying snow, is known in all latitudes, but at sea-level it is extremely rare inside the tropics
(the only cases being just inside in south China and south-
east Brazil), and unusual inside the thirtieth parallels. Polewards of the fortieth parallels it is common. To consider first
the lowlands and moderate elevations in the sub-tropics,
snow is by no means infrequent in winter on the north and
especially the north-east coasts of the Mediterranean, but it
does not lie long; Jerusalem, 30 miles inland on the plateau,
gets some heavy falls, and in 1920 large areas in its neighbourhood were covered with over 3 feet, 10 feet in drifts.
The plateau of the Shotts in Algeria and the Meseta of Spain
are also subject to severe snowstorms and bitterly cold winds
in winter, a striking contrast to the furnace heat of summer
days; patches of snow persist through the year on the north of
the Sierra Nevada. Snow may fall at sea-level in Algeria and
Tunis, but it is rare. A snow flurry has been noted near sea-
level in the Hawaiian Islands.

In the United States (interior) snow lies at times everywhere except in Florida, but not long enough to be of
importance in the extreme south; on the coasts it is negligible
south of lat. 37 N.

In South Africa it is almost unknown at sea-level, but the
mountains within sight of the coast, such as the Hottentots
Holland and the Drakenstein, above 3,000 feet glisten
white in the bright sunshine for several days in most winters;
the higher Drakensberg is often covered in winter. Snowstorms are known in the Karroo and on the High Veld of
the Orange Free State, the south of the Transvaal, and

South-west Africa as far as the tropic, but the snow soon melts.

Australia has little snow on the lowlands even in Victoria, but the Eastern Highlands south of the tropic get heavy falls down to about 3,000 feet, and a few sheltered spots retain patches all the year. The South Island of New Zealand gets some snow everywhere, and the mountains above about 7,000 feet are snow-covered always.

In higher latitudes the lowlands have less snow than might be expected. Heavy snowfall requires heavy precipitation and at the same time a low temperature, a combination more frequent on mountains. Lowlands in continental interiors certainly have cold winters, but the air contains little vapour; in summer vapour is abundant, but temperature is too high. Western seaboards have no lack of vapour in winter, but the temperature is not low enough; however heavy falls are not infrequent, occurring generally with easterly winds in front of a depression following a path on the south, in the case of the British Isles over or near the Channel or north France (Fig. 116, p. 351); spring and winter have most snow, autumn much less. The south and west coasts of Britain[1] have a mean of only 3 or 4 days with snow on the ground, but the number increases rapidly with altitude, favoured by the decrease of temperature and the increase of precipitation; the Chilterns and Cotswolds have about 15 days, the north-east (lowlands) of Britain 25 days, the highest hills of Wales, north England, and south Scotland over 50 days, the Grampians and the north-west Highlands over 100 days, and in these higher and more northern areas snow may be a serious obstacle to traffic of all kinds. Even in the north of the Pennines road-traffic is obstructed on 30 days a year on the average at 1,000 feet, and the roads are completely blocked on about 8 days at 1,000 feet, 25 days at 1,500 feet. But snow is a very variable element; years pass with little or none except on the hills; but in other years the 15-foot posts along some of the main roads across the Pennines are entirely buried, and fail their purpose as guides. In March 1916 10 feet of snow fell on large areas

[1] Manley, G., *The Meteorological Magazine*, 1947.

of the north Pennines, and on 29 March 1901 the higher slopes of Snowdon had 5 to 7 feet; 4 or 5 feet from a single storm is not uncommon on the lower hills, and 1 foot on the lowlands. Dartmoor, despite its southerly position, is liable to heavy falls; Holne Chase in the south-east of the moor had 6 feet in 15 hours on 16 February 1929, and in the same month trains were snowed up for 4 days on the main line south of Dartmoor; Tavy Cleave, a gully 300 feet deep, was filled with snow in March 1891. In bad storms drifts may attain great depths everywhere, and exceeded 20 feet on Salisbury Plain in the Christmas storm of 1927. In the exceptional winter of 1947 most of Britain was deeply snow-covered from 27 January till 13 March; drifts of 10 feet were common, and many hill-districts were under 15 feet of snow for several weeks. Traffic was seriously disorganized, and the resulting shortage of coal and other supplies put severe restrictions on industry.

The east of Asia gets little snow from the dry north-east winds of the winter monsoon, but snow does fall even inside the tropic. In most of Siberia the depth of snow lying rarely exceeds 3 feet in the lower Obi basin where it is most abundant, and 1 foot in the lower Lena where it is least. In South America Patagonia is too closely sheltered by the Andes to get much precipitation, snow or rain. But it is very different in the east of North America, for the Maritime Provinces are among the snowiest lowlands outside the polar regions, with a mean duration of snow-cover of over 120 days; the winter precipitation is heavy, in places heavier than the summer, owing to the vigorous cyclonic activity, and the vapour-laden winds from the Atlantic are soon cooled enough to give snow. On the east of the Great Lakes the onshore winds give as much as 17 feet of snow. Most of the Gulf of St. Lawrence has more than 8 feet. Even in Saskatchewan, in the far interior, the ground is snow-covered for 120 days, and the mean snowfall is 2 to 4 feet a year; it is more than 4 feet everywhere east of Winnipeg. North Canada, coniferous forests and Barren Grounds, has less snow owing to the intense cold, but the snowy season lasts longer. Asia has considerably more snow in the

taiga and tundra than farther south in the interior where
mountain-shelter and distance from the sea conspire with
high atmospheric pressure to keep the winter precipitation
low. The steppe lands are liable to frequent snowstorms
and blizzards, but the amount of snow is small, and each
fall is soon swept away or evaporated by the strong dry
winds.

Mountains that are high enough have snow even on the
equator. On the giants of equatorial Africa the snow-line
(or more correctly, the lower limit of glaciers) ranges, according to the amount of precipitation and the temperature,
from about 15,000 feet on the windward slopes to 18,000
feet and higher on the lee, and snow is known a few thousand
feet below those levels.

The high Alps have snow all the year round, and on the
Säntis (8,202 feet) only in July and August is rain more
frequent than snow. In the lower Swiss valleys (e.g. around
Altdorf) snow is as frequent as rain in December, January,
and February; from the beginning of May till the end of
October it never snows. In the higher Alpine valleys snow
often drifts to a depth of 25 feet in winter, and the passes are
closed to traffic for about 6 months.

The western mountains of North America also get extraordinarily heavy snow on their western slopes, the necessary
vapour being brought by the ocean winds from the Pacific.
On all the higher ranges the mean depth amounts to 16 feet
a year, and on many to far more—over 40 feet in the Sierra
Nevada (75 feet has been recorded in these aptly-named
mountains) and the Cascades, and 20 feet in the Rockies.
Mountains in the heart of Asia, equally lofty and even colder,
have much less snow owing to the lack of damp maritime air.
Further information about mountain snows is given in
Chapter XXXI. Some details for the polar zones are to be
found on pp. 224–226.

Blizzards

The interiors of Canada and Siberia, Greenland and
Antarctica are snow-covered in winter, all the precipitation
being in the form of snow. Because of the extreme cold of

those regions it falls as fine dry crystals, not large flakes, and in strong winds the snow-dust is swept up from the ground; at the same time snow may be falling from the clouds, and the raging winds are soon thick with the flurrying white particles. The temperature is far below freezing-point, often below zero, but not so low as it may be during calm weather, though to those unfortunate travellers who are out-of-doors it feels much colder owing to the rapid movement of the air. What with the cold, the bewilderment produced by the howling gale and the dancing snow-whirls, and the complete loss of direction in the opaque atmosphere, blizzards have claimed many victims.

Simpson[1] describes the blizzards of Antarctica:

In a true blizzard the wind is accompanied by clouds of driven snow. The snow is in the form of exceedingly fine grains which penetrate through the smallest chink or hole in a house or tent. The whole air appears to be full of drift, so that it is impossible to see any great distance, and when it is at its worst even a tent cannot be seen for more than a few yards. Not only does the drift make it difficult to see, but any one exposed to it seems to become bewildered and to lose all power of thinking clearly. For these reasons it is sheer folly to attempt to travel in a blizzard even when the temperature is relatively high and the wind at one's back.

Brehm's description of the buran, as blizzards are called in Russia and Siberia (purga in the tundra), portrays a very similar storm:

The wind changes and blows harder and harder from east, southeast, south, or south-west. A thin cloud sweeps over the white ground —it is formed of whirling snow; the wind becomes a tempest; the cloud rises up to heaven; and maddening, bewildering even to the most weather-hardened, dangerous in the extreme to all things living, the buran rages across the steppes, a snow-hurricane, as terrible as the typhoon or the simoom. For 2 or 3 days such a snow-storm may rage with uninterrupted fury, and both man and beast are absolutely storm-bound. A man overtaken in the open country is lost, unless some special providence save him; nay more, even in the village or steppe-town, he who ventures out of doors when the buran is at its height may perish, as indeed not rarely happens.

[1] Simpson, G. C., *British Antarctic Expedition: Meteorology.*

Hoar-frost

Hoar-frost is the beautiful thin deposit of glistening white ice-crystals on grass and twigs, consisting of the frozen supercooled droplets of water from calm air on clear winter nights. Meteorologically it is dew deposited at a temperature below freezing-point. It is common in winter in high latitudes, and not infrequent in middle latitudes; it occurs on the average on about 20 nights a year in south England, 40 in south Sweden, and it is by no means unknown in the northern Mediterranean lands, but its frequency varies greatly according to topography like the frequency of frost, being greatest in frost-hollows.

Rime (Plate 9, facing p. 240)

This is a much more copious deposit than hoar-frost, but like it consists of frozen supercooled droplets on twigs and similar objects. The air must be in motion, not calm as for hoar-frost, and the formation is more frequent and abundant in a fog or low cloud than under clear skies. The ice-crystals build out on the windward side of the twigs from the air coming into contact with them, and the supply is kept up by the passing current, the rime forming a sharp triangular prism pointing into the wind, not uncommonly to a thickness of an inch, so that the weight may break the objects bearing it. The circumstances of the deposit are the same as, at temperatures above freezing, produce the fog-drip (p. 278) which falls from trees in a damp drifting fog, and occasionally in very damp air without fog. On mountains covered for long spells with drifting cloud it may attain a remarkable thickness; the annual mean on a mast on the Brocken was about 80 inches. Unlike hoar-frost, it is deposited hardly at all on short grass, the surface air being too still.

Glazed Frost

For both hoar-frost and rime the air and its supercooled droplets must be well below freezing-point, and the freezing takes place so rapidly on contact that the deposit consists of minute loose crystals, dazzlingly white in the winter sunshine. A very different deposit is glazed frost, a varnish of thick, hard, transparent ice, on roads, walls, branches, telegraph wires, and similar objects. The layer may be ¼-inch thick or more, and is as smooth as if laid on like enamel. The circumstances are illustrated by an instance in England and much of western Europe on 21 December 1927. After a keen frost for several previous days the ground was at a temperature far below freezing-point, when a westerly breeze set in, bringing moist air and light rain. As soon as the drops touched the ground they froze, and in a very short time all objects out-of-doors were coated with clear ice. Road traffic was almost suspended:

The rain coated roadways and pavements with a thin sheet of slippery ice. Progress on the treacherous surface, alike for pedestrians and vehicles, was extremely precarious. Hospital staffs could not recall in any previous year conditions which had produced such a number of accidents. The total of broken arms and legs, injured shoulders, head injuries, and concussions made a formidable list. . . . Lorries with produce from the country arrived very late, and drivers told of hours occupied in crawling over ice-bound roads. (*The Times*, 22 Dec. 1927.)

Serious damage is done, branches and telegraph wires breaking under the weight of ice. In a severe glazed frost in the south-west of England in January 1940, wires were coated with cylinders of clear ice to 4 inches and more in diameter in many districts, and thousands of miles of telegraph- and power-lines were so much damaged by the weight that replacement was necessary; posts, walls, and windows along the Welsh Border had ice several inches thick. Pheasants found their wings ice-bound and were unable to fly.

Glazed frosts are most common in the eastern states of America and especially in Newfoundland, when a moist south wind from the sea blows over a frozen land. For the formation of glazed frost the objects on which it is deposited must be at a temperature well below freezing-point, and the air, with its supercooled droplets, a little, but not much, below freezing, and moving fairly fast. On contact the droplets are deposited and start to freeze, slowly enough for their liquid to spread into a continuous film of water, which in a few minutes is a varnish of clear ice; icicles also may be formed if the deposit is abundant enough for the water to drip. The 'icing' of aircraft in flight is usually a deposit of glazed frost.

Dew

Reference has been made above to dew, which is a common form of occult precipitation, and though it is not frozen a short note is appropriate here. The circumstances of its formation are described on p. 31. The amount is difficult to measure; one usual method is by collecting and weighing the deposit on a piece of filter-paper freely exposed, but the results can only be approximate. It is heaviest and most frequent in the humid tropics, but even at Batavia the amount is very small in comparison with the rainfall, being estimated at only about 0·008 inch of water a night on nights with dew, and the mean total for the year probably does not exceed 1 inch. In temperate and high latitudes it is negligible as a source of water-supply, but nevertheless it is an appreciable support for plant life during dry periods, stopping evaporation and providing some moisture to the ground and plants to temper the aridity.

CHAPTER XXIV

EVAPORATION

EXCEPT when the air is saturated water-surfaces evaporate; the loss of water by evaporation is hardly less important climatically than the amount of rainfall. The rate varies with the saturation-deficit of the air, which depends on its humidity, temperature, and rate of movement; the water may be at a different temperature from the air owing to the cooling by evaporation, the lag behind air temperature, or heating by direct insolation. Unfortunately records of evaporation are not very numerous, nor are they readily comparable since different types of evaporimeters give different results. In one type water contained in a shallow vessel is left fully exposed to the weather, and the fall in the level of the water gives a measure of the evaporation, allowance being made for any rain that may have entered; the record is affected by the shape of the vessel, area of the water-surface, exposure to sun and wind, and temperature of the water. In the Wild pattern of this type a shallow pan about 6 inches in diameter contains the water, and the

loss by evaporation is measured by weighing the instrument
at the beginning and end of the period; in the British Isles
a much larger tank is used, the Symons pattern, 6 feet
square and 2 feet deep, nearly filled with water, sunk in the
ground with its rim projecting 1½ inches. In the Piche
evaporimeter water contained in an inverted glass test-tube
9 inches long is allowed to evaporate from a small disk
of blotting-paper over the open, lower end, and the loss is
measured on a scale graduated on the tube. Yet another
type, the Livingston atmometer, used mostly for obtaining
data for botanical purposes, has an evaporating surface of
about 12 square inches of unglazed porous porcelain,
spherical, cylindrical, or flat, kept moist by its capillary
attraction of water from a bottle below, the loss of which
can be measured at suitable intervals.

Evaporation might be expected to vary inversely with
rainfall, but important exceptions make the relationship of
little value. The 'cold water coasts' (Chap. XXVIII) are
rainless, but the air is highly charged with vapour and
evaporation is very slow. In the interior of the continents in
temperate latitudes summer is the rainiest season, but it is
also the season with highest evaporation. Evaporation
increases rapidly with temperature and air-movement. The
highest figures come from the trade-wind deserts, as might
be expected from the appearance of the land—thousands of
miles of dust and sand-dune and sun-baked rock. The
Sahara and the Sudan provide the following, all taken with
a Piche evaporimeter except at Helwan where a Wild type
was used:

	Mean daily evaporation (inches)		Mean annual evaporation (inches)
	Month with most	Month with least	
Helwan . . .	0·42 (June)	0·11 (Dec.)	94
Wadi Halfa . .	0·87 (June)	0·35 (Dec.)	233
Atbara . . .	0·81 (May)	0·53 (Dec.)	246
Khartoum . .	0·77 (Apr.)	0·50 (Dec.)	213
Mongalla . . .	0·45 (Jan.)	0·11 (Aug.)	89

These excessive evaporation records are curiously similar to
the highest rainfalls of the globe.

In the deserts of Australia the mean annual evaporation
is over 100 inches, at Perth 66 inches, at Sydney 38 inches.
The semi-arid lands on the east and south-east of the deserts
are often almost as dry in summer as the deserts themselves,
and bush-fires are a serious danger:

Every summer the predisposing conditions arise which may lead to
an outbreak, and the utmost vigilance is needed. The vast stretches

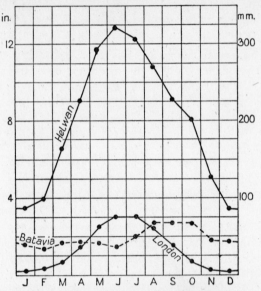

FIG. 87. Mean monthly evaporation; the mean annual total is 16 in.
at London, 25 in. at Batavia, 94 in. at Helwan

of unsettled country, the hard unwatered earth, the dry heat of the
Australian summer, the abundance of oils in leaves and plants—all
these combine to make the bush country an unrivalled carrier of fire.
Dry overland winds from the north or from the west may come to
fan any casual spark into a flame and to drive along the flames in
extending lines so that enormous areas of hundreds of miles are quickly
covered. (*The Times.*)

In the humid tropics evaporation is low, 20 to 30 inches
a year. The westerlies also have low evaporation, 16 inches
a year at London and about 25 inches in the interiors of the
continents; but even in the drier east of Britain loss by
evaporation exceeds rainfall in summer. The distribution
over the year is shown in Fig. 87.

The relation between evaporation and altitude is considered on p. 297.

The data that have been quoted are derived, it must be remembered, from instruments in which a water surface is always present, so that evaporation can be continuous. The actual conditions in nature are quite different, for the surface soon dries after rain and evaporation can then proceed only from water derived by capillarity from the sub-surface, a source which rapidly fails as the water table sinks. It is just in the driest and hottest hours and seasons that evaporation practically ceases, and hence the data from ordinary evaporimeters are not applicable.

In hot lands the value of the rainfall for practical purposes is greatly diminished by the large loss through evaporation; an annual rainfall of 40 inches is by no means abundant, and a total under 40 inches tends to check agricultural output; under the strong insolation of low latitudes the land dries out more rapidly than the evaporation records suggest. In temperate latitudes 40 inches of rain is plentiful.

On the oceans as a whole the mean annual evaporation is estimated by Wüst at about 37 inches; under the trades it is probably 40 to 50 inches, three or four times the rainfall. For an equatorial lake, 43 inches is the estimate for Lake Victoria.

Much of the solar energy received on the surface of the earth is rendered 'latent' by evaporation, and is carried in the resulting vapour from zone to zone.

CHAPTER XXV

THUNDERSTORMS. HAIL

THUNDER and lightning are a result of powerful updraughts to great heights with very copious condensation of vapour, almost always in cumulo-nimbus clouds (p. 188). The necessary conditions are high temperature and humidity in the lower air, a steep lapse-rate throughout a great depth of atmosphere to effect vigorous convection, and, in most types of thunderstorm, a light wind not varying much with height (strong and irregular winds deform and dissipate ascending columns by shear before massive clouds can form).

The immediate cause of the high electrical tension which produces lightning has been the subject of many researches. Sir G. C. Simpson[1] concluded that the source of the charge in the lower part of clouds is the breaking-up of raindrops. Raindrops may be minutely small, but experiment shows that there is an upward limit, a diameter of a quarter of an inch; a drop of larger size must soon break up. It is also known that raindrops cannot fall through still air at a greater speed than 24 feet a second, so that an upward current of the same speed prevents their descent. The process of the formation of the rain is the same in a thunderstorm as in other storms. An ascending current of damp air cools adiabatically and its vapour is condensed; if the ascent exceeds 24 feet a second the drops, being unable to fall through it, grow larger and larger till they attain the limiting diameter of 0·25 inch and break up. Thus a great deal of water accumulates in the higher levels, and the drops are continually growing and dividing, taking a positive charge at each division; the upper cloud is charged positively, most of the rest negatively as a rule, and discharges occur inside the cloud, or between cloud and cloud, or cloud and earth. A lull in the up-draught allows the water to fall to the earth in a torrential shower, sometimes called a cloudburst. This theory explains the fact that heavy rain is almost always associated with a thunderstorm, and that thunder is very rare in a light shower. But recent work has revealed difficulties.

Thunderstorm conditions are often present in the hot moist air of equatorial lands. In the trade-wind deserts the air is too dry; but thunder and lightning sometimes accompany the downpours of rain in tropical cyclones. In higher latitudes heat and moisture are often adequate in summer, but converging air-streams are needed to give the necessary up-draught. The air in the polar zones is rarely warm and damp enough to give the necessary condensation.

[1] London, *Proc. R. Soc.* 114(A), 1927; 161(A), 1937.

PLATE 9

Rime in Norfolk

Frequency of Thunderstorms

The 'frequency' of thunderstorms is the number of days on which thunder is heard; audibility extends for about 15 miles from the origin. Lightning without thunder is not counted, since it may be visible for hundreds of miles and is to be seen almost every night in parts of the tropics.

The Tropics

The humid tropics is the outstanding thundery area, at any rate on land. Thunder is recorded on more than 75 days in the year in the East Indies, Central and West Africa, much of the plateau of South Africa, the Amazon Basin, Central America, and Mexico. Java seems to be the most thundery region on the globe with over 200 days; the hot moist air, and the influence of the mountains, are very favourable to copious condensation. Outside the tropics the south-east of the United States has most thunder, on about 50 days, the moist warm air from the Gulf Stream being favourable.

The dry trade-wind deserts have less than 5 days a year with thunder. For a humid tropical land India is remarkably free from thunder, with only about 25 days.

In the tropics most of the thunder on land is in the afternoon and evening in the rainy season, the time of the heaviest convectional rain, and it is notably frequent on mountains:

MEAN NUMBER OF THUNDERSTORMS (TOTALS OF HOURLY OBSERVATIONS) RECORDED IN THE YEAR

	0000–0600	0600–1200	1200–1800	1800–2400
Java, Batavia (260 ft.)	67	18	196	89
„ Buitenzorg (800 ft.)	26	20	848	498

At sea the frequency is reversed, having a maximum at night; as an example, on the Atlantic, 0°–10° N., 20°–30° W., the mean percentage frequency is:

0000–0400	27	1200–1600	10
0400–0800	17	1600–2000	16
0800–1200	10	2000–2400	20

Batavia records 55 days with thunder in the 6 driest months, April to September, and 81 in the 6 rainiest. In monsoonal climates the tendency is to a pronounced maximum in the transition months at the beginning and end of the summer monsoon, and little during the height of the monsoon; this is strongly marked in India.

Middle and High Latitudes

Hot, moist, unstable air is most prolific here as in low latitudes, and this explains the main features of the frequency by locality, season, and time of day. The most thundery localities are continental interiors into which damp air penetrates, the favoured season is summer, time of day the afternoon and evening, as is illustrated in the following tables:

MEAN NUMBER OF DAYS WITH THUNDER

	J.	F.	M.	A.	M.	J.	J.	A.	S.	O.	N.	D.	Year
Valencia .	0·8	0·6	0·5	0·4	0·5	0·7	0·5	0·6	0·3	0·5	0·5	0·6	7
Cambridge .	0·1	0·1	0·4	0·9	2	3	3	3	1	0·5	0·1	0·1	14
Frankfurt a. M.	0·1	0·2	0·6	1	4	5	5	4	1	0·3	0·1	0·1	21
Munich .	0·1	0·1	0·5	2	7	10	11	8	4	0·5	0·1	0·1	43
Vienna .	0	0·1	0·4	2	5	6	6	4	2	0·2	0·1	0	26
Moscow .	0	0	0	0·7	2·6	3·9	4·8	2·6	0·4	0	0	0	15
Semipalatinsk	0	0	0	0	1·0	3·5	6·7	3·6	0·5	0	0	0·1	15

MEAN DIURNAL FREQUENCY (%) OF THUNDERSTORMS

	0000–0600	0600–1200	1200–1800	1800–2400
Edinburgh	5	21	58	16
Vienna	6	6	66	22

In the temperate belt the land has a marked excess over the sea. Much of the North Atlantic and North Pacific have less than 5 days, but central Europe and large areas of the United States over 25.

In Great Britain thunder is most frequent in the midlands, the east, and the north-east of England, where it is four times more frequent than in the oceanic south-west, but it is noteworthy that in winter the latter area, represented by Valencia in the table above, has thunder more than twice as often as the interior, though it is rare everywhere. The frequency increases considerably towards central Europe.

With regard to the synoptic conditions, thunder is least frequent in anticyclones. Tropical air contains the necessary

supply of hot moist air, but it is usually stable except over
a hot land where strong surface heating may give rise to local
convection; it is liable to develop more extensive activity in

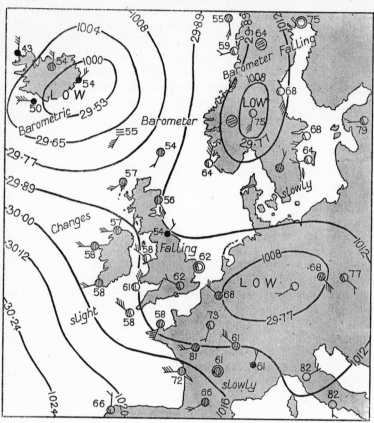

FIG. 88. Synoptic chart, 1800, 22 July 1924.
For meaning of the symbols see Fig. 11, p. 50

shallow secondary depressions and in cols with weak gradients (Fig. 88), where cooler air is brought into contact with
it, this being one case of the convergence which seems to be
a necessary condition for widespread thundery outbreaks.
Thunder is frequent but of short duration in cold fronts in
summer and spring with massive condensation in towering
cumulo-nimbus clouds; the undercutting of humid tropical
air, which has been lying for some time on a hot land, by a

vigorous polar current nearly always generates it along the front in a belt of heavy precipitation, rain or snow and hail, sweeping over extensive areas. A few peals may be heard in cold fronts in winter also, but rarely even on mountainous windward coasts, where, however, as has been mentioned above, it is more frequent in winter than in summer; the necessary lift is given by the elevated sea-board to deep polar air-masses, already unstable after their ocean passage and advancing rapidly; in summer polar currents are less vigorous and thunder is less frequent on these coasts. A thunderstorm is an impressive scene on a winter night in the Färoe Islands; the flashes flicker over the high west-facing cliffs of the islands, and the thunderstorm remains fixed there as long as it lasts, while the sea round about has only a gale of wind with rain or snow.

Shallow irregular depressions and cols are often the scene of thunder in summer, and the thundery conditions persist for days over large areas. On the day of the synoptic chart of Fig. 88 the air in the south of England was derived from central Europe which was having a very hot spell, and the temperature was high, 74° in London before the storm broke, but in the north it was much lower. With an abnormally steep lapse-rate convection carried the hot damp surface air to unusual heights, cumulo-nimbus clouds rising to over 23,000 feet. The temperature at South Kensington dropped 18° when the storm broke. The rain was extremely heavy locally, half an inch falling in 5 minutes; hailstones over half an inch in diameter fell in London, which had the worst of the storm, but thunderstorms of less intensity broke out over most of south England.

'Thermal' thunderstorms of small area often build up sporadically on summer afternoons when the air is hot and damp, and give torrential downpours while the surrounding country may be enjoying almost cloudless skies (Fig. 89).

Hail

Hail (the hard pellets of ice usually so called are referred to, not 'soft hail') is associated with thunderstorms. The pellets have characteristic structure, clear hard ice alternating with layers which are white and opaque owing to the presence of minute bubbles of air; hailstones with as many as 20 concentric layers have been recorded. They are formed by the freezing of drops of water in the upper part of lofty cumulo-nimbus clouds. The frozen drops fall through the cloud, condensing vapour and collecting water on their surface, which freezes. Carried up again by a vigorous

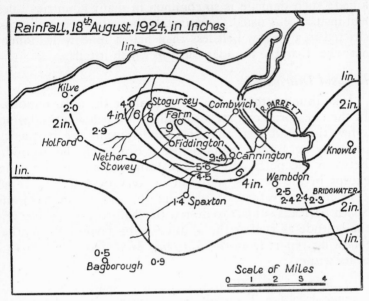

FIG. 89. Heavy local rain in Somerset (from *British Rainfall*, 1924)

up-draught, they receive another coat of water, and again fall, and the process is repeated several times. The opaque layers result from very rapid freezing when the stone is passing through minute drops of supercooled water, the transparent from the slower freezing of a coat of water. The necessary conditions for the ascent of large hailstones seem to be provided only by a very rapid uprush of air in thunder-clouds, and the structure of the hail itself provides evidence of the existence of such currents.

Hailstones larger than half an inch are occasionally re-ported; a diameter of 4 inches and a weight of 2 lb. are well authenticated, but it is difficult to credit the reports of stones a foot or more in diameter; some are spherical and many of the other common forms probably result from the breaking up of spheres, or from the cohesion of several small stones. Large stones can do serious damage to trees, which may be stripped of foliage and fruit, and to crops at a critical period of growth. The glass roofs and shades in market-gardens are broken, and tiles riddled; men and animals may even be killed; such damage is so common in many countries that hail-insurance is usual. Fortunately the hail is generally restricted to a narrow belt less than half a mile wide, much narrower than the thunderstorm in which it falls.

Regional Distribution

Like thunderstorms, hail is very rare in the polar regions. In the equatorial climate also hail is rare below altitudes of a few thousand feet, though thunderstorms are frequent, probably because it melts before it can reach the ground. Between the polar and the equatorial belts it is common except in the deserts, and can be very destructive. It is a prominent feature of plateaux (p. 317); the veld of South Africa is subject to destructive hailstorms in summer, the latitude as well as the altitude being favourable, as the following report from the *Mafeking Mail,* December 1915, bears witness:

. . . in the vicinity of Hildavale . . . there followed a hailstorm of exceptional violence. For nearly 5 minutes great isolated chunks of ice fell. We have the authority of Mr. Durand for stating that four of these chunks together turned the scale at 4 lb., and the measurements of one were: width 4 in., depth 4 in., and length $4\frac{1}{2}$ in. Numerous hailstones weighing over $\frac{3}{4}$ lb. also fell. Into ploughed land the bigger penetrated to a depth of from 2 to 3 in. and it would be better to imagine than experience a bombardment with such missiles had it been accompanied by a heavy wind. As it was, Mr. Durand's losses in livestock were considerable. Of one flock of sheep 14 were killed outright and 16 died later; 30 or 40, though very badly bruised and bleeding, are recovering. An ox had its eye destroyed, and a 2-year old heifer belonging to Mr. du Plessis was killed. Packing cases outside Mr. Durand's house were smashed to matchwood. The thatch on two rooms adjoining the homesteads was completely demolished, while at Mr. Odendaal's homestead one hailstone crashed through the veranda roof of corrugated iron, leaving a hole about 3 ins. in diameter. At the end of 5 minutes smaller hailstones fell, and continued for some 10 minutes. No great quantity of rain fell, in fact just before the water began to 'run' on the veld the storm ceased.

In India most hail falls in the thunderstorms of the hot-weather season from March to May, and the stones are often of great size. In higher latitudes it is most frequent in spring and summer; in a storm at Sydney, N.S.W., in December 1946:

More than 300 persons were treated by first-aid men or at hospitals for injuries caused by flying glass or for cuts and bruises by lumps of ice. Over wide areas the hail had the diameter of a penny-piece, and in some places there were larger irregular lumps the size of cricket balls, the largest so far verified weighing 4 lb. House-tops were damaged and thousands of windows were broken. Motor-cars had their roofs dented and tram-cars their windows broken. (*The Times.*)

Egypt gets hail in winter thunderstorms, which are not uncommon near the Mediterranean but much rarer inland in the desert, and hailstones over a pound in weight have reached the ground.

CHAPTER XXVI

SUNSHINE AND CLOUD AMOUNT

SUNSHINE, its intensity and duration, is a most important element of climate. Objects exposed to it are heated both on and beneath the surface much above the air temperature. The physiological effects on plants and animals are far-reaching, and still await full investigation. The aesthetic significance in landscape of bright sunshine needs no emphasis; a land of cloudy skies lacks a valuable source of pleasure and stimulation, and the poverty and weakness of the sunshine is a serious disadvantage in the westerlies.

The intensity of the insolation depends on the altitude of the sun and on the clearness of the atmosphere (Chapter XXVIII). In low latitudes the direct insolation is at least equally potent physiologically with the high air temperature, in the middle of the day more potent; white man finds it

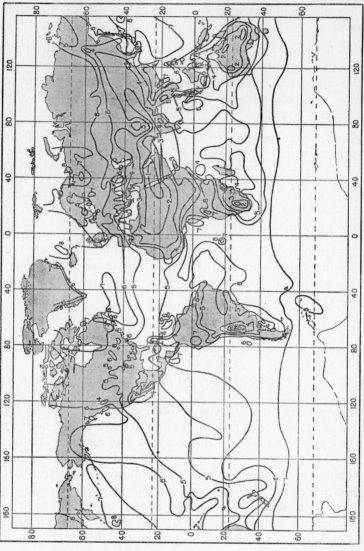

FIG. 90. Mean annual cloud amount in tenths of sky covered (after Shaw)

excessive, and must choose clothing which protects him against it while not unduly impeding the loss of heat from the body; the white loose-flowing garments ('burnous') of Arabs serve the purpose well. The unclothed negro is probably protected by the pigmentation of his skin. At high altitudes the sunshine gives a welcome addition to the reduced air temperature. In middle latitudes sunshine is sought, except in high summer, and poleward of about 50° N. it is a specially welcome but all too rare source of warmth and brightness; the strong light is one of the attractions of high Alpine health-stations.

Sunshine and cloud amount may conveniently be treated together, since the former varies, in most regions, inversely with the latter (if fog is included with cloud). Neither has necessarily a close relation to the precipitation, and some of the most arid tracts have low sunshine totals.

The duration of sunshine is usually measured by a Campbell-Stokes recorder, in which a clear crown-glass sphere, 4 inches in diameter, focuses the rays on a prepared card graduated to show hours. Bright sunshine burns the card, and the length of the burnt track is measured. A fairly bright sun is needed to burn the card, and there is rarely any record when the sun is within 5° of the horizon, or when it is shining through light clouds though still visible. This selectivity is perhaps an advantage, for a weak sun is not comparable in its biological effects with the sun at full strength; the ordinary sunshine recorder gives a record of the duration of sunshine of more than a certain intensity. Another recorder, the Jordan pattern, registers in a similar way the path of the light of the sun focused on sensitized paper; the record, depending on the actinic rays, is not necessarily quite the same as that of a Campbell-Stokes recorder. In the U.S.A. a thermometric recorder is used, which gives appreciably shorter traces than the instruments described above; but an increase in the tabulated records results from the practice of adding to the autographic trace a 'low sun correction', which is an eye-estimate of the time the sun is visible when it is so near the horizon as to be too weak to register itself; the combined effect is to increase the records from most of the region by about half an hour a day in summer, and to decrease them a little in winter.[1]

A rough estimate of the intensity of the sunshine at any moment is useful, and the following simple method is suggested by Sir L. Hill. A piece of black fur is exposed perpendicularly to the sun's rays, and a slender thermometer bulb is embedded in it. The fur is a very efficient absorber of the heat, and the difference between the temperatures in it and in the open air (shade temperature) gives a measure of the intensity of the insolation. Examples quoted by Hill are: at an Alpine station in midwinter the air temperature was 41°, the fur temperature 120° to 140°; on a calm sunny July day in England the air temperature was 72°, the fur 130°. Records indicate the great intensity of the winter sunshine in the high Alps, where for various medical purposes the low air temperature is an advantage. Arosa, 6,200 feet, has almost the same intensity at noon throughout the year, the greater transparency of the winter atmosphere balancing the lower altitude of the sun. Under the overhead sun in the clear air of the trade-wind deserts powerful insolation and intense light are accompanied by high air temperature.

Cloud amount is estimated by eye, in tenths[2] of the whole sky covered (e.g. 6 denotes 6 tenths covered); estimates can be rapidly and reliably made in daylight, but few night records are exact. The amount of cloud (Fig. 90) varies in most latitudes with the season, but much less on the sea than on the land. The sunshine and cloud in the main climatic regions will now be described.

Regional Distribution

The Trade-wind Deserts

To begin with the sunniest parts of the earth, the first place must be given to the trade-wind deserts in every month of the year. They are perhaps the only lands which by common consent have too much sunshine. Over wide areas the cloud cover is less than 2 tenths of the sky, in parts

---

[1] Sunshine Recorders, C. F. and E. S. Brooks, *Jour. of Meteorology*, 1947.
[2] In 1949 a new scale, in eighths, was introduced.

less than 1, in each month. Helwan, a few miles south of
Cairo, illustrates Saharan conditions:

HELWAN: MEAN DURATION OF SUNSHINE (hours a day)

Jan.	7·5	Apr.	10·8	July	12·6	Oct.	10·0
Feb.	8·4	May	11·6	Aug.	12·2	Nov.	8·8
Mar.	9·7	June	12·9	Sept.	11·1	Dec.	7·6

Year 10·3

The total for the year is 3,668 hours, 82 per cent. of the
time the sun is above the horizon. June to September, the
sunniest period, has more than 90 per cent. of the possible;
winter is a little cloudier owing to Mediterranean depressions and the occasional formation of stratus cloud by surface
cooling, but even January, the cloudiest month, gets 70 per
cent. of the possible. The 15 Januarys of 1906–20 had only
11 days on which the sun did not appear. In the same years
not a single day in the months May to October inclusive was
without any sunshine, and a day with less than 12 hours is
very rare in summer; Heliopolis, near Cairo, was well
chosen by the ancients as the centre for sun-worship. The
most usual clouds are cirrus and light cumulus. Farther
from the Mediterranean the Sahara is still sunnier. At
Asyût the cloudiest months, December and January, have
only 1 tenth cloud, and June to October less than a third as
much; August is almost cloudless. In such a climate we long
to escape the harsh and pitiless glare of the midday sun if
only in the shade of a group of palms, and still more desirable is a darkened chamber behind thick walls or under the
ground. In summer the cool peace of sunset with its glori-
ously coloured skies comes as a welcome relief from the
exciting and tiring brilliance of the day. And yet so essential
to the desert landscape is the bright light of the sun that
there is something depressing and ominous in a day when
the sky is overcast and curtains of rain sweep over the bare,
drab expanses. Most of the trade-wind deserts are sunny like
the Sahara; the south-west of the United States has over
85 per cent. of the possible annual sunshine (Yuma 97 per
cent. in June, but see p. 249 for the method of recording).

The trade-winds on the oceans are cloudier, especially in
winter; the typical sky is light blue with light alto-cumulus

and fracto-cumulus clouds over about half its expanse, but widespread cloud covers the cool upwelling water off the west coasts of the trade-wind deserts (p. 278). Very different are the skies of low latitudes in the west of the oceans, where the trades are hot and damp from their sea-passage; and the cloud is massive rather than extensive, largely cumulus and cumulo-nimbus, and hangs low over the mountainous islands and windward coasts.

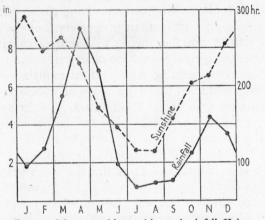

FIG. 91. Mean monthly sunshine and rainfall, Kabete

The Inner Tropics

With a mean for the year of 6 or more, this region is much cloudier than the last, and in most parts the afternoon sky is often overcast with massive dark cumulo-nimbus clouds. But in the mornings the sunshine is intense, and a topee or other head protection is used by some Europeans. In spite of the heavy rainfall there is much more sun than in many drier lands, the daily mean in many regions exceeding 5 hours (Batavia 8·3, Manila 5·7 hrs.). The mean at Kabete, Kenya, altitude 5,971 feet, is shown in Fig. 91; the least sunny months, June to August, have also the least rain, but January, the sunniest month, is one of the driest.

Large local and seasonal differences are found in this as in other elements of the tropical climate. At Manáos, in the midst of the forests of the Amazon, the mean cloud, 6 to

7 in each month, has little seasonal change, but at Pará the mean ranges from 4 in the dry season to 8 in the rains. The diurnal curves, too, show considerable differences; in general the night is much less cloudy than the afternoon, but Batavia has little difference during the rains, with 7 at night and 8 in the day; August, the driest month, has a larger range, from 4 in the early morning to 6 at noon. Abnormalities due to the land-breeze are mentioned on p. 119.

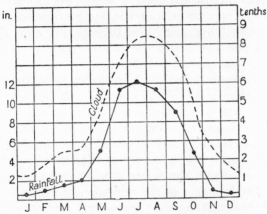

FIG. 92. Mean monthly rainfall and cloud, Calcutta

The Sudan and Monsoon Regions

The Sudan is Saharan in winter, humid-tropical in summer. At Roseires on the Blue Nile the cloudiest (and rainiest) months are June to September, with maximum cloud in August (6); winter is almost cloudless, with less than 1 from December to March; the curves of cloud and rainfall are in agreement. Most of the summer rain falls in the afternoon, leaving the mornings clear. The winter sky, though almost cloudless, is by no means always blue, for dust-haze and frequent smoke from bush-fires make it greyish, and the sun is seen as a pale disk. The South African plateau is notably sunny both in summer and winter; Kimberley (Fig. 101, p. 313) has 85 per cent. of the possible sunshine in August, 72 per cent. in February, the mean for the year being 9·4 hours a day, 79 per cent. of the possible. In the Kalahari and the north-west of the Cape Province the

mean cloud for the year is only 2. Most of the summer clouds
are cumulus and cirrus.

Monsoon lands resemble the Sudan, but the sky is clearer
and the sun brighter and more cheerful in the cool season.
North India is almost as sunny as the Sahara from October
to March, but in April the heat- and dust-haze dim the sun,
though there is little real cloud and no rain, and the dry heat
grows more intense every day. When the monsoon breaks,
the sudden increase in cloud is as pronounced as in rainfall, for almost overcast skies become the rule (Fig. 92).
The local peculiarities in the rainfall régimes in India are
reflected in the amounts of cloud.

China is similar; Peking is least cloudy in December (2)
and most cloudy in July (6); south and central China are
cloudier as well as rainier than the north. But the rainiest
parts of monsoon lands are not always the cloudiest. Some
of the mountains of India with excessive rainfall have good
sunshine records, owing partly to the strong periodicity of
the rain and cloud, the winters being dry and sunny, and
partly to the intensity of the rain when it does fall, for once
the sky is overcast the sunshine record cannot be depressed
farther, however heavy the rain. The east of N. America
differs from east Asia in respect of cloud as well as rainfall,
having almost the same amount in each season, with a
slight maximum in winter.

Mediterranean Lands

The regions with a Mediterranean type of climate, i.e. the
Mediterranean lands themselves, the Californian coast,
central Chile, the south-west of the Cape Province, and the
Perth region of Western Australia enjoy almost Saharan
skies in summer. The cloud is less than 1 in much of the
Mediterranean basin, and the south and east are especially
sunny, the sunshine much exceeding that of central and
north Europe in spite of the shorter days. Winter is the
rainy season, but even in winter a day without sunshine is
rare in the middle and south of the region, and the mean
cloud does not exceed 6 (Fig. 93). The mean monthly cloud
amount at Malta, a central Mediterranean station, is:

Jan.	5	Apr.	5	July	1	Oct.	5
Feb.	5	May	4	Aug.	2	Nov.	5
Mar.	5	June	3	Sept.	3	Dec.	6

The sunshine is a main attraction of the Mediterranean as a health and pleasure resort in winter. The brightness and exhilaration of air and sky, and the brilliance of the sunlight, both direct and reflected from the sea and the white limestone, delight all newcomers from the gloomy north;

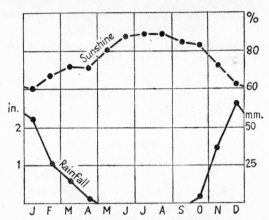

FIG. 93. Mean monthly rainfall and sunshine (percentage of possible duration), Alexandria

Nice has an annual mean of 7·2 hours a day, Paris only 4·8 hours. The gain in sunshine over even the sunniest parts of Great Britain is large:

MEAN MONTHLY SUNSHINE (hours)

	Athens	Falmouth		Athens	Falmouth
January . .	149	57	July . .	364	223
February .	156	84	August .	340	211
March . .	190	139	September .	272	161
April . .	215	181	October .	210	113
May . .	232	229	November .	129	73
June . .	292	221	December .	108	53
			Year . .	2,655	1,745

Attention has already been drawn to the fact that considerable, and even heavy, rainfall totals are not inconsistent with abundant sunshine; the coasts of Portugal and

Montenegro, with records among the highest in Europe, have good sunshine even in winter, since the rain is not of long duration though of great intensity. The cloud-forms are those of north and central Europe, but cumulus is more frequent and dull grey palls of stratus rarer in the Mediterranean.

The Westerlies

This is a cloudy as well as a rainy tract—'coelum crebris imbribus ac nebulis foedum' in the words of Tacitus, which truly indicate the outstanding drawback of the climate of almost the whole of the westerlies. Except in the far interiors of continents the sky has much more cloud than clear, with means exceeding 7. In summer the afternoons are cloudiest, with cumulus clouds in the damp atmosphere after midday; but in winter the afternoons are usually sunnier than the mornings, the sky often becoming overcast with radiation stratus in the night, and not clearing till the middle of the following day; in the lowlands in calm weather night inversion-fogs persist far into the day. The type of cloud is controlled largely by the weather, an all-powerful influence outside the tropics, but the seasonal control also is noticeable. In summer cumulus predominates in the hot hours, and sometimes masses of towering cumulo-nimbus, reminiscent of the tropics, give heavy thunderstorms. But in winter stratus is the prevailing form, and often an uninteresting and gloomy grey pall of strato-cumulus covers the whole sky; ragged nimbo-stratus in rapid movement, driven by the gale, may form a more exciting scene. The appearance in late winter of bright cumulus clouds reflecting the low sunshine is a welcome sign that spring is at hand.

Industrial pollution of the atmosphere in the many large towns in the westerlies reduces the sunshine seriously, by as much as 50 per cent. in winter in bad areas.

On the oceanic seaboards autumn and winter, the rainiest seasons, are also the cloudiest; short days and overcast skies combine to give Valencia, south-west Ireland (Fig. 94), a mean of only 1·3 hours of sunshine a day, 17 per cent. of the possible, in December; Stornoway in the Hebrides, in a higher latitude and nearer the most frequented cyclone

PLATE 10

Atmospheric pollution in the Potteries, Staffs.

tracks, has only 0·7 hour, 12 per cent. of the possible. It
becomes sunnier till May, which is the sunniest month with
6·7 hours a day, 43 per cent. of the possible, at Valencia, and
6 hours a day, 37 per cent. of the possible, at Stornoway; in
spite of its longer days Stornoway is still unable to equal
Valencia. June and July have rather less than May, but the
curve rises slightly in August and September before falling
to the December minimum. The Pacific coast of British

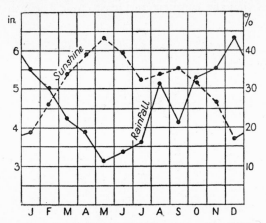

FIG. 94. Mean monthly sunshine (percentage of possible) and
precipitation, Valencia, Ireland

Columbia is similar, the cloud increasing to a maximum of 8
in December, but it falls to a minimum of below 5 in July
and August, the summers being considerably more sunny
than in the British Isles.

Much of these western seaboards is mountainous, and
has not only excessive rainfall but also very cloudy skies.
The slightest cyclonic disturbance caps the summits with
clouds, which may spread and enshroud the mountains for
weeks together, and the valleys are sunless and cheerless
under their low ceiling even if no rain is falling. Such are
the Lake District of Cumberland, the Western Highlands
of Scotland, and the fiords of Norway and British Columbia.

The monthly means of cloud amount on Ben Nevis,
Scotland, altitude 4,406 feet, are representative:

| Jan. | 9 | Mar. | 8 | May | 8 | July | 9 | Sept. | 8 | Nov. | 9 |
| Feb. | 8 | Apr. | 8 | June | 8 | Aug. | 9 | Oct. | 9 | Dec. | 9 |

The mean annual duration of sunshine is 736 hours, only 2 hours a day.

In general the rainfall and cloud curves rise and fall together in the westerlies on the oceans. The relationship is different on the lands; the cloud does not diminish nearly as rapidly as the rainfall with distance from the sea, for only in the most remote interiors does it sink to 5, and a striking feature is that the sunniest and least cloudy months are those

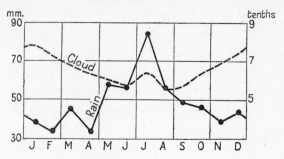

FIG. 95. Mean monthly precipitation and cloud amount, Potsdam

with most rain. Potsdam (Fig. 95) has most rain in summer, least in winter, but winter is considerably more cloudy than summer. The same is true of most of central Europe and Russia, the mean cloud in Russia being about 6 in summer, 8 in winter. In Siberia, on the other hand summer with 7 is rather cloudier than winter, 6; winter is much less cloudy in the intense cold of the far north-east, where the monthly means at Verkhoyansk are:

Jan.	3	Apr.	5	July	6	Oct.	6
Feb.	3	May	6	Aug.	7	Nov.	5
Mar.	3	June	6	Sept.	7	Dec.	4

Even in the deserts of central Asia the sky is far from clear, the mean cloud being 5 in both summer and winter in the Tarim Basin; Gobi is less cloudy in winter but equally cloudy in summer, when the Chinese monsoon is felt.

The interior of North America is cloudier in winter than in summer, and the means are lower than in Eurasia. The New England States have almost uniform cloud, 5 to 6, throughout the year. The annual mean is between 4

and 6 over the whole continent except the Pacific coast and
adjoining plateau and the St. Lawrence Basin. California,
Arizona, and New Mexico have about 3. The following
annual sunshine means show the advantage over Europe:
New York, 2,790 hours, Pittsburg, 2,320, Chicago, 2,650,
St. Louis, 2,700, Seattle, 2,070 (compare Kew, 1,460,
Glasgow, 1,090); America is most favoured in winter, with
more than twice the British totals, but the difference is in
part merely instrumental (p. 249), and it must be remembered that the U.S.A. is in lower latitudes than the British
Isles.

The lack of parallelism between the curves of rainfall and
cloud in these lands arises from the fact that the summer rain
tends to fall in heavy showers of no great length, leaving the
rest of the day clear, but in winter the less rain accompanies
long spells of cloud, and low stratus and fog may persist
without any rain. These long gloomy spells are among the
discomforts of life in the prairies and other steppe lands.

The duration of sunshine in the westerlies, and indeed
everywhere outside the tropics, is so much under the control
of the seasonal change in the length of the day that the
amount of cloud is no index to it, since the change in the
possible duration may easily override the effect of the latter.
In the higher latitudes, e.g. in Canada, the 20 hours of daylight go far to compensate plant life for the short summer.
Even the north of Scotland has hardly any real night at
midsummer, for the sun skirts so close below the horizon
that the glow remains. The lengths of the day in latitude
40° (New York, Denver, Rome, Peking, Melbourne),
latitude 50° (Winnipeg, London, Semipalatinsk), and latitude 60° (Great Slave Lake, Orkney Islands, Leningrad,
Tobolsk) are:

Latitude	Number of hours a day sun is above horizon	
	Midwinter	*Midsummer*
40°	9·3	15
50°	8	16·3
60°	5·7	18·7

The dark cloudy winters are the most unpleasant feature of the westerlies. 1927 had as many as 78 days on which the sun did not appear at all at Rothamsted, in the open country of south England; and in spite of a slight exaggeration, for 1927 was an unusually bad year, this record illustrates an important feature, the palls of cloud that may continue unbroken for a week; in the notably cold and snowy winter of 1947 London had practically no sunshine from 2 to 22 February, 21 days, and most of Britain, except the west of Scotland, fared little better. Greenwich, London, had 74 days without any sunshine even in the good year, May 1928–April 1929. Summer, too, can be cloudy enough, but two consecutive days without sunshine are rare.

The tundra lands are within the westerlies, but the high latitude and the low rainfall, less than 10 inches, are distinguishing features. Being for the most part inside the polar circles the range of possible daily sunshine is 24 hours; though the rainfall is low there is not much sun even in summer, owing to the frequent fogs and palls of stratus cloud. At Archangel November is the cloudiest month (9) and July the clearest (6).

Most mountains are very cloudy as well as rainy, and especially slopes facing strong winds from the sea. Interesting local peculiarities due to topography, altitude, season, and weather are mentioned on p. 295.

The Cold-water Coasts

The 'cold-water coasts' on the west of the trade-wind deserts show a striking discrepancy between rainfall and cloud, being among the least rainy but the most cloudy tracts on the globe. The conditions are described in Chapter XXVIII; the 'cloud' is largely low fog. Iquique, on the coast of the Atacama desert, Chile, is practically rainless, the mean annual rainfall being only 0·05 inch, but in the period June to September the cloud is 8, a higher record than even in the south of Chile where the rainfall exceeds 80 inches. In summer Iquique has much less fog, and the cloud is only 4. The upwelling water off these coasts (p. 278) is cool, and cools enormous areas of the oceans under the trades below the temperature of the air resting on them, a state conducive to cloud when the wind is strong enough to cause turbulence; the South Atlantic east of the meridian of Greenwich is cloudy for its latitude, and the sun is sometimes little in evidence all the way from the mouth of the Orange River to the equator.

The Polar Regions

The outstanding feature is the seasonal change in the length of day and night. On the polar circles the sun does not set at the summer solstice or rise at the winter solstice, giving 2 or 3 weeks of almost continuous day and continuous night at those times; the midsummer day and the midwinter night increase to 6 months at the poles.

Antarctica with its anticyclonic conditions has little cloud. Bright starry skies, brilliant aurorae, and low temperatures in winter are followed by long spells of sunshine in summer. The burn on the card of the sunshine-recorder is often unbroken for 24 hours, and Captain Scott's party at Cape Evans secured a continuous record of 66 hours 25 minutes (from 1305 on 9 December 1911 to 0730 on 12 December). The mean was about 14 hours a day in the summer months, and the total for the year was considerably more than in England, though the sun was above the horizon on only 246 days. The skies of the polar plateau are probably very clear, and explorers report long spells of sunshine in summer; the eyes must be protected from the dazzling reflection from the snowy wastes throughout the 24 hours. We may imagine the winter landscape—the white snowfields glistening under the bright moon that circles the sky for days without setting; or the moonless skies illuminated by the sparkling stars and the coloured streamers and curtains of the aurora.

The amount and the form of the clouds have been carefully observed on the coasts, especially round the Ross Sea, but records are uncertain owing to the commonest form of cloud being a very thin stratus of ice particles, 'a uniform layer of cloud which had no distinguishing features, and the height of which could not be determined . . . the moon and the stars could be seen through it'. Such a sky was usually entered as overcast, but so thin was the covering that some observers seem to have entered it as clear sky. But there is no doubt that the cloudy Southern Ocean surrounds a polar region of clear skies. The mean cloud at Cape Evans, Ross Island, was about 6—a figure, however, even more misleading than most mean values, since by far the commonest skies were completely clear or completely overcast, 6 tenths of cloud being rare. Cloud was least in early summer, most in February–March and October. After stratus the commonest forms were alto-stratus, alto-cumulus, cirro-stratus, cirro-cumulus, and cirrus. Low cumulus only appeared in summer, and then extremely rarely, and never over the snowfields. Fog was rare at Cape Evans, but frequent on calm nights and early mornings on the Ice Barrier owing to the intense cooling of the snow by radiation through the clear air.

The Arctic is less sunny than the Antarctic. In the summer months many channels of open water between the icefields give rise to differences of temperature and humidity between adjacent areas conducive to frequent fogs, and the sun when visible is often only dimly seen through the mist. No long records exist for an estimate of the duration of sunshine. In winter the sky is probably much clearer than in summer, but less clear than in Antarctica owing to the lesspronounced anticyclonic conditions, and the influence of the stormy westerlies which not infrequently penetrate far towards the pole.

CHAPTER XXVII

PHYSIOLOGICAL TEMPERATURE

THE human body is constituted to maintain an internal temperature of about 98°, and much departure from it is harmful and may be fatal. In cold environments measures must be taken to check loss of heat, in hot to facilitate it; in the latter case man's problem is to effect the cooling in a way that is comfortable and not likely to be injurious. It is easier to keep the body warm in cold climates than to keep it suitably cool in hot.

'Physiological temperature' denotes the feeling of heat or cold experienced by man, and it depends on several factors, of which the air temperature is only one, and not always the largest; others are (*a*) radiation, (*b*) evaporation, (*c*) air-movement. These have been treated as physical entities in earlier chapters, and we now consider their physiological effects.

(*a*) Radiation; the net result is the balance between loss by radiation from the body itself and receipt from the surrounding objects; the former depends on the amount, kind, colour, texture, of the clothing worn, the latter on the temperature and radiating power of the objects. In a room the balance is a large loss of heat by the body if the walls are cold and a much smaller loss if they are warm, the air temperature being constant. The radiant energy of the sun is a factor the magnitude of which depends on its intensity when it reaches the body, and the length of exposure to it. In the tropics long exposure in the middle of the day can be harmful; at the other extreme, in high latitudes and at great altitudes, as in the cold air on snowfields, the sunshine is a welcome source of warmth.

(*b*) Evaporation causes cooling and is a normal process which is necessary for health and vigour. It should not be excessive, but the healthy body can stand a great strain. The air makes contact with the lungs where it is heated to about 90°, and the skin where it is heated to about 70° according to movement and clothing. Even if the air temperature is well above 98° the body remains at 98° as long as the perspiration mechanism is working well, and the necessary amount of liquid to provide perspiration is supplied. But if this cooling process is checked by either internal causes—fatigue or injury of the perspiring mechanism, or lack of liquid to evaporate—or by external conditions, as when the air, at a temperature approaching 98°, in contact with the body is saturated with vapour, or is almost saturated and so stationary that evaporation from the body soon brings it to saturation-point, the body is unable to cool itself and heat-stroke results, it may be with fatal results.

Unacclimatized persons soon suffer in hot damp weather, as during the heat waves of summer in the east of the United States. In the hot deserts the temperature on summer days is above 98°, and may exceed 120°; contact with the body cools the air, not the body, in this case, and increases its humidity. But the air is so dry that the small increase is not important, for if the initial temperature is 115° and relative humidity 20 per cent., not uncommon figures, the humidity after the air is cooled to 98° is only 32 per cent.; fortunately a strong breeze is usual in the hottest hours. These regions are much more healthy than the humid tropics, where the air may be 20° cooler but is saturated with vapour, and the winds are light. Similarly the dry windy plateaux in the south-west of the United States are less debilitating in summer, in spite of their higher air temperature, than the moist sultry lowlands of the lower Mississippi and the Gulf coast. But cooling by evaporation can be excessive; on a cold, damp, 'raw' day clothes get damp and their insulating power is lessened, and much of the heat of the body is wasted in evaporating the droplets of water in the air. The body is specially sensitive to humidity at temperatures above and below normal; at normal temperatures considerable changes are hardly noticed.

For many purposes the wet-bulb thermometer gives a better indication of the temperature as affecting health and comfort than the dry-bulb, because damp skin evaporates in some respects like the wet-bulb. A wet-bulb temperature of 75° is oppressive for north Europeans, and the debilitating effect increases rapidly when that figure is exceeded; long exposure to such sultry heat may be injurious. The dry-bulb temperatures of the Australian summer are extremely high, but the dryness of the air reduces the physiological temperature, the maximum wet-bulb readings on summer days in the hottest areas being as much as 35° below the dry. In Victoria the wet-bulb thermometer rarely rises to 80° even in the greatest heat. The trade-wind deserts, the hottest regions of the earth in summer, are not unhealthy, though the days are unpleasantly hot; in Death Valley, California, a wet-bulb reading of only 70° has been recorded with the dry-bulb at 118°. The high summer temperatures of Mediterranean lands are much modified, for the wet-bulb does not usually rise above 70°; the highest recorded temperature at Athens was 106°, but the wet-bulb maximum was only 73°. In the British Isles the wet-bulb is not usually more than 2° or 3° below the dry-bulb in winter, and sometimes the two readings hardly differ for days together; on fine spring and summer days the difference may be 10° or 15°. In the humid tropics a wet-bulb depression of more than 15° is uncommon even in the hottest hours.

The wet-bulb thermometer, however, is not a perfect indicator of the physiological temperature, for the body, the human wet-bulb, is not maintained at the air temperature. The most significant value is the 'physiological saturation deficit', that is, the difference between the vapour actually present in the air (the absolute humidity) and the amount that saturated air at body-temperature contains, 43 g./m.^{3} at 98°. On a typical winter day in north-west Europe or on the Pacific coast of Canada the air temperature may be 40° and the relative humidity 80 per cent., so that the amount of vapour in the air is about 5 g./m.^{3}, and the physiological saturation deficit 38 g./m.^{3} (43–5); on a summer afternoon with air temperature 70° and relative humidity 60 per cent. it is 32 g./m.^{3}; in a desert with temperature 115° and relative humidity 10 per cent., 36 g./m.^{3}. The larger the deficit the more vigorous the evaporation, and consequently the cooling of the body, other conditions being the same.

(c) Air-movement intensifies the effect of low temperatures by renewing the air in contact with the body, and in a dry wind rapid evaporation adds its influence. The strong NE. winds which are frequent in west Europe in spring are notoriously trying, being both cold and dry. The damp winds of winter at a temperature of about 40° are also unpleasant, and they feel colder than the still air in the interiors of continents where the temperature may be 50° lower.

The interiors of continents in temperate latitudes have a healthy bracing climate in winter, but the far interiors of Canada and Siberia are too cold, especially when the wind is strong, to be comfortable or even healthy, and such heavy clothing must be worn that many of the advantages of a bracing climate are lost; fortunately calms and light winds are frequent. The winter of high Alpine valleys is very favourable to health and vigour, being dry and bracing and not unduly cold. The breathing is deeper, and evaporation is vigorous in the rarefied atmosphere. Additional advantages here are the calm air and the exhilarating sunshine, while the snow-cover prevents dust and makes a bright and cheerful scene. At the other extreme, in the humid tropics temperature is little below that of the body; the sluggish air is almost saturated, and the nights do not bring much relief. Europeans tend to lose vigour, and fall victim to various tropical diseases, which may be directly due to micro-organisms but might be resisted if the body retained its tone. Conditions are similar during the rainy season in the outer tropics, but the cooler and drier winters give a welcome respite. Heat waves claim many victims to heat-stroke in New York and neighbouring cities every summer, though they last only a few days. The unhealthy hot-house conditions are familiar in all crowded and unventilated rooms where temperature and humidity of the stagnant air are abnormally high.

Evidently the important physiological consideration is the cooling power of the air resulting from all the factors in combination.[1] Various instruments, 'katathermometers', have been designed to measure it; one, by Sir L. Hill, is essentially a large alcohol thermometer, graduated at $100°$ and $95°$ F.; before use the bulb is warmed till the reading is above $100°$, and it is then exposed in the air which is to be examined, and the time taken for the reading to fall from $100°$ to $95°$ is measured in seconds. The time varies inversely with the cooling power of the air, and the cooling power in calories may be obtained by applying a factor determined for the instrument. The range from $100°$ to $95°$ is a near approach to that through which the air in contact with the body passes. The perspiring body may be imitated by surrounding the bulb with wet muslin. The

[1] See Gold, E., 'The effect of wind, temperature, humidity and sunshine on the loss of heat of a body at temperature of $98°$ F.', *Q.J.R. Meteorological Soc.*, July 1935.

'eupatheoscope' is another instrument which records the integrated cooling power of radiation, air temperature, and air-movement.

CHAPTER XXVIII

VISIBILITY. FOG. ATMOSPHERIC POLLUTION

AIR is practically transparent, but extraneous matter, suspended particles, solid or liquid, reduce visibility. Visibility has always been an element of practical importance, and fog is still a serious danger for marine navigation, though less than formerly since the introduction of radar; rail and road traffic may be badly dislocated. For aircraft a range of vision of less than 2 miles presents difficulties, and fog makes landing hazardous; the higher the speed of the aircraft the more important good visibility becomes. In large towns smoke and other products of combustion, the commonest constituents of bad visibility, can be so abundant as to cause great nuisance, expense, and injury to health.

Observations of visibility are included in the daily routine at all meteorological stations. The international scale[1] is in terms of the distance at which objects can be recognized by a person with normal vision in normal light:

Code figure	Description	Range of visibility		
0	Fog	Less than	55 yards	
1	,,	Exceeding	55 yards, less than 220 yards	
2	,,	,,	220 ,,	,, 550 ,,
3	,,	,,	550 ,,	,, 1,100 ,,
4	Poor visibility, mist	,,	1,100 ,,	,, 1¼ miles
5	Moderate visibility	,,	1¼ miles	,, 2½ ,,
6	,,	,,	2½ ,,	,, 6¼ ,,
7	Good visibility	,,	6¼ ,,	,, 12½ ,,
8	Very good visibility	,,	12½ ,,	,, 31 ,,
9	Excellent visibility	,,	31 ,,	

Climatological tables should contain data of visibility, preferably expressed as the mean percentage frequencies of the several code figures, a point of importance in some

[1] A new scale was introduced in 1949.

climates. Hutts Gate, St. Helena, altitude 2,066 feet, is an
example, with the following means for winter:

Code figures	0–3	4	5	6	7–9
Percentage frequency	13	2	2	5	78

The table shows that the visibility at this station is usually very
good, but if not very good it is usually very bad; the explanation is that the trade-wind air itself is clear, but at times the
clouds are low enough to envelop the tops, among which the
station lies, and form a thick fog; intermediate values are
rare. For convenience we shall consider first visibilities
better than fog, and fog later.

The minute suspended particles which reduce visibility
may be:

(a) Crystals of sea-salt left after evaporation of fine spray
blown or thrown up from the sea; they are ubiquitous, even
in the heart of the continents, and, being hygroscopic, in
damp air they become minute droplets of saline water, much
larger than the original crystals. They seem to be the most
general cause of obscurity, and their effect is evidently much
greater in damp than in dry air.

(b) Hygroscopic particles resulting from combustion, for
the most part sulphur and nitrogen acids, the product of
industrial furnaces and domestic fires. Like sea-salt they
grow by the accretion of water even at humidities below
saturation.

(c) Smoke, mainly particles of carbon, comparatively few
but in places large and numerous enough to reduce visibility,
though, not being hygroscopic, they remain dry. Like (b)
they are derived from combustion; a main source in the
tropics in the dry season is bush- and grass-fires; forest-,
heath-, and grass-fires are frequent in higher latitudes in dry
regions and during dry weather. The contribution of combustion products was made obvious in the General Strike
in 1926, when, with the cessation of industrial operations,
the air over the 'blackest' counties of England became as
clear as in the open wilds.

(d) Particles of fine dust, sand, and various dry organic
substances, raised by strong winds from dry ground, and

carried to great heights. This is a major cause of obscurity in parts of the tropics; in West Africa the Harmattan is hazy, and may be foggy, with such particles, which are carried far out over the Atlantic by the NE. trade (p. 136). In the dust-storms of the Sudan (haboobs) and similar regions thick clouds of desert dust are raised to 10,000 feet and more; in the khamsin winds of lower Egypt daylight may be so much reduced that motor traffic uses headlights. Volcanoes throw very fine dust to such heights that it circles the globe.

(e) Rain, mostly when the drops are numerous and small, which may reduce visibility to less, sometimes very much less, than a quarter of the previous range. Snow in any quantity can be an almost opaque screen. But precipitation washes the air, and gives much-improved visibility afterwards.

Obscurity due to dry particles or to heat shimmering is called haze; mist and fog consist of globules of water.

The fine particles collect about their place of origin unless removed. Removal is effected horizontally by winds, and vertically by ascending currents. The latter depend largely on the stability of the atmosphere; in stable air under a strong surface inversion of temperature the particles remain near the surface, and increase till they form a dense haze or even a fog. In unstable air, on the other hand, vertical movements carry them up and dilute them throughout the depth of movement, thousands or even tens of thousands of feet; and the stronger winds at such altitudes disperse them still more. From this point of view surface visibility tends to be better in the warm hours when convection is active than in the night and early morning, better in summer than in winter; moreover, the humidity is lower in the former periods, so that the hygroscopic particles are smaller. But other factors may counterbalance: industrial smoke tends to a maximum in the day-hours all the year, the contribution of domestic fires is largest in the early mornings and in winter; the sand and dust mentioned above as blown from arid surfaces are usually at a maximum in the hot hours when the winds are strongest.

An inversion of temperature is a ceiling for the ascending currents, and stops further ascent; under it the polluting particles, in the absence of a strong wind, collect in sufficient number to form a stratum of murky air; an extreme case is the 'high fog' described on p. 275. Above the inversion we suddenly enter a bright atmosphere of striking transparency, in which features even 100 miles distant stand out clearly. The troposphere may contain more than one haze layer, each at an inversion ceiling.

Regional Distribution

Despite its variability some general features of the visibility in the major climatic regions can be indicated.

Inner Tropics. Visibility is good or very good nearly always, a range of 50 to 100 miles being frequent; a main reason is that the surface is warmer than the air, except at night, so that convection is active:

MEAN PERCENTAGE FREQUENCIES OF VISIBILITIES

Code figures		0–2	3	4	5	6	7	8–9
Mombasa,	Feb.,[1] 0900	—	—	—	1	5	27	68
	1500	—	—	—	—	—	23	77
	May[2] 0900	1	1	2	4	11	27	54
	1500	—	2	2	3	8	28	57

[1] Month with best visibility.   [2] Month with worst visibility.
(See p. 319 for Kabete on the plateau of East Africa.)

Exceptionally, visibility deteriorates owing to:

(*a*) Smoke-haze in the dry season, and, in a few areas and for short periods, dust blown up from the ground.

(*b*) Shimmering, often an obstacle to clear sight in the hot hours.

(*c*) The heavy precipitation of the tropics, which reduces visibility seriously, but as the rain is usually in localized showers aircraft can avoid it by altering course.

(*d*) Fog patches over swamps and other wet ground at night and persisting till about 0830, but they are of no great depth.

(*e*) Low cloud, which, especially on hilly ground, may

present difficulties for aircraft. The higher slopes of mountain masses, Cameroon Mt., Kilimanjaro, and other giants, are rarely visible, hidden as they are by masses of thick cloud.

At sea visibility is very good, and fog is unknown except in a few small areas.

Outer Tropics. During the rains the conditions of visibility are similar to those of the inner tropics. But the region contains extensive arid areas, where in the long dry season, though poor visibility due to vapour (fog, low cloud) is rare, smoke-haze, dust, and sand are frequent causes, an extreme case being the haboobs of the Sudan (p. 212). The cold-water coasts, with the adjacent seas to a distance of some hundreds of miles, of the outer tropics and the sub-tropics are liable to frequent and often dense fogs (p. 278).

Sub-tropics. In summer the 'Mediterranean' regions in the west of the continents have consistently good visibility, though with a tendency to slight haze in the surface air due in many cases to salt-particles. There is little cloud, rain, or smoke, and fog is very rare except on the cold-water coasts. In winter these regions resemble the westerlies, but the cleaner air and the brighter light favour better visibility. Cape Town (Wingfield aerodrome) has the following mean percentage frequencies of good visibility (code figures 7–9):

Dec.–Feb.,	0830	74%	June–Aug.,	0830	63%
	1500	94 ,,		1500	90 ,,

The Monsoon Regions resemble the outer tropics in the rainy season, when visibility is generally good except in precipitation, but low cloud tends to be persistent. The air is exceptionally clear for a few weeks after the rains, since the dust has been washed out, and the ground is still too damp to provide more. In winter dust-laden winds are a scourge in north China, reducing visibility to a fog; and in the hot dry months before the rains start the sun is seen through the hazy atmosphere as a lifeless disk in the whitish sky.

The Westerlies, except in the interior of the land-masses, have most of the possible causes of obscurity, especially in winter: high humidity, always prone to condense into low cloud which may hang on the hills for weeks, frequent precipitation, much fog of both the land and sea types, poor light in the winter months. Sea-fog is abundant especially on the Banks of Newfoundland and similar regions of convergence of warm and cold currents, and the surface air at sea is often thick with spray and rain in the frequent strong winds. Man adds his own contribution, for the great agglomerations of millions of people in Europe and the east of the U.S.A. send trails of smoke and other impurities hundreds of miles down wind, spreading as they go, when the lapse-rate is less than normal, and particularly when an inversion puts a low ceiling on vertical dispersal. Such trails are responsible for poor visibility, often amounting to gloom, under skies overcast with low cloud over great areas. But, on the other hand, visibility can be excellent in polar air in the higher latitudes far from industrial pollution, especially a few thousand feet above the surface; it is best in late spring and early summer, when the atmosphere is most unstable. The data for Croydon Airport, 10 miles south of the middle of London, show the difference there between the murky evenings and nights of winter and the clear days of summer:

MEAN PERCENTAGE FREQUENCIES OF VISIBILITIES

Code figures		0–2	3	4	5	6	7	8	9
Croydon Air-	Feb., 1800	8	3	19	54	12	7	—	—
port	July, 1300	—	—	—	3	14	20	61	2

The far continental interiors have fairly good visibility thanks to their low humidity, but the more humid tracts are subject to inversion-fog in winter, and in blizzards visibility is reduced to very few yards. The tundra lands are liable to fog of both the land and the sea types, the latter mostly in spring and early summer.

The Polar Regions have various conditions in accordance with the topography. The ice-caps of Antarctica and Green-

PLATE 11

Sea-fog pouring through the Golden Gate, California

XXVIII VISIBILITY 273

land are at one extreme, with notably good visibility all the year except in snow and occasional driving low cloud and shallow fog. At the other extreme, in summer the Arctic Ocean, being only partly ice-covered, is liable to be foggy; but in winter visibility is probably fairly good except in precipitation.

For the visibility on plateaux see Chapter XXXIII.

Fog

Fog or mist is the extreme case of reduced visibility, and is caused by an intensification of the processes mentioned above, with some additional factors. It is generally associated with very slight movement of the air, and a small lapse-rate preventing vertical movement. A surface, whether of land or water, cooler than the air is a predisposing condition, since the air on it is likely to be stable, and to retain its suspended particles. Fog is of little depth, 750 feet or less being an average on land and less than 500 feet on the sea. Land-fog in autumn and winter and sea-fog in spring and summer are the main types in middle and high latitudes.

Inversion-fog

Land-fogs are most frequent in the higher latitudes, where the ground is cooler than the air; autumn and winter are the foggiest seasons, relative humidity being highest, and the nights long enough for the necessary cooling of the ground; Kew (London) has on the average 43 days with fog in the winter 6 months, only 10 days in the summer 6 months. The cooling may cause only a deposit of dew if the air is quite still, till just after sunrise when the incoming heat starts slight convection which mixes the saturated layers of different temperatures and leads to general condensation; night and early morning are the foggiest periods. The condensation can often be watched on clear evenings, the cooled air with its filmy mist creeping slowly down the slopes to stagnate on the lowest levels, where the white sea grows deeper and deeper, till in the morning the valleys as seen from above

5071 S

resemble estuaries. In this case the necessary mixing is provided by katabatic movements.

When fog forms it screens the ground, but its upper surface radiates heat, and the cooled air sinks and intensifies the fog. If the low sun cannot dissipate it in the day-time it thickens and deepens night after night till it may cover thousands of square miles of land and adjacent narrow seas, the Strait of Dover, the estuaries of the Thames, Humber, and Mersey; Heligoland, though 35 miles from land, has a pronounced maximum of fog in the winter. But fog is less persistent on the sea, the water being warmer than the land.

Land-fogs are thickest and most persistent in valley-bottoms, where the ground is moist, the air in less rapid movement, and the basin-shaped topography favourable. Their frequency and unpleasantness are much intensified in the neighbourhood of large cities, whose domestic and factory chimneys pour smoke into the air; the site of even a small town announces itself from afar by its smoke-cap, and in London and similar cities the effect of the smoke, even without fog, can be impressive. The usual 'London fog' consists essentially of a wet and very dense fog of the ordinary valley-bottom kind, polluted by smoke; the temperature inversion traps both fog and smoke, and only too often in autumn and winter the thick, black, impenetrable veil holds up traffic and makes even progress on foot hazardous. The damage to health is partly positive, from the abnormally abundant sulphurous and other noxious products of combustion, and partly negative in that not only the short waves but almost the whole of the sun's radiation is cut off. The lower Thames valley is naturally subject to fog by reason of its topography, but the persistence, blackness, and chemical impurities originate in the fires of the city. The same type in a less intense form tends to afflict most large manufacturing cities in the humid temperate zones; in England the whole of industrial Yorkshire, Lancashire, Stafford, and other counties lose much of the insolation (p. 282), and the industrial towns in the valleys are subject to fogs little better than those of London. In the open country fog is clean and white, but in towns it is discoloured, greyish-yellow and gloomy.

'High fogs' are another striking and unpleasant affliction of large cities. On 23 November 1927 Londoners woke to find the city still shrouded in a darkness thicker than night, though the surface air was clear. Only in the late afternoon did daylight break through. In this case not fog but an accumulation of smoke about 1,500 feet above the ground was to blame. Smoke, when not carried away at once by the wind, usually disperses in convection currents and reaches an upper wind, but on this occasion it rose to the base of an inversion layer where its ascent was stopped, and the accumulation became so thick after a few hours that the city below was in total darkness. A similar occurrence on 23 January 1924 is described by the Advisory Committee on Atmospheric Pollution:

The amount of impurity registered by the automatic filters in Westminster and South Kensington was not unusually large, but a thick bank of cloud overhead, due no doubt to an inversion of lapse-rate, seriously obscured the daylight in most parts of London. . . . In Westminster from 11 a.m. to 1 p.m. the light gradually failed until the whole of the sky visible from the office window in Victoria Street appeared completely black, the darkness appearing to spread from a northerly direction; nevertheless shop window lights could be readily seen in the street approximately ¼ mile away, indicating that surface visibility was comparatively good.

A short account of atmospheric pollution is given at the end of this chapter.

Advection-Fog. The fogs previously described form *in situ*, with still or almost still air. Another type is brought by moving air and may be termed 'advection-fog'. The essential feature is the advance of an air-mass over a cooler surface, so that its lower layers are chilled below dew-point. The cooled air remains on the surface, the atmosphere being stable, and in time fog appears. But if the wind is strong enough to cause turbulence the mixing produces not fog but low stratiform cloud. Most sea-fogs are of this advection type, and they are for the most part restricted to middle and high latitudes, the surface of the sea being too warm in the tropics. They form in tropical air-masses moving over the ocean to higher latitudes (Fig. 96); spring and early summer are the foggiest seasons, the ocean-surface being then coolest relatively to the tropical air. Such fogs are well known off the south and west of the British Isles; at Scilly 67 per cent. of the days with fog (27 in the year) are in summer, and of these 60 per cent. are in the night and early morning; in winter night and day are equally foggy. But on the east and south-east coasts of Britain winter is the foggy season, since, as we have seen, the land-fogs spread over the intervening narrow channel; at Dungeness 59 per cent. of the fogs are in winter, and night-fogs preponderate strongly over day. Similarly in British Columbia the inner straits and inlets have land-fogs, with a maximum in autumn and winter (e.g. Vancouver, 8 days with fog in October), and the outer waters are rarely fog-bound in winter, but have an average of about 12 days a month with fog in summer when navigation is seriously impeded.

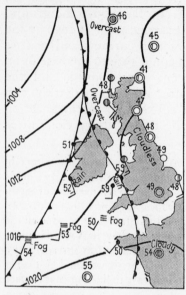

FIG. 96. Synoptic chart, 0000, 17 May 1947; sea-fog in a warm sector. For meanings of symbols see Fig. 22

The fogs of the Banks of Newfoundland are famous. They are due to the meeting of the warm Gulf Stream with the cold Labrador current, whose icebergs come south and melt in the warm water. The air is nearly or quite saturated with vapour, and dense fogs form if Gulf Stream air blows over the icy water, or if masses of warm and cold air mix. The Strait of Belle Isle has fog on 116 days a year, and a wide tract of the seas round Newfoundland is fog-bound for 70 days or more; the foggiest seasons are summer and autumn. The coastal waters east of Greenland are specially subject to fog in summer; the icefloes and bergs reduce the temperature of the air coming from the open water, and dense fogs persist for days; but their depth is not more than a few hundred feet, and the air may be clear and the sky cloudless above the strong inversion of temperature.

The formation and dissipation of fog was investigated by means of kite ascents on the Grand Bank by G. I. Taylor from the ice patrol s.s. *Scotia*, in 1913. This example is given in the official report:

'If the air is originally dry it may cool through quite a large range of temperature before the fog begins, but when it does begin it will be thick owing to a large temperature gradient. . . . In this connexion the ascent of July 29 is particularly interesting. On that occasion the air at a height of 240 metres was very dry, the humidity being only 50 %. It had been cooled through 6° or 7° C. since the sea temperature along its path began to decrease, but it was not yet saturated. At the surface the humidity was 88% and the temperature 16·3° C. The dew-point for air containing this amount of water vapour is 14·2° C. If the quantity of water vapour is not increasing or diminishing one would expect that, if the air explored in the ascent of July 29 were to continue on its course northwards over still colder water, a fog would be produced when the temperature had got down to 14·2° C. Fortunately it was possible to verify this. The *Scotia* proceeded northwards, moving in the same direction as the wind, which remained in the south for about 40 hours. The temperature of the air fell steadily from 16·3° C. at the time of the ascent, to 13·6° C. at 4 a.m. on July 30. During this period there was no fog, but between 4 a.m. and 8 a.m. a thick fog came up, and the air temperature fell to 12·6° C. At midnight, when the air temperature had fallen to 10·9° C. the fog was very thick. We see, then, that on July 29 the air had been caught in the act of moving up to a place where fog was bound to be produced. The only things which could have prevented its formation were an increase in wind force, which would have the effect of increasing eddy conductivity near the surface and so obliterating the negative temperature gradient, or a change in wind direction of such a kind as to cause the air to blow back again towards the warm water. Some 24 hours after the formation of the fog the wind direction did undergo such a change, and in a few hours the fog vanished.'

Advection-fog sometimes forms on land in countries subject to cold winters, when warm and damp, but gentle, ocean winds blow over a land-surface still snow-covered, or very cold after a frosty spell, and give a day or two of very unpleasant wet fog.

Fog, with more or less drizzle and visibility down to a quarter of a mile, may occur with light or moderate winds in the immediate neighbourhood of a warm front in temperate latitudes.

Trees, shrubs, and similar obstacles are effective condensers and collectors of the moisture in saturated air, even in the absence of fog; this is a main form of 'occult precipitation', and a valuable source of water-supply for the vegetation which itself produces it. A remarkable instance was reported from Table Mountain, Cape Province; in eight summer weeks an ordinary rain-gauge collected 5 inches of rain, while a similar gauge near by, containing a bunch of reeds, caught no less than 70 inches; the excess presumably consisted of the water condensed on the reeds from the driving cloud ('the table-cloth') and saturated air of south-easters. Similar observations have been made elsewhere.

From the point of view of visibility the low cloud that often shrouds hills in all latitudes may be considered as fog, though generically it is cloud.

The Cold-water Coasts

The seas off South-west Africa, Chile and Peru, Morocco, and California, are notoriously foggy; the circumstances are similar in all, and South-west Africa will serve as an example. The dominant, and almost constant, general winds (apart from the merely local sea-breeze on the coasts) are the trades which sweep over a vast area, blowing some points off-shore and wafting the surface waters with them; this surface drift is almost directly off-shore since the effect of the earth's rotation deflects it about 45° from the wind. Sub-surface water, derived from depths down to about 100 fathoms, wells up along the coast to compensate and it is much cooler than the surface water which it replaces; the Benguela Current is abnormally cool. The water is coolest close under the coast and warmer seaward, but the cold is appreciable for 1,000 miles out to sea. The approximate mean annual temperatures of the ocean-surface of the South Atlantic west of C. Frio, South-west Africa, are:

Distance (miles) off C. Frio	0	32	65	130	260	450
Temp. °F.		58	61	63	65	68	70

But the littoral, like most tropical coasts, has almost constant sea-breezes by day, intensified here by the cool sea; indeed along all this coast the prevailing winds are SW., blowing very strongly in places during the hottest hours in summer (but irregularities occur in the frequent depressions which travel slowly south near the coast). Winds from the ocean, passing over progressively cooler water, are saturated with vapour, and tend to be foggy long before they reach the land; the fog dissolves on the warm land, and is rare beyond 50 miles inland. A wind from the land—which is less frequent —brings a great change of weather, a clear atmosphere and bright sunshine. Diaz Point, Luderitz Bay, a representative station, records fog or mist during about 1,000 hours in the year; it usually clears in the afternoon, night and early morning being the foggiest periods. In spite of the fog and damp air the land is a desert, one of the most barren on the earth; a few plants manage to subsist on the fog-moisture, but most of the surface is bare. A rainstorm is very rare, but the occasional heavy downpours suffice to give a mean annual total of 1 or 2 inches; a light drizzle is not uncommon in the early mornings, but the region has no regular rain, being under the trade-wind, the drier here in the lee of the plateau of South Africa. At Walvis Bay the average number of days with fog is:

Jan.	2	Apr.	5	July	8	Oct.	1
Feb..	1	May	8	Aug.	8	Nov.	5
Mar.	4	June	11	Sept.	5	Dec.	2

Central Chile has a similar fog-coast, also under the influence of the south-east trade, with regular sea-breezes from the cool Humboldt current. Here again is an arid desert, the Atacama, even more arid than the Namib of South-west Africa owing to the lofty Andes on the east and a ridge of hills on the west rising directly from the coast and cutting off any slight rain that might be derived from seaward. The interior may be described as generally rainless but liable to receive a sudden shower at long intervals—an unbroken desert of brown earth and nitrates, hazy in summer with dust and heat. The coast itself is almost as rainless. Fog is frequent and tends to be persistent off central and much of south Chile.

Plate 10 (facing p. 256) shows the fog pouring in at the Golden Gate, California, which has an average of 40 days with fog in the year. The fog, and the cool California current, exert a notable effect on the air temperature; at San Francisco (Fig. 97) the summer months are chilly, and the air temperature actually rises as the clearer autumn comes on. The summit of Mount Tamalpais, 2,375 feet, which overlooks the Golden Gate from the opposite side, is more than 10° warmer than San Francisco in summer, for the

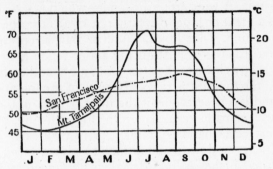

FIG. 97. Mean temperature at San Francisco (alt. 207 feet) and Mount Tamalpais (2,375 feet)

hill-top projects above the fog into the clear air and bright sunshine.

The conversion of fog into low cloud by turbulence when the wind increases is clearly seen on the cool oceans off these coasts. As long as the wind is very light the fog lies, but an increase in speed at once clears the surface and forms low stratus cloud. From the coasts the fog may spread inland for some miles, but, in the day especially, a slight wind is enough to start turbulence which turns it to low cloud.

Atmospheric Pollution

Much attention has been directed in recent decades to the pollution of the atmosphere by the products of combustion, a large factor in the bad visibility of industrial districts, and a cause of much damage to health as well as to vegetation, buildings, and other material objects (Plate 11, facing p. 272).

Measurements[1] give the following mean annual values

[1] *Heating and Ventilation of Dwellings*, Ministry of Works, 1945.

PLATE 12

Climatic contrast in spring between adret and ubac, Alps near Arosa, 6,700 feet

PLATE 13

Sea of clouds in the valley round the Diablerets, Switzerland

(average 1936–9) for the deposit in tons of total solids on a square mile:

London and neighbourhood:
Golden Lane, ½ mile from Guildhall 274
Kew, 7 miles W. from Guildhall 122
Rothamsted, 22 miles NW. from Guildhall 83

Glasgow:
Glasgow Cross, centre of city 361
Queen's Park, 2 miles S. 194
Glasahoil, 35 miles N. 133

Stoke-on-Trent:
Tunstall, centre 229
Loggerheads, 12 miles SW. 59

Pollution is decreasing appreciably with better methods of fuelling and the substitution of gas and electricity for coal; in London,[1] the mean annual deposit in tons of total solids, mainly soot, and liquid, mainly tar, on a square mile (average of 8 stations) was:

1915–18. 468, ranging from 624 at Southwark Park to about 280 at Wandsworth Common.

1934–7. 320, ranging from 432 at Archbishop's Park to 193 at Wandsworth Common.

And the mean annual number of days of thick smoke-haze (not dense smoke-fog) was:

	Victoria Street	Kew
1923–6	168	44
1934–7	161	33

It is estimated that more than two-thirds of the smoke is from the chimneys of dwelling-houses; the amount is largest in the daytime, with maxima between 0900 and 1100 and between 1900 and 2000, least about 0500. The pollution is much greater in winter than in summer.

The impenetrable 'London fogs' (not restricted to London), in the production of which meteorology and man conspire, are much less common than in Victorian times. Meteorological conditions predispose to good or to bad visibility in open country as well as in towns, and little if any change is feasible, but man-made pollution could be reduced much more than has yet been accomplished, with

[1] *Smoke Abatement in Greater London.* Report of a Conference, 1938.

great gain to health and amenity. Manchester gets only half the sunshine of the country a few miles away, and the damage done by atmospheric pollution is reckoned at over £1 million a year. In 3½ years (excluding 6 months for which complete records were not available) Southport had 4,503 hours of bright sunshine, an industrial district of Lancashire not far away only 2,195 hours.

PART IV
MOUNTAIN AND PLATEAU CLIMATE
CHAPTER XXIX
INSOLATION

ALTITUDE climate, on mountain or plateau, is a local modification of the lowland climate of the region. The modifications common to all mountains in greater or less degree are
our subject, though the Alps are frequently referred to
since they have been more fully observed and studied than
other systems.

Mountains share the features of the free atmosphere in
respect of pressure, insolation, and some other elements, but
themselves, in accordance with their position and their lie in
relation to the general air-currents, exert a strong influence
on the direction and force of the winds, the temperature,
cloud, and precipitation. Only generalities can be described
here, and their application in particular cases must be worked
out for the local conditions.

Some special features of the climate of plateaux are
described in Chapter XXXIII.

Perhaps no feature of a high mountain ascent leaves so
vivid a memory as the brightness of the sunlight, intensified
by the reflection from the virgin snows, and enhanced by the
pure dark-blue transparency of the sky. In winter the low
altitude of the sun is compensated by the reflected light, and
the brilliance of the heights is the greater by contrast with
the gloom of the lower valleys.

The higher we ascend the more of the atmospheric
blanket is left below; at 8,000 feet about a quarter of the
mass of the atmosphere is below us, at 18,000 feet about a
half. At 8,000 feet we are above half of the vapour, and
most of the suspended dust. The liquid and solid impurities
decrease rapidly upwards, and even at 4,000 feet their effect
is so much diminished that a further ascent does not make
very much difference to the intensity of the insolation (apart

from topographical influences, as in the case of a temperature inversion with its effect on humidity); 1·59 calories on a sq. cm. a minute was recorded at Davos (5,120 feet), 1·55 on Mont Blanc (15,000 feet), 1·64 on Mount Whitney (15,000 feet), and 1·67 in a balloon at 23,000 feet. Up to 4,000 feet the peculiarities of mountain climate are not prominent, but at 6,000 feet most are strongly developed.

The intensity of the insolation is outstanding. Though the air temperature may be much lower than at low altitudes, the sun's rays are so powerful that objects are strongly heated, and the body may be seriously sunburnt and inflamed if exposed for a few hours; invalids who wish to take a sun-cure should acclimatize themselves gradually. The light reflected from snow is hardly less powerful than the direct sunshine.

According to Dorno,[1] on clear days some 75 per cent. of the insolation penetrates to 6,000 feet, and only 50 per cent. to sea-level, but in average conditions the reduction by the passage through the atmosphere is much greater, and a smoky city near sea-level gets little direct insolation. It is one of the incidental advantages of mountains that they have few large towns to pollute the atmosphere. Davos gets 50 per cent. more direct radiant energy in a year than Potsdam, 200 per cent. more in winter; Davos is in a high valley in the interior of the Alps, 5,101 feet above the sea, and its records are the more striking in view of the fact that the surrounding mountains deprive it of 3 hours' possible sunshine a day; Potsdam is near sea-level in the north German plain, a region of much cloud and damp air. The following table (after Götz) shows in more detail the advantage of Arosa, another Alpine station, over Potsdam, in respect of the heat (cal./cm.²) received in a day on a horizontal surface, assuming the mean duration of sunshine at the station:

	Alt. ft.	Jan.	Apr.	July	Oct.	Year
Potsdam	350	20	204	267	76	53,200
Arosa	6,200	86	276	350	176	81,900

The intensity of the sun's rays may be realized by letting them fall on a piece of dry black fur in which is embedded

[1] Dorno, C., *Physik der Sonnen- und Himmelsstrahlung*, Braunschweig, 1919.

a small thermometer bulb; a reading of 120° to 140° may easily be obtained, though the air temperature is only 70°. It is said that at Leh, 11,500 feet above the sea in the upper Indus valley, water has been made to boil (boiling-point 191°) by exposing it to the sun in a small bottle blackened on the outside and shielded from the air by a larger transparent vessel.

Ultra-Violet Radiation

High altitudes have the further advantage that their insolation is absolutely as well as relatively richer in the short, ultra-violet, wave-lengths. These waves are intercepted in the lower atmosphere with its solid and liquid suspensoids, particularly in industrial districts, and only with exceptionally good transparency can waves of even 0.35μ reach sea-level; a manufacturing town is estimated to receive only one-third of the ultra-violet radiation of the clean open country-side. When the sky is clear very high altitudes get a small part of the waves as short as 0.33μ; according to Dorno the ratio of the intensities of the ultra-violet band as a whole at 250 feet, 5,000 feet, and 10,000 feet is 40 : 61 : 90. But even at considerable heights the short-wave insolation is much reduced proportionately to the whole; the same authority gives this estimate:

Percentage Composition of Insolation for Mean
Altitude of the Sun

	Ultra-violet	Light	Infra-red
Outside the atmosphere .	5	52	43
Davos (5,121 feet) .	1	40	60

The excess of short-wave intensity at high over low altitudes is larger with a low than with a high sun, larger, therefore, in winter than in summer, and the advantage of the heights is enormously increased since low valleys and plains lose not only the short-wave, but also a large proportion of the long-wave insolation in winter, in their long spells of cloud. Götz gives values which illustrate this:

Ratio of ultra-violet radiation, Arosa (6,102 ft.) to Chur (1,936 ft.
in upper Rhine valley)

Alt. of sun .	10°	30°	60°
Ratio .	2·91	1·49	1·34

Ultra-violet rays[1] are invisible, but they have a powerful chemical and therefore physiological action; it was the reduction of silver chloride by some then-unknown form of radiation outside the violet end of the visible spectrum that first drew attention to them in 1801. The group embraces wave-lengths from 0·2 to about 0·4 μ, nearly as wide a range as that of the band of the spectrum, 0·4 to 0·7 μ, which we perceive as light, and the different wave-lengths have different properties. The shorter ultra-violet waves, less than 0·33 μ, are almost entirely filtered out in the high stratosphere by oxygen and ozone, and only a small proportion of those about 0·33 μ reach the troposphere. Most of the waves that do enter the troposphere are intercepted there, reflected or scattered, and those that reach the lower atmosphere come in greater amount from the blue sky than in the direct rays of even an overhead sun, the proportion of scattered to direct being far greater when the sun is near the horizon. Ultra-violet rays cannot penetrate ordinary soda-glass but they pass through quartz, and it seems desirable that quartz-glass should be used in preference to soda-glass for the windows of houses since so much of our life is spent indoors, in order that full advantage may be taken of the scanty ultra-violet radiation available; the smoky atmosphere of towns is an effective screen, much more opaque to these short waves than to the longer which are visible as light (and even these latter are seriously weakened).

Ultra-violet rays ionize gases, and have many organic effects, coagulating protoplasm and, in excess, killing living cells. Living tissues absorb the rays, and the skin of our bodies is a necessary protection for the cells below; wave-lengths about 0·30 μ are most effective in forming the brown pigment in the skin which is the protective agent, the shorter waves being less effective, and those of less than 0·26 μ having hardly any effect (Dorno). Vitamin D, essential to growth and well-being, is formed by the action of ultra-violet rays on one or more of the group of substances known as sterols, which are contained in living tissues. The same rays cause sunburn, and at high altitudes serious injury, both local and

---

[1] See papers by Dobson, G. B. M., in *Report of the Oxford Meeting of the International Commission on Solar Radiation*, 1936.

general, may result; sun-bathing and other light-treatment, under the rays of the sun or of an artificial source, should be in expert control, especially until the subject is acclimatized.

Many authorities are enthusiastic believers in the value and even the necessity of ultra-violet rays for health, and in their high efficacy in the treatment of numerous maladies. In view of the stronger short-wave insolation at great altitudes a sojourn in the high Alps, at Davos or Leysin for example, is recommended; sun-bathers may pursue their cure by exposure to the blue sky without direct sunshine. If an Alpine sojourn is not feasible at least irradiation from some artificial source of ultra-violet rays, such as the mercury-vapour lamp, should be used. Tuberculosis and rickets, both in men and animals, are amenable to the treatment, which is also recommended for refractory lesions including contusions, ulcers, and abscesses, the beneficial action being both local and general; but there is no agreement as to the exact effect of the rays, whether they act by killing the bacteria directly—this would seem impossible at any depth under the skin—or by forming on the surface of the skin exposed to the rays irradiated compounds which circulate throughout the body, or by a general tonic stimulation. It is for wave-lengths about $0.30\,\mu$ that the highest therapeutic value is claimed, and, as already stated these are the rays that only rarely reach even high levels in the troposphere; hence the advantage of mountain-stations. But some observers regard the whole of the spectrum, as much the infra-red as the ultra-violet rays, as the effective agent, while others incline to attribute the therapeutic benefits chiefly to other features of the high Alpine environment, pure bracing air with a low temperature and low humidity, exciting scenery, regular life and exercise, and suitable clothing. The stimulus of the change of habits and environment is in itself certainly a considerable factor.

Slope and Exposure

At high altitudes direct insolation is a larger factor than air temperature in the heating actually experienced; hence the marked contrast between sunshine and shade. The sun's rays traverse the clear air without warming it, but they strongly heat objects on which they fall; in the sunshine we feel warm or even hot on a calm day in winter, though the air temperature is low. The larger the angle of incidence of the insolation to the surface the greater its power, and therefore the angle and direction of slope of the ground are major considerations. In the Alps the altitude of the midday sun is less than 45° for 6 months of the year; the northern slopes are then largely in shadow while the southern are getting almost perpendicular rays, and hence the striking differences between the two sides of many mountain ranges. Götz gives data for Arosa:

Mean heat, g. cal./cm²., received in 24 hours on south-facing (S) and north-facing (N) slopes (angle with horizontal)

	S 75°	S 15°	0°	N 15°	N 75°
15 June	154	314	306	280	38
15 Dec.	238	130	73	13	0

The bottoms of deep valleys lose much sunshine owing to the shadow of the surrounding mountains. Villages and farm-houses avoid shadowed sites and choose slopes that get the sun early and keep it late. Some valleys have settlements perched on their sides at great altitudes, where they enjoy in some cases 2 or 3 hours more sunshine than the lower villages. The loss is serious in high latitudes; in Norway there are villages so shaded at the north of steep mountains as to lose the sun entirely for several weeks in winter.

The snow-line tends to be higher on the sunward than on the shady side, but it must depend also, and often to a greater extent, on the amount of snow that falls on the two sides, and this may exceed the former influence. Very steep slopes cannot hold the snow, and therefore have a snow-line much higher than the normal; on the other hand, the snow that slips from the higher slopes collects below, and may lie abnormally low in patches.

Near the equator the limit of perennial snow, or more correctly the lower limit of glaciers, is determined by the amount of snowfall and the shade of the massive cloud on the side with most precipitation; Kibo (Mt. Kilimanjaro), 19,300 feet, has ice down to about 15,000 feet on the south-west, but hardly any below the summit on the dry north.

PLATE 14

Ober-Gurgl, Tyrol, in winter

The glaciers on Mt. Kenya descend on the average to about 15,000 feet. In the equatorial Andes the snow-line is at about 15,000 feet in the eastern, 19,000 feet in the western Cordillera. In the Himalayas it is estimated at 16,500 feet on the south slopes in Nepal, 19,000 feet on the ranges facing Tibet, the heavier precipitation on the south giving a lower limit in spite of the greater heat; in the Kuen-Lun at 16,000 feet.

The Pyrenees are both warmer and drier on the south side than on the north, and no perpetual snow is to be seen from Spain, though the highest 2,000 or 3,000 feet of the north slope is snow-covered always. In the Alps the snow-line is lower on both the southern and still more the northern ranges than the central zone, owing to the greater precipitation on the exterior ranges; its mean altitude is about 9,000 feet, but it ranges more than 1,000 feet on each side of the mean, according to the precipitation, exposure, slope, size, and form of the massif. Glaciers, of course, advance far below the snow-line, the Lower Grindelwald descending to 3,800 feet. In the south of Norway the snow-line is about 5,000 feet, in the north about 3,000 feet, and near the poles it descends to sea-level.

The more rapid melting on a sunward slope is specially prominent in spring and early summer (Plate 12, facing p. 281). A sunny Alpine slope at 10,000 or 12,000 feet may have no snow except in occasional patches, the bare rock is strongly heated by the almost perpendicular rays, and the air may be warmer at 8,000 feet than at sea-level; on crossing the ridge we find the shady slope deep in snow for the upper 3,000 or 4,000 feet. In the Alps the sunny slope is the adret or sonnenseite, the shady the ubac or schattenseite, and other regions have their local names. The ubac is often left under its natural pine forest, while the opposite slope is rich pasture. Villages and chalets show a strong preference for the sunny slopes. The contrast is very pronounced in the Alps in the great east–west valleys such as the Engadine, and is most striking in spring when the north-facing slopes are still deep in snow, the south almost clear. In many valleys 90 per cent. or more of the population live on the sonnenseite.

CHAPTER XXX

AIR TEMPERATURE. SUNSHINE AND CLOUD. HUMIDITY

THE general fall in temperature with height in the free atmosphere is explained in Chapter VIII. But mountains introduce complications, for the heating and cooling of the ground is superposed on the wider effects. In calm weather the amount of heating by day and cooling by night, and hence the range of air temperature, depend largely on the area of ground in contact with the air. In flat country this is similar everywhere, but mountains have large local differences; at one extreme is the isolated peak projecting high into the free atmosphere, at the other the deep and steep-sided valley where the air is enclosed below and on each side by the ground. Woeikof suggested a useful distinction between convex and concave topography; convex slopes conduce to equable, concave to extreme temperatures, the former resembling maritime, the latter continental conditions. In powerful sunshine the rocks at high altitudes are more heated than at low, but an isolated peak has so small an area of contact with the atmosphere that the air temperature is not much affected, the less since the air is usually in rapid movement and does not remain long in place. A nook at a high altitude, facing the sun but sheltered from the wind, feels warm, and the temperature of the still air is high; but we find a great difference in the wind which rushes past outside. At night the rocks cool rapidly, but again the effect on the atmosphere cannot be large. The air heats but little by day, and cools little by night, like the free atmosphere round about. On the other hand, an enclosed depression has maximum contact with the air, and the air has less movement than on the heights; high temperatures are the rule on sunny days, very low temperatures at night. The daytime heat is most noticeable in summer, the night cold in the long nights of winter. The cold depends on the wider topography as well as on the immediate surroundings, for the larger the area of elevated mountain slopes draining into the depression, the more intense it is likely to be.

The chilled air collects in cold damp 'lakes' which begin to be noticeable as soon as the sun sets. The clearer the sky the more rapid is the cooling of the rocks; and the calmer the atmosphere the steadier the descent of the cooled air. The effect is most prominent in winter, for in summer the bottoms are so much heated during the day that they keep the air warm far into the short night. On a winter morning it is not unusual to find them filled with a cold fog, or sometimes roofed over with a low pall of cloud, but on ascending the slopes we come suddenly to a level where we break through the gloom and enter a new and unexpected world, bright with the sun shining from a deep-blue sky and reflected from the sparkling white mask of snow. Still higher we may look down on the upper surface of the sea of cloud which fills the bottoms (Plate 13, facing p. 280).

The deep trench of the Lauterbrunnen valley was filled with mists, and snow was falling steadily. As the train toiled up to the Wengeralp, a bright light pierced the hanging cloud, and the next instant we rose out of the mist into a perfect morning. Above, the Jungfrau, the Mönch, and the Eiger swept up into a stainless sky. Below, the silvery surface of the cloud sea stretched over all Northern Switzerland. (From a report of a winter ascent on the Eiger, January 1929.)

The Himalayas, Alps, and similar systems have isolated summits at a less altitude than many of the upper valleys, but in winter they enjoy brighter weather since they stand well above the fog of the surrounding lowlands; the highest summits and ridges are always clear of this type of fog. Many of the higher valleys also, which offer a free outlet for the chilled damp air that drains into them, are exempt, and for this reason among others are favourite resorts for invalids. Davos is an example; Ober-Gurgl (Plate 14, facing p. 288), the highest village in the Tyrol, is similarly situated, and it too has a reputation as a winter health-resort. The elevated shoulders of the larger glaciated valleys are also usually above the fog and are suitable sites for winter cures: such is Montana, on the south-facing alp overlooking the deep trough of the upper Rhone.

As a contrast to Ober-Gurgl, Plate 15 (facing p. 320) shows Zwieselstein, a village some miles down the same valley, but deeply enclosed by steep slopes. The cold air collects in the little basin in calm weather, and the winters are very cold, but only in calm weather can inversions of temperature be strongly developed, and mostly in the anticyclonic calms and long nights of winter. The Alps, being dominated by the 'barometric backbone' of Europe, are frequently subject to such conditions.

In a continental climate enclosed upland valleys at great altitudes may have remarkable extremes of temperature. Sven Hedin[1] noted this in the Pamirs of central Asia:

> The variations of temperature are enormous, not only in winter but also in summer. At Fort Pamir (12,000 feet) at 7 o'clock in the morning of 11 January, 1894, the thermometer recorded a temperature of −36° F.; one hour after noon it was 53·6° in the sun—a difference of nearly 90° F. in the course of only 6 hours. The amount of radiation is almost inconceivable. At a time when the temperature of the air was just at the freezing point, the black-bulb insolation thermometer actually registered 133°.

The rapid changes of temperature between sunshine and shade, wind and calm, are prominent everywhere above about 5,000 feet. Even on snow-covered mountains the heat may be excessive in a sheltered spot in the sunshine, and change to bitter cold within a few minutes when the sun ceases to shine and the wind springs up.

The lower slopes of deep valleys facing the sun are very warm on summer days; even at considerable altitudes sunny slopes are notably warm, for in addition to the powerful isolation the valley-breeze blowing over the heated ground in its ascent is as warm high up the valley sides as below. The upper Rhone valley in Switzerland is often extremely hot and enervating, for the altitude is only about 1,500 feet, and during a spell of summer weather with clear skies and bright sunshine Sion, Sierre, and the neighbourhood are suggestive of the south of Italy. The resemblance is heightened by the semi-arid type of natural vegetation in the bottom of the valley, favoured by the dry hot air and the low

---

[1] Sven Hedin, *Through Asia*, ch. xiv.

rainfall; some tracts are covered with a saline deposit. The limit of cultivation is remarkably high in these valleys—the vine is profitably grown up to 4,000 feet, cereals to 6,500 feet, and trees flourish to 8,000 feet. For agricultural purposes the low rainfall is eked out by an elaborate and ancient irrigation system fed from the melting snow and ice above. Ruskin was impressed by the heat of Sion—'the air in the morning stagnant also, hot, close, and infected; one side of the valley in almost continual shade, the other (it running east–west) scorched by the southern sun, and sending streams of heat into the air all night long from its torrid limestones'—this only after hot summer days, for the valley is filled with cold air on winter nights and even on some winter days the cold lake is not dissipated.

Evidently no constant relationship connects temperature and altitude; the accepted average gradient of 1° for each 300 feet of elevation is merely a mean value which rarely occurs. The heights are usually colder than the lowlands, but in strong sunshine the valleys are abnormally warm, and in still nights abnormally cold. Hence the gradient is steeper by day than by night, in summer than in winter, and, in the tropics, greater on the dry than on the rainy side of mountains. In the following table for Alpine stations Lucerne is on the Swiss Plateau, the Rigi is an isolated summit (convex relief), and Bevers is in the deep valley-bottom of the upper Engadine, overlooked by lofty ranges (concave relief); Bevers and the Rigi have approximately the same altitude but quite different topography.

MEAN TEMPERATURE °F.

Station	Alt. ft.	July Mean	0700	1300	January Mean	0700	1300	Range, July–Jan.
Lucerne	1,480	65	62	71	30	27	32	35
Rigi	5,863	50	49	52	24	22	25	26
Bevers	5,610	53	48	62	14	8	22	39
Difference								
Lucerne–Rigi	−4,383	15	13	19	6	5	7	9
Rigi–Bevers	253	−3	1	−10	10	14	3	13

The type of weather helps to determine the gradient, since

only in calm anticyclonic conditions are inversions of temperature prominent. This is shown by an example from Switzerland:

Station	Alt. ft.	1881. Temp. at 0700, °F.		
		25 Dec.	26 Dec.	27 Dec.
Altdorf	1,480	20	19	23
Rigi	5,863	13	27	35
St. Gothard Pass . . .	6,877	−2	24	30

The three stations are not far apart; Altdorf is in a valley-bottom, the Rigi is an isolated summit, the St. Gothard Pass a ridge station. On 25 December the weather was cyclonic and the wind strong, and temperature decreased with altitude. But with the arrival of an anticyclone on 26 December a strong inversion of temperature was established in the calm air; on the 27th at 0700 it was 12° colder at Altdorf than on the Rigi, in spite of the altitude being 4,000 feet less.

In middle and high latitudes the gradient is less at night than by day, less (about two-thirds, but much less in some cases) in winter than in summer; in the tropics it is a little less in the rainy than in the dry season. The difference stands out clearly in a comparison of the two sides of some highlands; of the stations in the following table Addis Ababa, 8,005 feet, is on the Abyssinian highland, Hillet Doleib, 1,283 feet, on the River Nile in the Sudan on the west, and Berbera, 31 feet, on the desert Somali coast on the east:

DIFFERENCE OF MEAN MONTHLY TEMPERATURE

	Jan.	July
Hillet Doleib–Addis Ababa	21	18
Berbera–Addis Ababa	19	39

In an extensive mountain-system the larger upland massifs are much warmer on summer days than the smaller massifs and the lowlands, correction for altitude at the standard rate being applied; thus in Switzerland Quervain has shown that the Pennine Alps, the Oberland, and the Bernina district are 10° warmer at midday in July than the Swiss Plateau; the excess persists in appreciable degree during the daytime all the year except in the winter months when the large massifs are colder than the lower levels. Again, on a gentle slope or a plateau the decrease of temperature with height is much less in the warmer hours and the warmer season than on an isolated mountain; the relation is the opposite in winter (Kimberley and Durban, **Fig.** 103, p. 314). These facts show that no uniform rate of correction of temperatures for altitude is possible.

Sunshine and Cloud

The katabatic descent of cold air explains many of the sunshine and cloud features. The valleys and lowlands have much low cloud (often really fog) and little sunshine in winter as compared with summer, but the high valleys and the summits are more favoured:

Station	Alt. ft.	Cloud, tenths		Sunshine, hours a day	
		Jan.	July	Jan.	July
Säntis . . .	8,202	5	7	3·9	5·3
Arosa . . .	6,200	5	6	4	6
Davos . . .	5,121	4	5	3·2	6·7
Chur . . .	2,001	5	5	—	—
Zürich . . .	1,542	8	5	1·4	7·7

The good sunshine records in winter, in spite of the short days, on the Säntis, at Arosa, and at Davos are noteworthy. The long duration and the intensity of the sunshine, both direct and reflected from the snow, are of great physiological importance. Industrial cities of north-west Europe have only a little more than a quarter of the winter sunshine of the high Alps.

But the high Alps do not enjoy these advantages in windy cyclonic weather. Rising air expands and cools at about 1·6° in 300 feet, so that it usually reaches its dew-point in the course of the ascent. The clouds thus condensed may enshroud the heights for days and the sun never breaks through, so that at these times the valleys and lowlands, being farther removed from the clouds, are more favoured. Again, the tops are cloudy during the midday hours in settled weather in summer also, owing to the valley-breezes which set in every morning and blow up the valleys. Wisps begin to form before noon, and for several hours the highest summits are cloud-capped, often thickly enough to have thunderstorms. Towards evening the valley-breeze dies away and the clouds disappear. Thus in fine summer weather the mountain tops have their clearest skies in the night and early morning; in high ascents mountaineers aim at reaching their objective and starting down again before the clouds thicken. The Sonnblick, 10,190 feet, has most sun, 40 per cent. of the possible, in June between 0700 and 1100, the amount falling to only 23 per cent. between 1600 and 1700; but in December it has most, 50 per cent., between 1000 and 1500. Klagenfurt, in the bottom of a basin in the same district, has most, 66 per cent., in June between 1000 and 1100, but the amount does not decrease much till after 1500.

In almost all respects the highest altitudes have climatic advantages in winter. The high valleys are almost equally favoured with the summits, and they have the advantage of calmer air and a continuous snow-cover, as well as accessibility and other conveniences for human settlement.

To summarize, the peaks and elevated valleys are less cloudy and have drier air in winter than in summer, in the night and early morning than in the afternoons. The low valleys have less cloud, more sunshine, and drier air in summer than in winter, in the middle of the day than in the night and early morning.

Humidity and Evaporation

Low humidities are usual on the summits and in the upland valleys of such systems as the Alps during the calm and bright anticyclonic spells of winter as well as of summer, and notably low values may occur in the subsiding air; the change to cyclonic weather, however, with its strong winds, thick cloud, saturated air, and driving rain or snow, may be as abrupt as it is complete; the changes in humidity from one extreme to the other can be as sudden as in temperature. At very high altitudes the excessive evaporation from the body, particularly in the usually strong winds, is one of the trials of climbers; a report by a member of a Mount

Everest expedition describes the conditions at about 27,000 feet:

The constantly and rapidly repeated intake of breath and catching at the back of the throat seem to have a curiously drying effect. Whatever the cause the result is a pronounced desiccation of the whole system. In the great cold the thirst seems not to make itself felt until late in the day, when it becomes intense. There is little doubt that this tremendous desiccation of the body is one of the primary causes of breakdown and failure at great heights. (Col. Norton in *The Times*.)

On the other hand, at moderate altitudes of 6,000–12,000 feet the dry air adds to the delights of winter sports. We may walk or ski through snow the whole day without clothes or boots being wet though they may be covered with snow. And probably it is a main cause of the marked feeling of well-being, exhilaration, and energy. It explains the rapid disappearance of the snow and the drying of the ground in spring.

Complex factors govern the relation between the amount of (physical) evaporation and altitude. Evaporation increases as atmospheric pressure decreases, but at the same time it decreases with decrease of temperature (both air temperature and the heat of direct insolation) and increase of relative humidity (the summits are colder and more humid than the valleys except at times of anticyclonic inversion). Another control is air-movement, which increases with height on the average, though with important exceptions; the stronger the wind the greater the evaporation. The result, as estimated from observations and calculations in the Alps and in the western mountains of America, is that evaporation (the mean amount for a period) decreases somewhat, but not much, with height on mountains. From the physiological point of view, however, another, and preponderating, factor is the internal heat of the body, the temperature of which remains at about 98° while the air temperature normally falls rapidly with height; the larger difference between body and environment is the chief cause of the physiological facts mentioned above.

Evaporation on plateaux is treated on p. 318.

CHAPTER XXXI

PRECIPITATION

In Chapter XXI some account is given of the effect of mountains in increasing precipitation; even low ranges stand out hardly less prominently on the map of rainfall than on that of relief. Windward slopes have most rain, leeward least, and in a region with prevailing winds from one direction the difference is large. In complex mountain-systems each ridge has its rainy windward and drier leeward slopes, the totals becoming less on corresponding slopes from windward to leeward of the whole system and the deep inner valleys having least; in the Himalayas the precipitation exceeds 150 inches on the ranges overlooking the Plains of India, and diminishes to 3 inches or less in the valleys in the north, as at Leh in the upper Indus valley.

The Alps have most rain on the exterior ranges, less on the interior, and least in the enclosed inner valleys such as the upper Rhone (24 inches at Sion), the upper Adige (16 inches at Glurns), and the Engadine (most of it with less than 30 inches); Fig. 68 (p. 193) illustrates the relationship between altitude and precipitation.

All types occur—drizzle, steady cyclonic downpour which may continue for days without intermission, violent thunder-storms on summer afternoons. Even without rain falling, much occult precipitation is deposited on the vegetation from clouds swept past by strong winds; measurements on Table Mountain, Cape Province, are given on p. 278. Chapter XXIII contains some account of the snowfall.

Inversion of Rainfall

Precipitation increases with altitude up to a certain height. Theoretically it is heaviest where the clouds first deposit rain or snow, since the temperature is highest there and for any given ascent and cooling the condensation is more copious than at higher levels where the temperature is lower; and, moreover, the gaps in the higher ranges give passage to the

winds which are thus saved further ascent. As a result precipitation may decrease with altitude in the higher altitudes,
instead of increasing as is usual lower down, a distribution
sometimes called inversion of rainfall. Circumstances
of locality and season should determine the position of
maximum, which should be higher in summer than in winter.
In the humid tropics observations in the Dutch East
Indies seem to prove an increase of rainfall up to about
8,000 feet (much lower levels on some mountains) and a
decrease above. In middle and high latitudes the available
data are not consistent; in the Alps the precipitation, as
shown by the best series of observations, increases up to the
tops of the ranges; but on the Pic du Midi in the Pyrenees the
zone of maximum seems to be at about 4,000 feet in winter,
6,000 feet in summer, in the Western Ghats at 4,500 feet,
in the north-west Himalayas at 4,000 feet. It must be noted,
however, that the readings of rain-gauges in high mountains
are not always reliable and may be seriously in error, particularly in the higher latitudes, since their catches are influenced by strong winds and by the drifting of snow, an
important consideration. Moreover, it is difficult to find sites
for rain-gauges suitable from the standpoint of practical
convenience as well as of meteorology, and to obtain the
readings in remote areas, difficult of access, at regular short
intervals.

The inversion in the Tian Shan of Central Asia is of
importance in the life of the nomads. In winter most precipitation is around 9,000 feet, a zone of forests, above which
it is so much less that the pastures have little snow and
the herds are driven up to graze on them. In summer
these same pastures get enough moisture for the growth
of grass, the maximum rainfall occurring higher than in
winter, and good grazing goes on up to about 14,000
feet.

Snow-cover

The presence or absence of a snow-cover is the outstanding
feature of the round of the seasons. Much snow has to be
melted everywhere, and especially on the higher slopes,
before the warmth of spring is felt. In the high Alpine

pastures the spring flowers do not open till the beginning of
April, but to this delay is due the glorious display in late
spring and early summer, for plant life starts so late that it
has a race against time to complete the life-cycle before the
snows of autumn draw the veil. All plants must be ready to
flower at the earliest opportunity, and by the end of June
the meadows at 5,000 or 6,000 feet are a richly coloured
paradise—in remarkable contrast to the snows of winter, and
to the slush of brown and decayed vegetation in the late
spring under the melting snow. In April the Alps are still
snow-covered down to about 6,000 feet, a figure, however,
subject to great local variations with precipitation, drifts,
exposure, and slope. The main passes even at 6,000 feet
may be completely blocked with 20 or 30 feet of snow well
on into May, and the roads over them closed till the middle
of June.

The earliest and latest dates on which the ground is
snow-covered are important; depending on altitude, slope,
amount of precipitation, temperature (including the heat of
direct insolation), they differ widely in a large mountain
system. The following table for the Eastern Alps shows that

	Arlberg Pass		Hohe Tauern		Upper Trentino	
	1,000 m.	2,000 m.	1,000 m.	2,000 m.	1,000 m.	2,000 m.
Mean date of beginning of first snow-cover . . .	31 Oct.	21 Sept.	15 Nov.	6 Oct.	27 Nov.	15 Oct.
Mean date of end of last snow-cover .	21 Apr.		15 Apr.		3 Apr.	
Mean number of days on which ground is snow-covered .	140	240	120	200	100	200

the west of the region, represented by the Arlberg Pass
district, which has the heaviest precipitation, is the earliest
to be snowed up; the interior ranges in the east including
the Hohe Tauern are much later, and latest of all is the
upper Trentino in the south with a southern exposure. The
date of the last snow-cover and its duration have the same

order reversed. The ground is considered to be snow-covered when at least half of it at the observer's level is under snow; it is not necessarily snow-covered throughout the period between the first and last cover. For the Eastern Alps the mean duration by altitude has been computed by Conrad (but there are large variations with topography and position on relation to the snow-bearing winds):

At 1,000 ft.	.	.	47 days
,, 2,000 ,,	.	.	89 ,,
,, 4,000 ,,	.	.	142 ,,
,, 6,000 ,,	.	.	200 ,,

CHAPTER XXXII

WINDS

Mountains as Obstacles to the General Winds. Lee depressions

MOUNTAINS deflect the general winds of their region, and in addition the air-movements within a system itself are much complicated by the topography. To consider the former, an extensive highland presents a formidable barrier to the winds, and an air-mass approaching it is deflected either upwards to cross it or sideways to avoid it. Rising air cools (p. 71) and its density, so far as it depends on temperature, rapidly increases; even if the ascent is caused by heating from a warm surface as on a hot sunny day, it is soon checked unless the air is inherently unstable; and forced ascent due to an obstacle in the path, without any surface heating to aid buoyancy, is stopped the sooner, long before the air can surmount such ranges as the Alps (the Alps are favourably situated for the development of these movements, which have been carefully observed and studied by local meteorologists, and this description is largely based on them). The possible ascent depends on the stability of the air, stable air resisting ascent strongly, and very unstable air possibly rising high enough to cross the ranges; but probably surface air is rarely forced up directly to 9,000 or 10,000 feet above sea-level, where gaps are wide and numerous enough to afford it passage, unless the air-mass is unusually buoyant and heavy condensation assists the buoyancy.

Consequently in many cases a large horizontal deflexion will take place, and polar air advancing from the north or

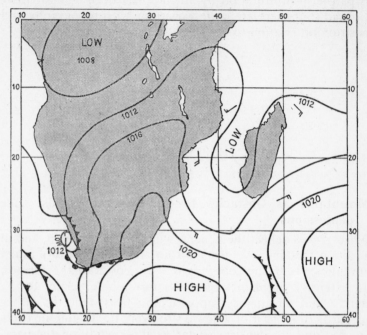

FIG. 98. Synoptic chart, morning of 13 April 1945, showing a lee depression west of Madagascar

north-west outflanks the Alps by taking advantage of the passages offered by the Rhone valley on the west (often appearing there as the mistral in winter), and by the Danube on the east. However, the whole air-mass is forced upward to some extent, and the higher layers cross the ranges, some-times without even being cooled to dew-point, but at times with the condensation of lofty and massive cloud, for turbu-lence may carry it thousands of feet above the summits. Thus a lower and an upper layer must be distinguished in the body of air facing the obstacle; the former, of a usual depth of about 5,000 feet, circumvents (while suffering some elevation also), the latter surmounts the ranges. Fronts associated with the air-masses are also necessarily affected, their lower sections being stopped or turned aside with the adjacent air, the upper advancing and crossing the ranges with the higher strata, so that these 'upper fronts' out-distance their lower sections.

Other results of the check to the advancing air are the formation of a minor ridge of slightly higher pressure where the air is piled up in front of the barrier, and a corresponding tendency to low pressure in the lee, over the Gulf of Genoa and Lombardy in the case of air-masses approaching the Alps from the north, and these lower pressures may develop into closed 'lee depressions'.

Another, almost daily, example of the formation of lee depressions is provided by Madagascar; the continuous escarpment, 800 miles long and 5,000 feet high, deflects the trade, which sweeps round the north of the island as a very strong E. wind, and round the south as a NE. wind, and a prominent lee depression, without fronts however, is usually present west of the barrier (Fig. 98). The features sketched above are of great importance for the meteorologist who is concerned with the weather of any region containing large mountains.

Local Winds

There remain the local winds inside a mountain-system, which result, in part at least, from the details of the topo-graphy; some are associated with disturbed, others with settled weather. To consider the former, the wind is normally stronger at high altitudes, both in the free atmosphere and still more among mountains, where, in unsettled weather, swirls and gusts, irregular in direction and force, interspersed with lulls, confront us in the ravines and gaps, and round the peaks—a wild and chaotic scene when dense cloud, driving rain, or flurries of snow add to the confusion, and a serious trial for the mountaineer without adequate equip-ment, the more so if it has followed abruptly on the calm weather and blue skies of an anticyclone. Evidently the turbulence is an expression of the irregularities of the moun-tain features, and it is hardly possibly to reduce it to orderly description.

The air-movements in settled weather are of quite a different kind, being notably regular in both time and place. They will now be described.

Mountain- and Valley-winds

In the morning about 1000 the wind begins to blow up every valley, strengthens till afternoon and dies away before sunset; an hour or so later the current is reversed, a cold wind descending from the heights and continuing till morning. Towards 1000 the valley-wind appears, and the sequence is repeated day after day, with striking regularity as long as the weather is settled—a great daily respiration of the mountains comparable with the coastal respiration of land- and sea-breezes, to which, indeed, it also bears a resemblance in its causes. The disturbances of cyclonic weather mask, or eliminate, these local currents, the weakening of which foretells a deterioration in the weather. The valley-winds carry vapour to the mountain tops where it is condensed into heavy cloud, sometimes with precipitation and thunder. A few minor exceptions to the up-valley direction of these diurnal winds occur, where long valleys slope up to a low col from both sides, and a stronger wind in one of them may continue over the col and for some distance down the other side; they have been called Maloja winds, from the Maloja Pass at the head of the Engadine where their occurrence was first investigated. The valley-wind is of moderate force when at its strongest in the early afternoon, but it may be quite light or attain gale force, according as it is counteracted or reinforced by the general winds and controlled by the topography. The wind brings a welcome moderation of the heat which, without it, is excessive in deep valleys on sunny days in summer.

The mountain-wind at night is even more regular than the valley wind, for, except in disturbed weather, the chilled surface air gravitates down the slopes into the valleys which it descends with the true mountain wind. The mountain- and valley-winds vary greatly in strength; on the whole the latter is a more massive current, but the low temperature of the former makes it the less welcome, and the bottoms where it is prominent are shunned for that and other reasons by human settlement; deep enclosed basins amid snow-covered mountains are filled with inversion 'lakes' of intensely cold air on winter nights despite low altitude. True mountain- and valley-winds are best developed in long wide valleys of gentle slope, hardly at all in narrow ravines.

Theory of Mountain- and Valley-winds

Alpine meteorologists attribute this daily mountain respi- ration to two separate processes, one going on in the valleys themselves, the other of much wider extent. The first depends, for the day effect, on the heating of the slopes by the strong insolation; the air ascends them more or less directly, rather than blows along the valleys; glider-pilots find good thermals close along the sunny sides of valleys. In valleys with one side facing the sun, the other in shade, the anabatic movement on the former is accompanied by a katabatic movement on the latter, best developed where the slope is snow-covered; a strong katabatic 'glacier wind' may blow regularly, by day as well as at night, down long valley-glaciers, anabatic currents ascending one or both slopes above them. The anabatic movements are merely shallow local currents on the slopes, but their combined effect is a general drift up the valleys towards the summits. Corresponding to this effect of diurnal heating is the kata- batic night effect, which gives rise to a down-slope creep merging into a down-valley wind.

The other process embraces not only the mountains them- selves but also the lowlands round about. It is a much wider phenomenon than the local slope-winds just described, and gives rise to the true mountain and valley circulation which covers the whole region. A mountain-mass and particularly its deep and wide valleys are strongly heated by the insolation on a clear day, and in turn heat the adjacent air which becomes warmer than the free atmosphere at the same level over the plains. In this respect the mountains are compar- able with an island, and, like the island's sea-breeze, a move- ment of the lower atmosphere sets inward to balance the outward movement in the high levels; the in-blowing surface air is directed along the valley lines which it follows upward, forming the valley-wind. The contributions from the many valleys converge towards the summits, adiabatic cooling condenses their stores of vapour, and heavy cloud, rain, and thunder may be almost daily occurrences. The outward movements in the higher atmosphere are usually too diffuse to be readily observed, another resemblance to the sea-breeze circulation. Night brings a reversal; the mountains rapidly lose their heat, the air round them is colder than the free atmosphere, and a 'land-breeze'—here the mountain-wind—descends the valleys and blows outward to the plains, while in the high atmosphere a diffuse inward drift maintains the circulation.

This general daily pulse is reinforced by the local slope-winds described above, and in the valleys they can hardly be distinguished.

Föhn Winds

In great contrast to the regular, fine-weather, mountain-and valley-winds are the föhn winds of deep valleys in large mountain-systems such as the Alps, Himalayas, Andes, and Caucasus, and on the borders of lofty plateaux; they are prominent both in the north and south valleys of the Alps, and are cyclonic winds associated with low-pressure systems moving across north-west or central Europe or along the Mediterranean, the former generating the south föhn (i.e. a föhn wind from the south in the valleys trending north) and the latter the north föhn; the special characteristics of squalliness (in force and direction), heat, and dryness for which they are known are a modification imposed by the topography. The following account refers to the Alps, but the main features are common to föhn winds everywhere.

Many valleys are noted for the not-infrequent occurrence of these hot dry winds in the winter half-year. For days previously the weather has been unusually cold, the snow-covered valley being filled with cold damp stagnant air, often laden with fog or low cloud which has gravitated from the higher slopes during an anticyclone. Then comes a sudden change; the wind blows down the valleys, first in spasmodic gusts, later as a strong steady current, with a rapid rise in temperature, sometimes as much as 40° in 24 hours, a drop in humidity, and notably good visibility. The snow melts

so fast that in some valleys the wind is called 'schneefresser'.
Structural damage may be done by the more violent gusts,
and the air is so dry that the wooden houses are liable to
catch fire from stray sparks, and whole villages have been
burnt down. Notices such as the following are to be seen in
villages:

DAS RAUCHEN

bei Föhnwetter im Freien ist bei einer Busse von Fr. 2–10
verboten.

BUCHS, den 20. März 1911.

Der Gemeinderat.

The föhn is usually over within a day or two, but it may
last for 3 days or even a week, and the abnormal dry warmth
has a depressing nervous effect. But it is of value in clearing
the ground of snow—a service bought at times at the cost of
heavy floods—and in some valleys in hastening the fruit
harvest in autumn. Many valleys have an average of 30 to
40 föhn-days a year:

MEAN MONTHLY NUMBER OF DAYS WITH FÖHN

	J.	F.	M.	A.	M.	J.	J.	A.	S.	O.	N.	D.	Year
Innsbruck .	3	3	6	6	5	2	2	1	2	5	4	3	43
Bludenz .	4	3	3	3	2	1	1	1	4	3	4	4	32
Altdorf .	4	4	6	6	6	3	2	2	3	5	4	4	48
Martigny .	3	3	5	6	4	1	1	1	3	5	6	2	39
Castasegna* .	8	10	10	9	7	5	4	3	3	3	5	8	74

* On south side of Alps, near Maloja Pass

Spring and autumn have the highest frequency.

The föhn resembles in some respects the sirocco of
the south Mediterranean, and, before its meteorology was
seriously studied, it was thought to be identical, the warmth
and dryness being derived from the Sahara. But this view
proved untenable. As already stated, föhns are cyclonic
winds, the south föhn associated fundamentally with a depression over north-west or central Europe, the north with
one over Italy; but a feature so extensive as the Alps modifies

the winds that approach it and causes local high pressures
to build up along the windward side, and low pressures in
the lee (p. 303) to which the winds which actually cross the
ranges are immediately due. The föhn peculiarities result
from the passage of the ranges; in order to reach the valleys
the winds have to cross them and descend; descent causes
compression and therefore heating and drying. But if the
southerly current is to be maintained it must be fed from the
south side of the Alps, and as much heat is lost in the ascent
as is gained by the descent to the same level on the north;
no warmth can be gained. But another consideration is
involved, for as the winds rise and cool on the south side they
are soon unable to contain their water vapour; the front of
the mountains is covered with thick clouds and the torrents
roar under their load of flood and pebbles. But conditions
are very different on the north; the masses of cloud ('föhn
wall') can be seen coming over the ranges and pouring
through the passes, but as the wind carries them down
they rapidly dissolve, and after a few hundred feet of
descent they disappear. Now the evaporation of the clouds
uses as much heat as is liberated in their formation, but
the former process is completed in a few hundred feet
of descent, the latter has continued for several thousand,
and hence its effect is much greater. An example will make
this clear (Fig. 99). It is assumed that the south wind
reaches the foot of the Alps at a temperature of 70° and
almost saturated with vapour, being the damp tropical air
of a depression. Ascending it cools adiabatically 1·6° in
300 feet, so that at 3,000 feet it has cooled 16° to 54°, and
by that time clouds have formed, rain falls, and the dry
adiabatic lapse-rate is reduced to the saturated rate, at first
about 0·8° in 300 feet. This continues to the top of the
range, which is taken to be 9,000 feet, and there the temperature will be about 38°. Descending the lee slope the
air is heated adiabatically, at first at the saturated rate till the
clouds are evaporated; but much less cloud is present to be
evaporated than was formed in the ascent, for the condensed
vapour has been falling as rain and a small descent will
suffice to effect the evaporation, during which the temperature will have increased about 1° (taking the rate of heating

to be the same as the rate of cooling while clouds were forming in the ascent). In the remaining 8,400 feet to its original
level the air heats at the dry rate of 1·6° for 300 feet, and
should attain a temperature of 85°. Such high readings
are not found, one reason being that the north valleys are
3,000 or 4,000 feet above sea-level, but even a temperature
of 45° or 50° is a very noticeable change from the previous
cold.

Southerly winds are faced by the concave curve of the

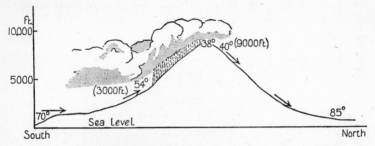

FIG. 99. Temperature changes in an air-current crossing a range

Alps, which hinders lateral spread and forces a greater
volume of the air upward over the mountains. The warm
air contains much vapour, and the rainfall on the windward
ranges is very heavy; as a result the föhn in the north valleys
is strongly developed—notably more than the north föhn in
the south valleys.

Föhn winds may occur without precipitation and cloud on
the heights, and the liberation of latent heat of evaporation
fails as an explanation. In some of these cases the air is
warmed by descent in an anticyclone covering the mountains, and blows down the valleys, often both on the north
and the south sides. Such an anticyclonic föhn may be complete in itself, or it may be only a preliminary stage before
cyclonic influences appear and force air to cross the ranges
as described above. Another type of föhn without much, or
any, rain on the tops seems to be associated with polar air
coming from the north and finding its passage barred by
the Alps, where in some circumstances it piles up till it

overflows the ranges and descends into the south valleys with adiabatic warming and drying.

Only deep enclosed valleys have the remarkable oases of warmth of the true föhn, for the air loses its heat as it spreads over the plains (though the föhn effect may still be very perceptible). The most favoured spots are where side valleys from the high ranges on the south join the great

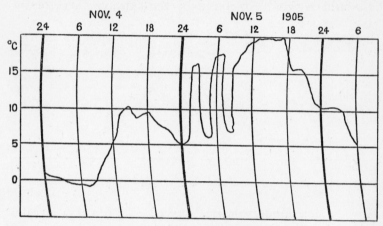

FIG. 100. Temperature during a föhn at Rotholz, Inn valley, near Innsbruck which began at midnight, 4–5 November (Ficker)

longitudinal valleys of the upper Rhone, Rhine, Inn, and other rivers; and in the Ill valley round Bludenz, and the upper Aar, Linth, and Reuss valleys. Föhn winds are less pronounced on the south of the Alps, since the wind blows from the north and is therefore cool in its origin, and these valleys themselves are warm thanks to their southern aspect, so that the warmth of the föhn wind is not heightened by contrast.

Explanation is required for the descent of warm air into the narrow valleys which were filled with cold air, a condition of stable equilibrium, for the warm wind might be expected to pass overhead and leave the cold air in possession. The turbulence between two air-masses of different velocities is a main cause of the mixing, and thus of the removal of the cold air; and the arrival of a depression in north-west or central Europe causes the cold inversion layer to drain away,

and the potentially warm air aloft to replace it, this reaching
the valley floors first in turbulent spasmodic hot gusts and
later in a more steady current, as is shown by the temperatures
in Fig. 100.

The investigation of the föhn of the Alps has given the
clue to many other warm winds. The coasts of Greenland
are an example; the interior is a lofty plateau of snow and
ice, and yet when the wind blows strongly from it temperature rises on the coasts so much that the natives find it
unpleasantly warm; instances are: at Godthaab on the west
coast, 64° N., on 23 January 1883 the temperature rose to
45° (31° above the mean for the month), and the relative
humidity fell to 12 per cent.; Denmark Island on the east
coast, 70° N., on 13 July 1892, had a maximum temperature
of 59° (19° above the mean for the month), and relative
humidity down to 34 per cent.

The 'chinook' winds of Alberta, Montana, Wyoming, and
Colorado are better known. The Rocky Mountains fall
steeply to the high plains on the east, and in favourable
isobaric conditions the strong damp west wind from the
Pacific is so warm after its descent that the winter snow is
melted and the pastures laid bare for grazing, a great boon
to ranchers. A rise in temperature of 100° from the preceding icy blasts of a blizzard or the inversion-cold on the snow
is not unknown.

The berg winds of S. Africa are remarkably hot and dry
winds from the interior which are prominent on the littoral
all round the Union and in South-west Africa, blowing
approximately at right angles to the coast; the strong sunshine from the clear sky adds its effect. They are most
prominent in the west where they may last for two or three
days; they are often dusty and contrast strongly with the
normal cool ocean air; in South-west Africa their mean
frequency is about 50 days a year (most in winter); they
bring temperatures above 90°, and Port Nolloth has recorded
115°. Unlike the föhn winds described above they are not
associated with cloud and rain, and the common explanation
is that the air descends from the plateau in the interior, where
in spite of elevation the days are as hot as near sea-level,

under the influence of a depression off the coast, and is
heated adiabatically. But this fails to account for some of
the peculiarities on the west coast, where the berg winds are
strongest and hottest in the night and early morning, and
are replaced by the cool sea-breeze in the afternoon.

The 'bohorok' along the east foot of the mountain range
(about 7,000 feet) of Sumatra is a föhn on the equator, distinguished not by heat but by low humidity which sometimes
damages crops.

CHAPTER XXXIII

PLATEAU CLIMATE

A PLATEAU is an extensive area at a considerable and fairly
uniform height and possesses continentality, and the modifications it imposes on the general climate of its region differ
in many ways from those of an isolated mountain of the same
height. The larger and higher the plateau, the stronger is
its influence. The modifications are similar everywhere, but
the prominence of the various features differs with the latitude. Many plateaux have considerable populations, and the
physiological effects of the climates have given rise to some
discussion.

Atmospheric pressure

The reduction, being a function of the altitude, is the
same as on a mountain side or in the free atmosphere, about
34 mb. (1 inch) in 1,000 feet in the lower levels; it begins
to be appreciable in its direct and indirect effects above
6,000 feet, where the pressure is 800 mb. (24 inches); some
European settlers on the plateau of East Africa consider that
even at 5,000 feet the reduced pressure is physiologically
harmful, but it is unlikely that a person of normal physique
and good health is conscious of it up to 8,000 feet, the
upper limit of most European settlement. Above 12,000 feet
some newcomers are subject to mountain-sickness (Chapter
XII); the inhabitants of the high Andine plateaux above
15,000 feet have developed prominent physical peculiarities,

and have difficulty in acclimatizing themselves to the low-lands when they descend for agricultural employment. But whatever the direct effects may be, the indirect physiological effects of altitude through sunshine, temperature, and humidity are considerable.

Temperature

The distinction between the heat of the direct sunshine and the air temperature is more evident than near sea-level.

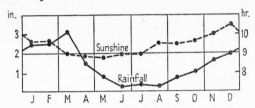

FIG. 101. Mean monthly sunshine (hours a day) and rainfall, Kimberley, S. Africa

The atmosphere is clearer, the sky less cloudy, and the sunshine longer and more powerful, and a large contributor to the total heat experienced. The strong glare of the light makes it advisable to wear dark glasses in regions with light-coloured surface and little vegetation. All this has been described for mountains in Chapter XXIX; but the effects are more pronounced on plateaux owing to their clearer skies and more abundant sunshine. The contrast between sun and shade is prominent, the clouding-over of the sun being felt at once, so much as to be an important feature on many plateaux. The mean sunshine and rainfall at Kabete, near Nairobi, are shown in Fig. 91 (p. 252); Kimberley, Orange Free State (Fig. 101), with its liberal sunshine in both summer and winter, rainy and dry seasons, illustrates the remarkably sunny skies of South Africa. The plateau of the south-western states of North America has similar totals (p. 251), but the land is more arid. The Meseta of Spain (Madrid, altitude 2,149 feet, 2,920 hours of sunshine a year, 8 hours a day) and the steppes of Anatolia are very sunny for their positions on the globe.

The mean monthly temperatures on plateaux near the

equator are lower than at sea-level, the gradient being about
the normal 3° for 1,000 feet in all seasons, so that the mean
annual range is similar; but the daily range is far greater
on the plateau, as is illustrated by Equator and Mombasa,

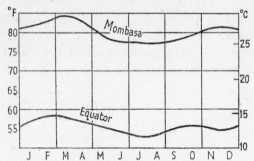

FIG. 102. Mean temperature at Mombasa (alt. 52 ft.)
and Equator (9,050 ft.), Kenya

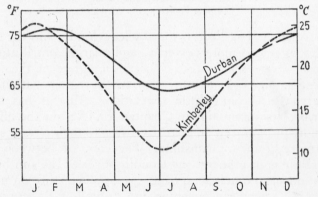

FIG. 103. Mean temperature at Durban (alt. 260 ft.) and Kimberley
(4,042 feet)

Fig. 102. The days are warm, hot in the sun, but as the sun
sinks the surface cools quickly in the clear air under the almost
cloudless sky, and the change from the heat of the day is
very noticeable.

Plateaux in the sub-tropics, in South Africa, the Mediterranean region, the Andes, have an equal, or larger, daily
range; and, contrary to the case on equatorial plateaux, the
reduction in mean monthly temperature from sea-level
varies much with the season (Fig. 103); summer is as hot on

the plateau as below, the summer days often much hotter, but winter, notably the nights, much cooler, a result of the lower sun, the long nights, the clear sky, and the dry air; and bitterly cold winds and snow may sweep across from high latitudes.

In the middle of the day the sun can be hot enough to cause sunburn, but as soon as it sets heavy coats must be donned, and it may freeze before dawn. Even on the Rhodesian plateau inside the tropic frost occurs on winter nights, and on the higher plateau of Bolivia (altitude about 9,000 feet):

Early in the morning and late in the evening, when the sun is below the horizon, the cold is liable to be intense even in September and one suffers from almost frozen feet. In the winter, when the winds blow and the frosts are yet more severe, the dry cold is so trying that even the natives cover up their faces in thick woollen masks, and wrap shawls about their heads and ponchos over their bodies. But as soon as the sun is a little way above the horizon, its direct rays scorch the traveller with their great heat, so that he soon begins to pray for the night, as the lesser evil of the two. . . . By day the burning sunshine so envelops all the brown, dry, dusty ground that everything in view seems to vanish in brightness; and the eye, unprotected by dark glass, cannot gaze steadily in any direction. . . . When the sun is hottest little cyclones raise dust whirlwinds which dance along, often by scores at a time. (SIR MARTIN CONWAY.)

The chilled air drains into the hollows, perhaps more on plateaux than elsewhere:

I noticed during the drive (over the veld) what I have often noticed out here, the layers of cold air. Sometimes the wraps became quite oppressive at the top of a hill or even climbing up it; then in crossing a valley or narrow ravine we seemed to drive into an ice-cold region where we shivered beneath our furs; again in five minutes the air would once more be soft and balmy, crisp indeed and bracing, but many degrees warmer than those narrow Arctic belts. (BARKER, on S. Africa.)

Bolivia again provides another good example, the deep valleys incised in the Puna being filled at night with very cold air. But the level tracts are extensive enough to retain a cold layer of air, and are often colder than the mountain sides or the free atmosphere at the same altitude.

Asia has plateaux of great altitude (Tibet) and in high
latitudes (Mongolia), where the winters are extremely severe.
Even the Tarim River is deeply frozen for 3 or 4 months,
and water for domestic purposes has to be transported in
the form of blocks of ice. Yet in summer the heat is intolerable:

> In the beginning of June summer—the Asiatic summer—was upon
> us almost before we were aware of it. The sky glowed like a gigantic
> furnace. The temperature rose to 100° F. in the shade; the black-bulb
> insolation thermometer showed 150°. The queen of the night was
> powerless to infuse coolness into the superheated atmosphere of east
> Turkistan. And every afternoon the desert wind blew in across the
> ancient capital, dry, burning, impregnated with fine dust, filling the
> streets with a stifling impenetrable haze. (SVEN HEDIN, describing
> Kashgar.)

It is true that the Tarim Basin, though in one sense a
plateau, 3,000 feet above the sea, is at the same time really
a great depression, bounded on three sides by lofty ranges,
a configuration which intensifies the extremes of temperature.

Tibet, with plateaux of from 14,000 to over 17,000 feet
above the sea, has monthly means below freezing-point
most of the year. Iran, on the other hand, with its lower
altitude and latitude, is distinguished by blazing heat in
summer, but a winter journey over the salt wastes of the
interior in the face of the icy blasts and snow flurries from
the north is no pleasant experience. Anatolia has colder
winters owing to the proximity of the steppes of Russia, and
contrast with the genial climate of the Mediterranean coasts
makes the cold of the interior the more noticeable.

The plateau of the Shotts in Algeria is in a higher latitude
than the Transvaal, and another factor giving it colder
winters is proximity to the land-mass of Eurasia. It can
be bitterly cold in winter, and severe snowstorms have cost
the lives of men caught unprotected. The invalid fleeing
from the cold of north Europe must cross not only the
Mediterranean Sea but also the plateau before he can be
immune in the sheltered oases of the Sahara. As on other
plateaux of similar altitude the summers are very hot, hotter

than on the shores of the Mediterranean, owing to the fierce
sunshine that beats down on the parched plains, and the
summer days recall those of the Sahara. The Meseta of
Spain has a similar but less extreme climate.

Precipitation. Evaporation

Precipitation tends to be low, partly as a result of the
frequent elevated rim forming a rain-shadow. The régime
depends on the region; the plateaux of Ecuador and East
Africa have the equatorial double maximum, but with much
drizzle in the mornings of the cool season. The veld of
South Africa has the tropical régime, with rain in summer
and almost rainless winters; the plateau of the Shotts, the
Meseta of Spain, and Anatolia have the Mediterranean dry
summers but a pronounced maximum of precipitation in
spring with much snow, a steppe feature. These are brown
lands during much of the year, green only when revived
by the rains.

The rain often falls in heavy showers, and at times in
violent thunderstorms (Chapter XXV). The thunderstorms
and hail of South Africa are well known; Johannesburg has
on the average 111 days a year with lightning:

> The crops in the citrus orchards over a large area in the northern
> Transvaal have been destroyed by hail, and donkeys, pigs, goats,
> and other animals, including apes and game, have been killed. The
> damage is estimated at many thousands of pounds. (*The Times*,
> 8 November 1927.)

The bitterly cold hailstorms of loftier plateaux have been
mentioned by many travellers; Sven Hedin describes one
in north-east Tibet:

> Sept. 22. . . . The weather took a disagreeable turn. The sky
> darkened in every quarter, and a hailstorm of unparalleled violence
> burst over the lake. The clouds drove towards us out of the east like a
> solid black wall, accompanied by fierce hissings and whinings like the
> sound of steam escaping from the boiler of a locomotive. The surface
> of the lake turned dark grey. The mountains on the shore became lost
> in the haze; louder and louder grew the roar of the storm. We could
> see and we could hear how the drops of water splashed up with a
> perceptible hiss as the hailstones thrashed the dead smooth surface of

the lake. The hail came down in blinding showers, but finally passed over into snow and rain. Then the wind changed, and a terrific gale set in from the west. It blew right in our teeth and nearly froze us to death. The horses literally toiled against it as though they were struggling up a steep hill.

Evaporation is, in general, much more vigorous on sub-tropical plateaux than on adjacent lowlands, in opposition to the usual reduction with altitude. Bulawayo, Southern Rhodesia, 4,470 feet, has a mean of 75 inches a year; Pretoria, 4,471 feet, 60 inches; the plateau of Palestine about 100 inches. These plateaux have considerable evaporation in their dry winters, when the air is dry though cool, winds brisk, and sunshine abundant, but more in the rainy season, which is warmer, with much sunshine and little rain for the latitude, and most of all in the hot dry spring months:

MEAN MONTHLY EVAPORATION (in.)

	J.	F.	M.	A.	M.	J.	J.	A.	S.	O.	N.	D.	Year
Pretoria[1] .	6·4	5·0	5·3	4·4	3·5	2·8	2·9	4·0	5·5	7·4	6·2	6·7	60·3
Johannesburg[1]	6·5	5·7	5·1	5·1	5·1	4·3	4·9	6·6	7·9	8·4	7·6	7·4	74·6
Alice Springs[1]	12·7	10·9	9·5	6·9	4·9	3·4	3·7	5·2	7·3	9·6	10·9	12·2	97·2
Kabete[2] . (Kenya)	6·8	6·2	6·2	4·8	3·7	3·6	3·4	2·3	5·7	7·4	6·0	5·6	61·7

[1] Tank.
[2] Wild evaporimeter.

The Highlands of Kenya (Kabete, altitude 5,971 feet, in above table) on the equator share the large evaporation records of the sub-tropical plateaux, and are dry and invigorating, in marked contrast to the humid lowlands and coasts; they provide white settlers with a pleasant climate, in which work of all kinds is possible.

Visibility

Visibility is good or very good generally on plateaux, thanks to their elevation above the lower atmosphere, and the average is better than on most mountains at the same altitude since cloud-fog is less frequent and the air is drier. Kabete illustrates equatorial plateaux:

MEAN PERCENTAGE FREQUENCIES OF VISIBILITIES

Code figures	0–2	3	4	5	6	7	8–9
Kabete, Feb.,[1] 0900	—	—	—	—	1	2	97
1500	—	—	—	—	—	2	98
Aug.,[2] 0900	—	1	1	2	5	18	72
1500	—	—	—	—	2	4	94

[1] Month with best visibility.   [2] Month with worst visibility.

For a sub-tropical plateau we have data for Beaufort West, altitude 2,850 feet, on the Karroo, Cape Province:

MEAN PERCENTAGE FREQUENCIES OF CODE FIGURES 7–9

Dec.–Feb.	0830	94	June–Aug.	0830	86
	1500	96		1500	87

—truly a clear atmosphere.

PART V

THE WEATHER OF THE WESTERLIES
(with reference mainly to north-west Europe)

CHAPTER XXXIV

THE PRESSURE-SYSTEMS OF THE WESTERLIES. ANTICYCLONES

In the general account of the westerlies in Chapter XV attention was drawn to the irregularities of pressure which are a prominent feature; the barometer is subject to rises and falls of greater magnitude than in any of the other zones, and their occurrence appears to be quite erratic, and very difficult, if not impossible, to forecast with any accuracy; they are evidently closely connected with the changeable weather which characterizes the belt (unlike the semi-diurnal rise and fall which is the chief movement of the barometer within the tropics, and is independent of the weather). The idea of the 'climate' of any region outside the tropics is a generalization based on such manifold and irregular types of weather that no description of it can be adequate unless it includes some account of the daily weather. There is abundant material available for the study of the westerlies of the north hemisphere in the detailed synoptic weather charts published officially in most countries, in which thousands of observations of all elements of the weather at stations on land and on ships at sea over most of the hemisphere, taken simultaneously under standard conditions and telegraphed to central offices, are plotted.

The charts show an endless variety of pressure-systems; the forms of the isobars, the movements of the systems, the details of the weather, are never repeated exactly, but we soon learn to recognize types (Fig. 104). The main distinction is between those with higher pressure than round about, and those with lower pressure.

They vary greatly in size, high-pressure systems being the larger on the average, some exceeding even 3,000 miles

PLATE 15

Zwieselstein, Tyrol

across; depressions may be over 1,500 miles in diameter, but many are much smaller, 500 miles or less.

The largest members of the former class are anticyclones; extensions, commonly called wedges, project poleward from many of them between depressions. Two anticyclones are joined—or separated—by a 'col', of low pressure in relation to the anticyclones, high pressure in relation to the

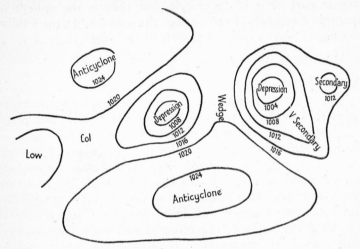

FIG. 104. Diagrammatic types of pressure-systems; the values of the isobars are arbitrary

depressions on the other two sides (relations corresponding to those of a col in a mountain-system with its mountains and valleys, from which isobaric cols are named). Cols are the scene of a great variety of possible winds and weathers, and they are favourable to the formation of fronts.

Low-pressure systems, 'depressions', are of a generally circular shape; but many have bulges in their isobars enclosing 'secondaries', which may be deep enough to have their own closed isobars. Some secondaries are 'troughs' or elongations with rounded ends, others are V-shaped, with isobars converging sharply and containing a warm, cold, or occluded front, in which stronger winds and more disturbed weather are usual.

The details of the weather in the various systems are not

described in this book, as a useful introduction may be found in many other works, e.g. *The Weather Map* (Meteorological Office, pub. H.M.S.O.). The synoptic charts issued daily by the Meteorological Office will soon give familiarity with actual pressure-systems, their movements and weather. The structure of even a simple type cannot be studied without a full consideration of the upper atmosphere in which the largest part of it is developed, but that is the sphere of synoptic meteorology rather than climatology. In the following pages only a general sketch of the surface elements is given.

Anticyclones

The large high-pressure systems, anticyclones, many of them thousands of miles across, travel slowly and often erratically. The pressure-gradient in the central region is weak and the winds are light, blowing clockwise in the north hemisphere with an outward component across the isobars in the surface layers. The air is subsiding slowly, at a rate probably of the order of one or two hundred feet in an hour, and becoming warmer and drier, down to a few thousand feet from the surface; the more violent forms of weather, strong winds and heavy rain, are absent, but beyond this it is not possible to generalize. A useful distinction is between anticyclones with fair or fine weather, and those with dull or gloomy.

The first type may be subdivided into systems with clear, bright skies, and those with some cloud. In those with clear skies (most summer anticyclones are such) 'radiation weather' is in the ascendant—abundant sunshine, high temperatures in summer, clear frosty weather with very cold nights in winter, the temperatures being the more extreme in the absence of wind so that advective effects are small and local influences have the more scope. Though in high summer the heat may be excessive, such anticyclones give the longest spells of pleasant weather known in the westerlies. The other class, anticyclones with cloud, are less pleasant. The descending air is checked by friction as it approaches the surface, and spreads outwards above a shield of stagnant air, cold and dense in winter, some 2,000 feet deep; this shield is often

roofed over with a pall of unbroken stratus, and cold gloomy
weather persists. Above the cloud-layer a strong inversion
of temperature marks the base of the descending air, and the
sky extends blue and cloudless to the horizon. The long
monotonous spells of dull grey stratus, and the low, but not
very low, temperatures with small range from day to night,

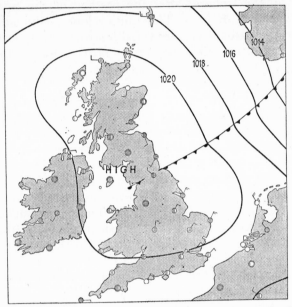

FIG. 105. Synoptic chart, 0600, 30 July 1947, showing an anticyclonic
system with front. For meaning of symbols see Fig. 22, p. 64,

make the weather on the surface depressing. Most of these
cloudy anticyclones are in winter.

The second type gives worse weather. The anticyclones
as wholes are high-pressure systems, but they contain
irregularities which may cause very broken conditions. The
skies over wide areas are more overcast, gloomy, and depressing than in the anticyclones described above; the
weather is damp and cold, 'raw' in winter, and drizzle or
light rain may persist for hours—weather not at all suggestive of warm, dry, descending air. The conditions are
really cyclonic, and it is possible in many cases to diagnose
the irregularities in the synoptic chart, for some anticyclones

contain minor low-pressure systems, large enough to appear as small closed depressions with their own cyclonic weather; others are crossed by fronts active enough to give disturbed weather in a belt of some width (Fig. 105); some fronts are in cols separating areas of slightly higher pressure, subsidiary anticyclones, not so pronounced, however, as to be shown by the isobars; after the passage of the front the weather may turn fine. Thus anticyclones, comparatively stable as they usually are, are variable structures; the weather in each can often be known only by observation, and eludes forecast.

Origin of Anticyclones of North-west Europe

Most large anticyclones come from the permanent or semi-permanent high-pressure systems. They are of two classes. In summer most come from, or are a part of, the sub-tropical high pressures of the North Atlantic, which extend farther north-east than usual to cover at least the south of the British Isles, or from which an anticyclone buds off and travels slowly to the region. These are 'warm' anticyclones, formed by the slow subsidence of air from the upper atmosphere (p. 106), and they provide warm tropical air, the surface layers of which get damp, cool, and stable as they advance over the cooler sea, and may be fog-laden round our coasts in summer. The stability favours persistence of the system.

The other class comprises 'cold' anticyclones; two origins may be identified, but they do not include all cases. Many come south from the polar region, often in the polar current in rear of a depression. Others originate in the winter high pressures of Eurasia, which either spread west and cover our area or send detached offshoots when the continental anticyclone is intense. These cold anticyclones have been conditioned from the cold surface on which they rested; they are shallower than the warm type, and have a strong inversion of temperature by their origin. Reaching warmer surfaces they are warmed, soon become unstable with the formation of cumulus cloud, and tend to break up; but, on the other hand, they may be remarkably persistent in winter over Europe, and pour floods of cold air over the British Isles, with skies which may be almost cloudless for days, or over-cast with strato-cumulus. These systems of continental origin are often stationed over Scandinavia and its neigh-bourhood, from which we derive lengthy easterly spells (p. 350).

Many anticyclones are 'strays', which do not lend them-selves to classification.

The air-mass in front of an approaching anticyclone is polar, and provides air with the ordinary polar features in rear of a preceding depression. An anticyclone with an elongated north–south axis on the North Atlantic sends air-masses south from high latitudes, bringing very cold weather to our islands. In strong contrast, the air-mass in rear is variable; it may be continental, hot, dry, and hazy in summer, cold or very cold and dry in winter; such are the easterly winds which give the hottest summers and the coldest winters to the British Isles; or it may be of maritime origin, damp and cool in summer, very mild and damp in winter.

Long, gently curving reaches of isobars steer air-masses from remote distances, with their qualities of temperature and humidity which appear of notable intensity in our lati-tudes.

The tracks of anticyclones are erratic in detail. They advance slowly, much more slowly and irregularly than de-pressions, from their origins described above. They tend to move from areas of negative to those of greatest positive barometric tendency (p. 342). They have a strong tendency to remain stationary for some days, giving us persistent spells of weather (Chapter XXXVIII).

Wedges of High Pressure

These are distinct from the large anticyclonic systems, though they are often spurs projecting from them. Of more or less prominent wedge- or ridge-form, they separate the pairs of a series of depressions and travel with them, much more rapidly than anticyclones and often undergoing much modification. They have a vigorous current of polar air in front, cool and fresh with the bright skies and cumulus clouds usual in polar air, feeding the leading depression. But the signs of the new depression approaching from the west are soon visible in the thickening cirrus, even before the rise of the barometer in the wedge is checked, and the calm of the central axis gives place to southerly winds and low cloud. The weather in front of a wedge is the finest and most exhilarating experienced in the westerlies, but it does not last long.

CHAPTER XXXV

FRONTAL WEATHER

THE weather of most of the globe, of middle and high latitudes in particular, may be most conveniently treated as it is found firstly within the body of air-masses, each of them having its own fairly stable and uniform type throughout according to season, and secondly in the transition belts or 'fronts' which separate air-masses, which also have their distinctive weathers. Air-masses are described in Chapter VII; fronts are more complex, and some general account is a useful preliminary to the study of the frontal depressions of the westerlies in which they are responsible for most of the bad weather and the many abrupt changes, as is shown by the fact that on the ocean west of Britain (according to measurements in the remote western isles of Scotland) 82 per cent. of the mean annual rain falls in fronts; at Kew 65 per cent. of the winter precipitation is in fronts, but in summer only 49 per cent., the summer precipitation being largely of convectional type.[1]

Fronts

Fronts are shown on synoptic charts by lines drawn where the frontal surfaces separating air-masses meet the ground; the surfaces slope up, in middle latitudes at a very small

[1] *Characteristics of Rainfall Distribution in Homogeneous Air Currents and at Surfaces of Discontinuity*, A. H. R. Goldie, Meteorological Office, Geophysical Memoirs, No. 53.

angle with the horizontal. The discontinuity cannot be absolutely sharp for some mixing results from diffusion and turbulence; it is rather a zone of a width on the ground of some 10 to 50 miles, but its passage is usually easily recognized by eye-observation as well as by instrumental records. Discontinuities in the atmosphere are comparable with the divides, often sharp, between currents of water in the oceans, and between the streams from tributaries in a deep river which may retain their individuality for miles. On a synoptic chart the discontinuity where a front crosses an isobar is shown by a small but sharp bend, always directed outwards from the lower pressure.

Discontinuities can be of enormous length, thousands of miles across ocean and continent (e.g. Fig. 56), but shorter fronts often appear on synoptic charts, and many are too short and weak to be shown. They may be almost straight, or curve gently, or have abrupt changes of direction and movement and various forms of junction with each other. Some move rapidly, others change little for several days (p. 347). Fronts are most numerous, active, and conspicuous in low-pressure systems, in which the tendency to convergence brings air-masses into contact—and into conflict when they are of different densities or moving at different speeds. In anticyclones the divergence tends to eliminate fronts.

The boundary, or frontal surface, between two air-masses is a stable feature when the air movements are adjusted to the conditions, including the pressure-gradients, a process which takes some time. The slope is related to the conditions; it increases with the magnitude of the rotational deflexion of the earth and therefore with latitude, from horizontal, theoretically, at the equator with the less dense air lying above the more dense, to a maximum at the poles; the greater the difference of velocity of the winds in the two air-masses, the steeper is the slope; the denser of adjacent air-masses moving with the same velocity tends to spread horizontally below the other. The slope rises in the direction of the colder air, which protrudes as a flat wedge under the warmer; the greater the difference of temperature, the less steep is the slope; in middle latitudes the average slope is of the order of half a degree.

In the case of air-masses moving under balanced forces along the isobars, no disturbance, apart from diffusion and turbulence, occurs at the frontal surface. But in practice disturbing influences are always present. Friction with the surface slows down the air in the lowest layers and deflects it across the isobars from high to low pressure. The winds are never quite steady, and their changes prevent the attainment of the perfect geostrophic balance. Pressure is usually changing differently in different areas, and here again the movement of the air lags behind the geostrophic value. The result is a thrust of the air from one side or the other of the front, and ascent with the usual adiabatic cooling and condensation of vapour. Moreover, air-masses are subject to changes of direction and velocity, the equilibrium of the front is thus disturbed, and one of them may force its way across, converging with its neighbour, and if warmer overriding it, if colder undercutting it; these frontal conflicts are the immediate cause of our bad weather, as will be described later.

The precise process which gives rise to convergence at a front on any occasion can often only be guessed. Convergence will continue until the front is adjusted to the new conditions, but there is necessarily a lag, and if the process responsible for the change continues the front may be 'active', and the weather may persist, for some time.

Fronts of the three types common in the westerlies will now be treated, with special reference to their occurrence in depressions, which, being areas of convergence, have many. The structure and development of depressions as wholes is described in Chapter XXXVI.

Warm Fronts

Where warmer air overrides colder the frontal surface is a 'warm front', sloping upwards over the cold air at an angle of about half a degree. The warm air is cooled in its ascent and a belt of cloud extends the length of the front, and forward some 400 or 500 miles (Fig. 106). The cloud is thickest and lowest, almost down to the surface, near the surface front; it consists of a great depth of nimbo-stratus with alto-stratus above it and partly hidden by it, from which continuous rain falls. Farther in advance only the higher and thinner cloud types are found, alto-stratus at 10,000 to 20,000 feet, thin enough for the sun to be seen as through ground glass, but thickening ominously behind into a sullen grey; forms of cirrus are the first visible forerunners at such high and cold altitudes, over 25,000 feet, that they consist of ice-crystals and are too thin to give rain; the delicate feathery cirrus is followed by cirro-stratus, a very thin sheet often with haloes of sun or moon.

Thus to an observer in the cold air on the ground the warm front gives clear warnings high overhead, for the first cirrus, 500 miles in front, is seen in some cases 24 hours before its arrival. Cirro-stratus with haloes, thickening to alto-stratus with rain and low nimbo-stratus with heavier rain, lead in the (surface) front. Temperature is low in the cold air-mass under the frontal surface, particularly when it comes from the east in winter; visibility is variable according to the degree of stability; detached patches of cumulus, grey and gloomy in the dull light, float about and merge into the higher clouds. Steady rain may persist for hours, 5 or 6 frequently, to take off slowly when the surface front passes; a belt of fog or nimbo-stratus down on the surface may mark its passage. Most of the rain

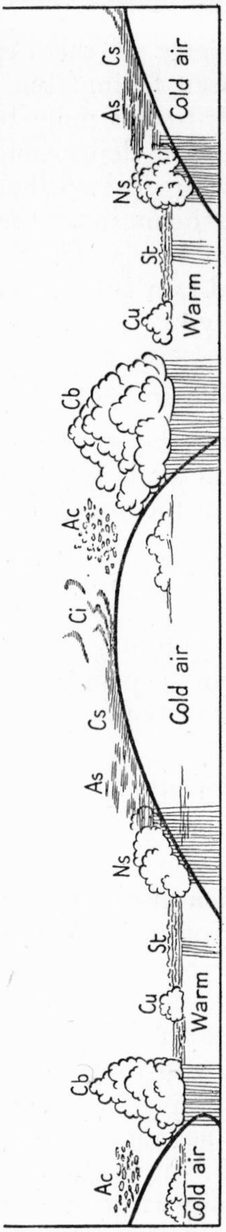

FIG. 106. Section through two depressions. Ac, Alto-cumulus; As, Alto-stratus; Ci, Cirrus; Cs, Cirro-stratus; Cu, Cumulus; Cb, Cumulo-nimbus; Ns, Nimbo-stratus; St, Stratus

is within 200 miles of the surface front and 300 miles of
the centre of the depression. Meanwhile the barometer
has been falling, but the wind is fairly constant, blowing
usually from a point between east and south or south-west.
Occasional depressions have a second, minor, warm front
following close on the first.

On the mean for the year in Britain (based on five stations,
Butt of Lewis, Tiree, Eskdalemuir, Aberdeen, Kew) warm
frontal rain falls considerably more heavily at night than in
the day.[1]

The Warm Sector

After the warm front comes the warm sector, in which
tropical air is lying horizontally before it is forced up the
slope of the warm front. The rain stops, temperature rises,
the wind veers, the barometer steadies. Cloud may be extensive but is not massive enough normally to give heavy rain,
though light rain and drizzle may fall and in summer
convection may give showers and even thunder on hot days.
Visibility is poor. On the hills this sector is the most prolific
source of rain.

Cold Fronts

Beyond the warm sector the cold polar air in rear of the
depression undercuts the tropical air at the cold front, a belt
of much disturbance, the details of which are not simple; it
is narrower than the cloud-belt of the warm front, and its
slope, about 1°, is steeper. Frowning cumulus clouds, often
cumulo-nimbus, are characteristic, towering up to great
heights and giving heavy precipitation in short showers, at
times with thunder. The barometer rises and temperature
falls sharply (e.g. Fig. 117, p. 352, on Nov. 12, at 0100). It
is a line, rather than an area, of disturbance—hence 'line
squall', 'ligne de grain'. Cold squalls blow out from it.
Visibility is good, usually very good, except in precipitation.

But other clouds complicate the picture. Nimbo-stratus

---

[1] *Rainfall at Fronts of Depressions*, A. H. R. Goldie, D.Sc., Meteorological Office,
Geophysical Memoirs, No. 69.

with intermittent rain is present in a wider belt both before
and behind the cold front, and alto-cumulus is characteristic.
These varied clouds can hardly be explained by the advance
of polar air simply as a sharp wedge under the tropical air,
for that would tend rather to repeat the cloud sequence of the
warm front, in the opposite order and in closer formation
since the slope is steeper. In part the explanation seems to
be that the cold front advances more rapidly a few thousand
feet aloft than on the surface, and the upper projecting 'nose',
unstable above the warm tropical air below it, descends
cascade-like from time to time, and is a main factor in the
convection clouds and squalls. The outbursts of strong
winds and angry clouds are often abrupt, and die away more
gradually. A cold front in a V-shaped secondary on the
south of a depression may be of great vigour, its squall line
violent and of great length (in some cases from the north of
Britain far into Europe), sweeping scythe-like across the
region. Many U-shaped troughs are without fronts, and
their weather is no worse than cloudy unless a closed secondary develops.

The favoured part of the day for cold frontal rain is the
afternoon, when it is both heaviest and most frequent,
especially inland and in summer.

The cold front is the advance-guard of polar air, in which
the sky is at first cloudless, but scattered cumulus soon
appears and grows, the surface air being warmed by the
ocean, and in greater degree by a hot land in summer.
Showers, at times with thunder, result from the instability,
and in winter snow may be widespread on the mountains in
the north. Moreover, the polar air usually has not one, but
several fronts, and each repeats the disturbance of the first.
Before the sequence is complete signs of the new depression
coming up from the west may appear.

A cold front contains exciting boisterous weather, with
vigorous squalls and gusts, massive spectacular clouds,
heavy showers of rain, snow, thunder, all of short duration
and interspersed with bright blue skies, in strong contrast
to the dull, persistently overcast skies, and steady rain, of
warm fronts. Where the meteorological situation is reinforced by favourable topography, secondary disturbances of

great violence may develop in the cold frontal belt, thunderstorms of more than usual intensity, and revolving storms of enormous velocity but small area, including sandstorms and waterspouts, and, most fearful of all, tornadoes.

Occlusions

Depressions contain a third kind of front, the 'occluded front' or 'line of occlusion'. The warm sector overruns the cold sector in front, but is itself overtaken by the polar sector in rear, and is thus raised on both sides and soon lifted above

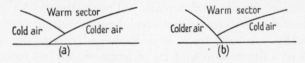

FIG. 107. Warm (*a*) and cold (*b*) occlusions

the surface, the depression becoming 'occluded'. Adiabatic cooling of the warm and humid uplifted air gives overcast skies with persistent moderate or heavy precipitation in a wide belt, for the depression slows down, and may be almost stationary, after occlusion, so that the precipitation continues for several hours with weather even more gloomy than in a warm front. In addition to the elevation of the warm sector as a whole a warm or cold frontal effect is usually present, according as the polar air is warmer or colder than the cold air in front which it overtakes under the uplifted warm sector (Fig. 107); this contributes to the precipitation.

Not seldom the thermometer seems to give the lie to the temperatures implied in the terms cold and warm, or polar and tropical, applied to air-masses and fronts, as when, to take a frequent example, a cold front brings a rise of temperature and humidity. The explanation is that surface air is not representative of the whole mass, being affected by local adventitious conditions. At night, particularly on land under a clear sky in winter, the surface air may cool 10° or 15° below the normal for the air-mass, and by morning a warm sector may be colder than polar air newly arrived from the ocean.

Sunshine and cloud, rain, wind, altitude, all may make surface air non-representative. Observations a thousand feet
above the surface are more representative.

Tornadoes

These whirls, the most violent winds on the globe, are
associated with cold fronts in regions which are specially
favourable for the conflict of very hot, moist, tropical air with
cold polar. They are most common in the middle and upper
valleys of the Mississippi and Missouri, where air from the
Gulf of Mexico meets polar air from the cold north, but they
occur occasionally in other countries in middle latitudes,
including England. Their favourite seasons are spring and
early summer, in the afternoon, but no season is exempt.
The following description is by R. de C. Ward[1]:

Briefly stated, a tornado is a very intense, progressive whirl, of small
diameter, with inflowing winds which increase tremendously in velocity as they near the centre, developing there a counter-clockwise
vorticular ascensional movement whose violence exceeds that of any
other known storm. From the violently agitated main cloud-mass
above there usually hangs a writhing funnel-shaped cloud, swinging
to and fro, rising and descending—the dreaded sign of the tornado
(Plate 16, facing p. 336). With a roar as of 10,000 freight trains comes
the whirl, out of the angry, often lurid west or south-west, advancing
almost always towards the north-east with the speed of a fast train;
its wind velocities exceeding 100, 200, and probably sometimes 300
or more miles an hour; its path of destruction usually less than a
quarter of a mile wide; its total life a matter of perhaps an hour or so.
It is as ephemeral as it is intense. In semi-darkness, accompanied or
closely followed by heavy rain, the tornado does its terrible work.
Almost in an instant all is over. The hopeless wreck of human buildings, the dead, and the injured, lie on the ground in a wild tangle of
confusion. The tornado has passed by. It is spinning away toward the
north-east, perhaps to carry destruction to other peaceful towns and
scattered farm-houses which lie in its path. . . .
We may roughly classify the damage done by tornadoes as follows:
(1) that resulting from the violence of the surface winds blowing over
buildings and other exposed objects, crushing them, dashing them
against each other; (2) that caused by the explosive action; and (3) that
resulting from the uprushing air movement close round the central

[1] *Q.J.R. Met. Soc.*, 43, 183.

vortex. Carts, barn-doors, cattle, iron chains, human beings, are carried aloft through the air, whirled aloft, and dashed to the ground. . . . Beams are driven into the ground, nails are forced head-first into boards; cornstalks are driven partly through doors. Harness is stripped from horses; clothing is torn from human beings and stripped into rags. In one place the destruction may be complete, with every building and tree and fence levelled to the ground. A few feet away the lightest object may be wholly undisturbed. . . . The explosive effects are many and curious. The walls of buildings—one or more of them—fall out, sometimes letting the roof collapse on to the foundations; or the roof may be blown off, leaving the walls standing. . . . It is natural, and unfortunate, that when once the proper conditions have been established, several tornadoes may develop over the same general region. . . . February 19, 1884, was the most remarkable and the most disastrous tornado day on record. Some 60 tornadoes occurred, mostly in the southern States. The loss of life was 800, 2,500 persons were wounded, and over 10,000 buildings were destroyed.

Weather Forecasting

Forecasting depends on the recognition on a series of synoptic charts of the pressure-systems and their fronts, if any, their character, developments, and movements. Numerous upper-air observations are available, and are very necessary in the analysis. Though much success is often attained it must be admitted that it is still a matter largely of empirical art as well as of science. Even a small error in the assumptions on which a forecast is based may have very large effects on its correctness. Thus, a slight miscalculation of the speed or the track of a front or a depression may vitiate the forecast seriously; let us suppose that a front is recognized over the ocean 600 miles west, and its assumed speed is 20 m.p.h., giving an expected time of arrival 30 hours later; but the actual speed proves to be 25 m.p.h., and the forecaster's time-table will be wrong, through this error alone, by 6 hours. A mistake of a few degrees in the expected track of a depression in winter may involve the difference between warm rain and widespread snow.

Much of the theory of the structure of depressions and anticyclones as commonly expounded seems straightforward and satisfactory, but observation of actual weather soon shows that it is not complete, and that few, if any, systems are fully covered by it. The weather along most fronts, for instance, is far from homogeneous even where the environment seems uniform; in many cases examination may reveal a reason, but not in all. If nature followed a diagrammatic scheme more closely and exclusively, weather forecasting would be a more exact science than it can yet claim to be.

CHAPTER XXXVI

THE ORIGIN AND DEVELOPMENT OF DEPRESSIONS

EVER since simultaneous weather observations have been plotted on charts, lively speculation has been roused as to the origin of the numerous and varied pressure-systems shown by the isobars travelling across the oceans and continents. Many theories have been propounded, optimistically received as a basis for forecasting the weather, and soon abandoned in the light of further knowledge of the facts and physical processes. It is now generally agreed that pressure-systems may arise in different ways, and it is not always possible to decide between them with conviction. Low-pressure systems, 'depressions', are by far the commonest in the westerlies, and most originate on the semi-permanent fronts (Figs. 57, 58, pp. 156, 157) in the west of the oceans in sub-tropical latitudes, or on the other fronts in higher latitudes which separate tropical air derived from high levels in the sub-tropical anticyclones, from polar air derived from the interior of North America or elsewhere in high latitudes; both air-masses are usually moving east at different speeds, but in some cases the polar air is moving westward. Since 1920 the theory of their origin as wave phenomena, worked out mainly by Norwegian meteorologists, has been widely accepted.

Frontal Depressions

According to this theory, from time to time the frontal equilibrium at some part of the polar front is disturbed, with the formation of a wave on the shear plane where the warm air flows over the wedge of cold air, the two currents having different speeds. This is an ordinary unstable wave, comparable with waves in water but of great length, 400 to 2,000 miles; it shows itself on the surface by a sinuosity, or wave, in the isobars (Fig. 108), in which the warm tropical air thrusts poleward into its neighbour. The polar air is

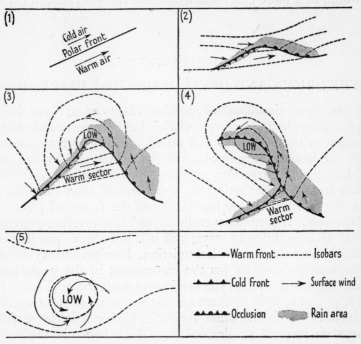

FIG. 108. Development and decay of a wave depression

deflected round the bulge, the tropical air in which maintains its course, and the disturbance rapidly develops with their interaction. Barometric pressure falls in a fairly definite way justifying the name depression, and a closed isobaric system of a roughly circular shape forms; the direction of the polar stream is much altered, to SE. and E. on the leading side, between W. and N. in the rear. The warm sector is triangular, with its apex near the middle of the depression. All the time the disturbance travels in some easterly direction, carried along apparently by the warm tropical air in which it arose.

PLATE 16

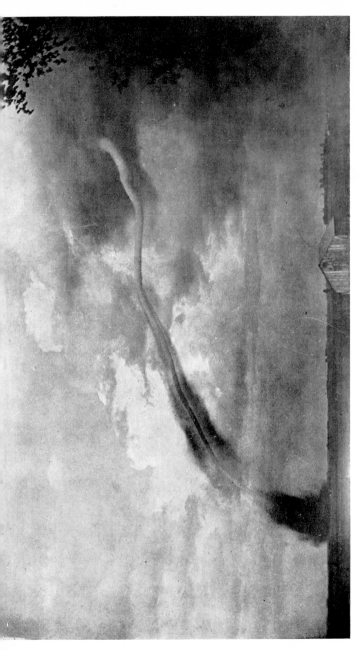

A tornado, Minnesota, U.S.A.

The stages in the development (for the north hemisphere) are shown diagrammatically in Fig. 108, from the incipient wave to full frontal activity and then decay after occlusion,

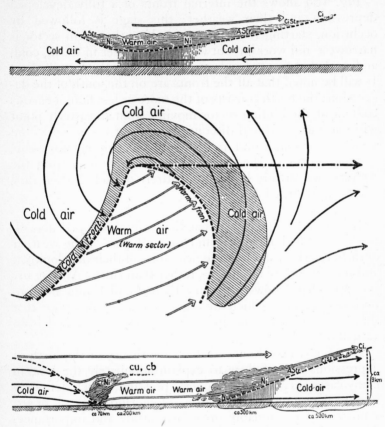

FIG. 109. Diagrammatic structure of a fully-developed frontal depression (Bjerknes)

the system degrading into a gentle whirl with cloud but little rain, and no strong winds, and gradually dying out.

But depressions are rarely solitary. Another tends to form on the trailing cold front behind the first, and to repeat its development; families of about four are a usual series, each originating a little south of its predecessor. The surge of polar air in rear of the last may make its way far south to join the trade, which is in part thus maintained. A family of depressions, with this polar outbreak, is seen in Fig. 39, p. 123.

Fig. 109 shows the internal fronts of a fully developed depression and their weather; this stage is followed by occlusion, starting from the apex where the warm sector is narrowest and working outward; the weather in warm, cold, and occluded fronts has been described in the last chapter. It will be noted that all the fronts are on the south of the depression; the north consists of the more or less homogeneous cold air of the leading sector moving from an easterly point without abrupt frontal discontinuities, but nevertheless the weather is cloudy and rainy (snowy in winter) for some distance north of the centre. Most depressions from the Atlantic are already largely or entirely occluded when they reach the British Isles.

It must be emphasized that the 'fully developed depressions' described above account for only part of the weather of the westerlies, and that the principles of their development and movement are tendencies rather than rules. Almost any synoptic chart shows a confused variety of fronts and isobaric formations, which diverge so much from type that they can hardly be classified and have to be studied individually.

One serious weakness in the wave theory of the birth of depressions is its failure to explain adequately the low, in many cases very low, atmospheric pressure, which definitely implies the removal, or 'eviction', of enormous masses of air, a process of presumably great magnitude and importance. Though pressure and isobars may be of less significance in the structure than air-masses and fronts, it seems impossible to ignore the physical bearings of this eviction, and the variations in pressure (in the British Isles between about 925 and 1,050 mb.). Shaw calculated that in a large depression over the North Atlantic on 31 January 1926 over 2 million million tons of air must have been removed.

Polar fronts are not the only birthplace of frontal depressions. They are liable to form wherever the field of pressure is such as to bring air-masses with contrasted qualities of temperature and humidity into contact. Thus many spring up as 'secondaries' on the fronts of primary depressions, which provide the necessary juxtaposition. The cold front or occlusion which trails behind well-developed systems is a likely, and frequent, origin, and secondaries may originate within the polar current in rear of the primary (p. 340). A secondary begins as a mere bulge in the isobars of a primary, and may soon grow into a deep disturbance with its own closed isobars, but many, with very disturbed weather, continue as only slight irregularities on the isobars. They are similar to primaries in their weather, and cause a renewal of clouds and rain, with winds possibly of gale force, particularly on the south side. They tend to move anticlockwise round the primary, and when very active they may absorb it. Most secondaries are in the south of a depression.

It appears, then, that depressions develop on an existing polar front of great length, which may be regarded as an essential element in the general circulation, and themselves modify that front, and give rise to successors. Each depression is capable of producing many secondaries.

It will be obvious that the frontal depressions of the westerlies are not revolving systems of winds, despite the name 'cyclone' still sometimes applied; most of the air involved does not make even one circuit of the centre before it rises from the surface and leaves the depression in the upper atmosphere; and the movement is fundamentally different from the rotation, at great speed, of the air in tornadoes, dust-devils, and waterspouts, and on a larger scale in the inner zone of tropical cyclones. But it seems likely that, at any rate in their later stages, some depressions do consist largely of what may be described as rotating disks of air. And the depressions that start as tropical cyclones and are carried into the westerlies are at first rather systems of rotating winds than frontal depressions.

Other Origins

Three classes may be distinguished:

(*a*) Some depressions enter the westerlies from the tropics, being the last stage of tropical cyclones; they may become rejuvenated and develop fronts, but most are whirls of little and diminishing intensity. The other classes are more important, thermal depressions and lee depressions.

(*b*) Thermal depressions. The formation of low pressures by the expansion of a column of air by local heating was explained on p. 104. The process is responsible for the shallow thermal depressions common in hot humid lands in summer but not in the cool climate of north-west Europe, though they are not unknown there, for heavy cumulus clouds, showers, and thunder are familiar features in hot summer weather, and these local convectional effects are capable of forming shallow depressions, which may continue active for some days, with convectional rather than frontal weather. In China and other lands with a monsoonal indraught of hot moist air thermal depressions are a main element in the summer climate. In the westerlies the secondaries in the rear of a depression that form in polar air heated over a warm sea are probably thermal; but the warmth is only relative for the weather is usually cold and showery, a bleak type very different from that of the thermal depressions of hot lands.

(*c*) Lee depressions. The mountains of the British Isles are not high and continuous enough to give rise to lee depressions, which, however, are not uncommon in middle latitudes. Their mechanism is described in Chapter XXXII. They are frequent in the Gulf of Genoa and the plains of Lombardy, when the cold front of a large depression passing over north-west Europe, and the massive polar current behind it, sweep across France and Germany to the Alps. The Alps, concave to the south, are well shaped to deflect air-masses approaching from the north, and to divert them into the Rhone valley and the Danube lands, forming depressions in the concave arc on the south. These are intensified by both convectional and frontal developments, convectional since the cold air of the upper levels crosses the ranges in advance of the surface front and descends to the warm lowlands and seas beyond, undercutting the warm damp air there, frontal in the interaction of the polar air from the Rhone valley and the Danube lands with the Mediterranean air; dense cloud, heavy rain, and great turbulence result.

Most of the depressions, and hence most of the bad weather, of the north Italian region are of this type. Lee depressions are not prominent on the convex north of the Alps. They are an ordinary form of disturbance in other regions where long ranges lie athwart the passage of stable air, as in central China in winter.

All depressions, whatever their origin, may deepen or fill up without any obvious reason, the pressure change occurring either on one side or over the whole cyclonic area, irrespective of changes due to the movement of the system. An area with increasing pressure (an 'isallobaric high') has diverging surface air, which is supplied by descent and therefore has a tendency to fine weather, and one of decreasing pressure (an 'isallobaric low') has converging surface air, ascent, and cloud and rain.

CHAPTER XXXVII

TRACKS AND SPEEDS OF DEPRESSIONS AND FRONTS

The tracks and speeds of pressure-systems and fronts are not only of theoretical interest but of practical importance for the weather forecaster, since the weather elements are relative to position in the system, the movements of which are of hardly less significance than the form. Experience has established certain principles which seem to govern the movements. These will be indicated first, and then some of the actual paths will be described. The movements of fronts will be considered later.

Movements of Depressions

Depressions are carried along in the general atmospheric current towards the north-east, somewhat poleward of the polar front on which they start. Five principles are available for estimating their speed and track. (1) The movement of the last few hours will continue, allowance being made for the changes in progress and for approach to mountain ranges and other features which may cause deflexions; (2) a symmetrical system will move towards the largest negative pressure tendencies, that is towards the area in which pressure is falling most rapidly, and away from positive tendencies.

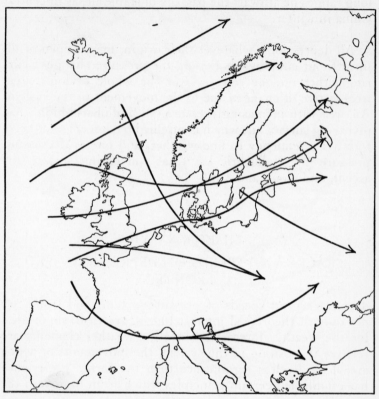

FIG. 110. Some main tracks of depressions in Europe (based on van Bebber)

The tendencies in the last three hours are reported by synoptic stations, and if it is desired they may be shown on the synoptic chart by isopleths, 'isallobars', which are useful for other purposes also; but a general deepening or filling-up of a depression will itself cause tendencies in the whole area which must be allowed for; (3) the track and speed are those of the geostrophic wind in the warm sector; when the depression is occluded it slows down, and may remain almost stationary. The isobars in the warm sector are generally straight and parallel; unfortunately most depressions lose their warm sectors before reaching north-west Europe, and over the oceans where warm sectors do exist the

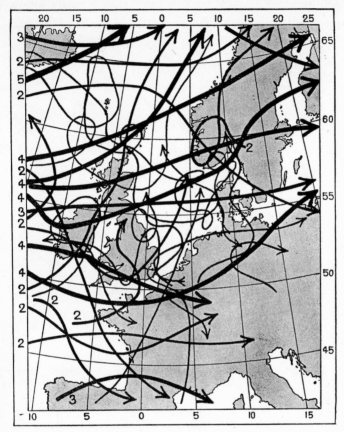

FIG. 111. Tracks of depressions in 1926; the figures indicate the number of depressions which followed the tracks. (Meteorological Office, London)

observations are usually inadequate for the accurate charting of the isobars, so that this method can give only an approximate estimate; (4) the system moves with the winds in the middle troposphere at about 15,000 feet; (5) the movement of the system is that of the strongest winds in any considerable area in it.

If the indications agree they may be accepted with some

confidence, but without any certainty that a change will not soon occur in the whole situation.

To pass now from theory to the tracks actually followed,

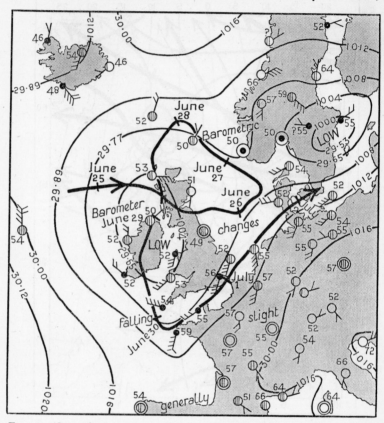

Fig. 112. Synoptic chart, 0700, 29 June 1927; the thick line shows the track of the depression. (For meaning of symbols see Fig. 11, p. 50)

in the North Atlantic region depressions have a distinct tendency to choose the warm waters of the North Atlantic Drift. The region of lowest pressure, and of deepest and most numerous depressions, is that part of the Norwegian Sea where temperature is highest for the latitude, the warm water being propitious for cyclonic growth and activity. The most frequented paths lie south-west to north-east between Britain and Iceland, and round the north of Scandinavia. But there are many others, and secondaries usually keep farther south, often crossing the British Isles, or coming in over the Channel Entries and passing up the English Channel; this latter track is the more important in view of the weather associated with it in England (p. 350). Some depressions advance from the north-west over the North Sea into Europe. The entries to the Baltic Sea and the south

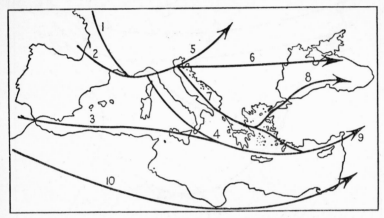

Fig. 113. Some main tracks of depressions in the Mediterranean region

of the Baltic itself are much frequented. Many attempts have been made to map these paths as definite belts. Fig. 110 is based on the tracks plotted by van Bebber.[1] Such maps have their uses, but a glance at the actual courses followed in a single year in the British Isles region (Fig. 111) shows that generalization is extremely uncertain, perhaps impossible. Probably the tracks are more erratic in this region than elsewhere. Fig. 112 gives the track of the depression responsible for the completely overcast skies and heavy rain which disappointed thousands of would-be observers of the total eclipse of the sun in the north of England on 29 June 1927.

The Mediterranean lands owe their winter weather to depressions, some of which are derived from the North Atlantic. They are more uniform in their movements than

[1] *Meteorologische Zeitschrift*, 1891.

those on the ocean, and the mean tracks of Fig. 113 are more reliable than those of Fig. 110 for the North Atlantic; possibly the strong contrast in temperature and humidity between land and sea is a factor in localizing the depressions.

In North America also (Fig. 114) the movements are more uniform than on the North Atlantic, especially in the east of

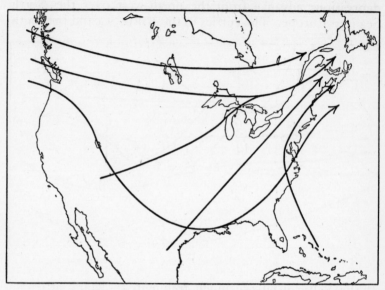

FIG. 114. Some main tracks of depressions in North America

the continent, and a control seems to be exerted by the warm Gulf Stream, and the large inland waters of the Great Lakes and the St. Lawrence.

Depressions leaving the North American coast can be traced day after day on the Atlantic. An east-bound ship may remain in the same sector and experience similar winds and weather for several days, the barometer on board being fairly steady. But in winter west-bound ships have to plough through one storm after another in rapid succession, since the speed of the ship is in this case added to that of the depressions, and the barometer shows a series of steep rises and falls (Fig. 115). In winter probably the wildest tract on the globe is the ocean between Newfoundland, Scotland, and Iceland, where the largest liners often have to reduce speed, and the mountainous seas may carry away boats and heavy fittings, but in summer the normal weather is fairly settled.

The westerlies of the south hemisphere are the scene of wild cyclonic activity. No sufficient material exists for detailed mapping, but it is likely that the pressure systems move from west to east over the almost unbroken expanses

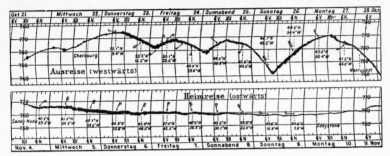

FIG. 115. Pressure and winds recorded between the English Channel and New York by SS. *Kaiser Wilhelm der Grosse* on an outward (upper diagram) and homeward (lower diagram) voyage, 1902. (Schott)

of the Southern Ocean on rather less erratic tracks than those of the north hemisphere.

The speed of depressions is very variable, at any rate in the north hemisphere; they may remain stationary, or almost stationary, for several days; some advance fairly uniformly, others change suddenly and erratically. The average off north-west Europe ranges from 18 m.p.h. in summer to 27 m.p.h. in winter; it is rather more in America. On the Atlantic speeds up to 60 m.p.h. are not uncommon in winter, but the average is about 30 m.p.h.

Movements of Fronts

Each front in a depression has its own movements, which are independent of the system as a whole, so that the fronts change their relative positions. The movement of a front is evidently that of the two air-masses it separates, and its speed may be got from the speed of the geostrophic wind (on either side of the front), the component of which at right angles to the front is the approximate speed of a cold front or of an occluded front, and rather more than the speed of a warm front. Hence for any isobar interval the more nearly normal the front lies to the isobars, the greater is its speed; a front lying parallel to the isobars tends to be almost stationary. Since a long front usually cuts the isobars at different angles, and the pressure-gradients along it vary, its movement differs in different parts. The sharper, less diffuse, fronts usually move more slowly. At best the rules merely indicate the speed of the front at the time, but are no sure guide to the future. As with depressions as wholes, it must be assumed that the front will continue its recent tendency unless some reason to the contrary can be seen.

The movements of anticyclones are treated in Chapter XXXIV.

CHAPTER XXXVIII

SPELLS OF WEATHER. PERIODICITIES

THE high- and low-pressure systems described in the preceding chapters may be regarded as the smaller units which control weather, each of the depressions operating for not more than 3 or 4 days as a rule, the anticyclones for longer. But weather has a pronounced tendency to recur; a depression is followed by another similar to it, advancing on almost the same track, and sometimes five or six form a connected series. The weather changes are repeated with each system, the 'spell' lasting perhaps a fortnight. Or a single system may maintain an almost fixed position for days or weeks, and give equally persistent, but more uniform, weather. Often the spell is broken abruptly, and a new type starts. These spells may be regarded as the larger weather units, and they are certainly worthy of classification, though it must be admitted that they do not cover more than a small part of the whole confused picture of the climate. It is at the time of change of spells of this kind that forecasts usually fail. As long as any series continues the forecaster's task is comparatively easy, and even empirical rules may guide him. But to forecast the change from one type to another calls for a deeper knowledge of the atmosphere than we yet possess.

As long ago as 1887 Abercrombie published a useful classification for the British Isles, based on the forms of the pressure-systems, their positions and movements, which is summarized below; the original description is to be found in a new edition of his work, *Weather*, Abercrombie and Goldie, 1934, which should be consulted. In all the types anticyclones seem to be the strong and persistent features which dominate the movements of the depressions.

Southerly type. The British Isles are between a large stationary anticyclone over Europe and persistent though fluctuating low pressures on the north-east Atlantic, with the isobars trending SW.–NE. The weather is mainly cyclonic and possibly rainy, winds generally southerly, sky overcast with low cloud, air damp, all these features often changing in detail though persisting in type. However, an important distinction is between E. and SE. winds, bringing air from the interior and east of Europe, cold and dry in winter, hot and dry in summer (but the type is not common in summer), and those between S. and SW. from the ocean, moist in all seasons, mild in winter, cool in summer; the former, continental, type approximates to the easterly type of weather described below, which is common in winter. The southerly type is most frequent in autumn. The essential feature is the persistence of the high pressures over the continent, which seem to hold firm against any advance of depressions from the ocean; depressions which come up are deflected and pass far to the north-west, but Britain is more or less within their outskirts, and hence has fluctuations of pressure and variations in wind direction, but no large or lasting changes of wind or weather, for though the oscillations give considerable changes the main type persists.

Northerly type. A belt of high pressure along the axis of the North Atlantic between the Azores and the Arctic (often uniting large anticyclones over those regions), and low pressures over Europe give us northerly winds; the type may last some days but is much less persistent than the Southerly type; it is most persistent in summer. The northerly winds bring polar maritime air, and the weather in

our west and midlands areas, at its best, is bright with clear
blue skies, exhilarating, and cool (cold in winter, but not
much below freezing, since the winds, though polar, are
from the ocean); but hard white cumulus cloud and showers
are likely, and at worst the skies in the east of Britain are
overcast, bleak and rainy if secondaries develop and travel
south down the North Sea or along our east coasts; and even
without definite secondaries the east has a tendency to
gloomy skies and passing showers, snow in spring, owing to
the turbulence set up in the surface air, which has acquired
heat and moisture over the sea, when it reaches land.

Easterly type. A strong stationary anticyclone over
Scandinavia, extending west over the Norwegian Sea to
Iceland and often east into north-east Europe and Asia, is
the essential feature; pressure decreases southward in north-
west Europe to the sub-tropics, and the winds, contrary to
the normal, are between NE. and E., or even SE. Depressions may be stationary, or travel slowly, over the north of
France and the English Channel (some moving slowly westward, in opposition to the usual easterly direction), so that the
associated weather tends to be of long duration.

This type occurs in all seasons except autumn, and is
prominent in spring. The wind is easterly, usually north-
east, steady and fairly strong, the air dry, cold physically
and colder physiologically owing to the piercing strength
and persistence of the wind, and the type is notorious as
being the most trying experienced in the British Isles for
weak constitutions. The weather may be anticyclonic and
fine with almost cloudless skies, but usually the surface air
is hazy, not seldom to the point of gloom in lee of industrial
districts owing to the inversion of temperature commonly
present at about 2,000 feet; long rainless spells are frequent.
But if cyclonic influences assert themselves as depressions
move up slowly from France or along the Channel, the
weather can be perhaps the most unpleasant known in
Britain, and it is the more persistent owing to their slow
movement; the winds are still easterly, but the sky is overcast with a gloomy pall of low, amorphous, grey cloud, the
air is hazy, the temperature low, and precipitation con-

tinuous for hours though not heavy. In winter and spring
most of our snow falls in these circumstances, as in the very
severe weather of February and March, 1947 (Fig. 116).
If the northern anticyclone spreads east over central Russia,
the British Isles being within its southern flank, our air is

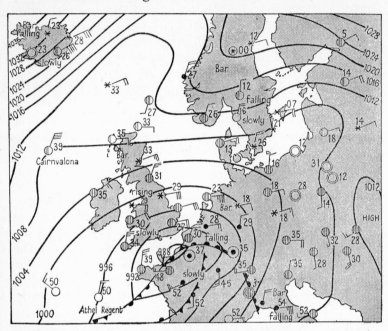

FIG. 116. Synoptic chart, 1800, 21 February 1947; widespread snow in Britain.
For meaning of symbols see Fig. 22, p. 64

derived from the Continent, and in winter it can be very cold;
such a distribution tends to last for several days, or weeks,
when once well established, giving our most severe spells of
frost. On the other hand, in summer this type, when definitely anticyclonic with no disturbances within range, can
give extremely fine, almost cloudless, hot weather; in 1947
it persisted through the end of July and all August into
September, with uninterrupted NE. winds over most of the
British Isles, a rainless and exceptionally hot and cloudless
spell.

In the Southerly type also Europe (central as well as
north Europe) is covered by an anticyclone, but the British

Isles are then under cyclonic influences from the Atlantic, and in winter the weather is usually warm and damp.

Westerly type. This is distinguished from the types already described by being dominated not by sluggish but by

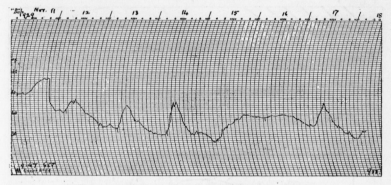

FIG. 117 *a*. Barogram, Radcliffe Observatory, Oxford

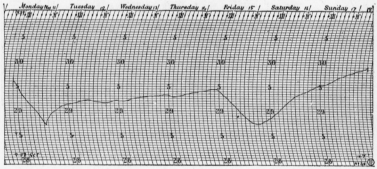

FIG. 117 *b*. Thermogram, Radcliffe Observatory, Oxford

rapidly-moving pressure-systems. It is most frequent in autumn, and the most characteristic weather of that season is associated with it. The sub-tropical high pressures are in their normal position, or extend rather less far north, and vigorous depressions pass eastward on the ocean, most of them having originated on a polar front in the west. Their usual tracks lie between Scotland and Iceland, but some depressions, the majority secondaries, cross our islands. The outstanding feature of the weather is its changeable nature as

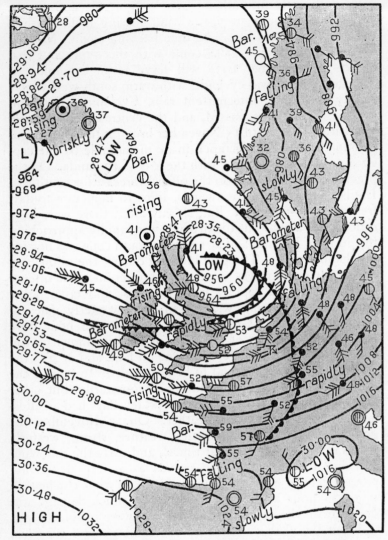

FIG. 118. Synoptic chart, 1800, 23 November 1928; widespread gales.
For meaning of symbols see Fig. 11, p. 50.

the air-masses and fronts pass. Temperature varies abruptly,
without much respect to time of day (Fig. 117), but its
mean is not notably high or low. This type is prominent
when it brings gales, which may blow hard for days, full

gales with little intermission, not only at sea and on the coasts, but inland as well, the wind veering from south to west as the centres pass, and then backing again. Most of our series of autumn gales come with this type, and that of 10–30 November 1928 will serve as an example. At first the weather was cyclonic, with warm south-west winds, cloudy skies, and intermittent rain. Cyclonic activity increased as the days passed, and the centres passed nearer the British Isles, until 15 November brought the first serious gale in the English Channel, made memorable by the capsizing of the Rye lifeboat with the loss of 17 hands. On the previous morning at 1000 the official forecast for south-east England was 'south-west winds, light to moderate to-day, freshening to-morrow'. But, shortly after, there were indications that a vigorous disturbance was rapidly approaching the north of Ireland, and at 1345 the south cone was hoisted in Channel ports. The gale blew up during the night, and the following day was even more boisterous. An intense secondary moved rapidly from the west and crossed the British Isles, causing widespread south-westerly gales in southern districts. Gusts of over 90 miles an hour were registered, hundreds of telephone lines were blown down, and much other damage was done on land and at sea; the cross-Channel services had to be suspended. In rear of the depression the weather became fair temporarily, but other disturbances approached, and the next few days had an alternation of storm and fine weather. On 22 November the general inference was 'unsettled weather, strong westerly winds reaching gale force at times', and early the following morning the expected gale arrived as a deep depression crossed central Scotland (Fig. 118). The wind reached 88 miles an hour at Liverpool and again much damage was done; again the cross-Channel packets were unable to sail.

From the 10th to the 23rd the same general type had persisted, as is shown by the barogram (Fig. 119). After the gale of the 23rd pressure rose, as it had done after the previous disturbances, and the weather became fair. But this was thought to be merely another temporary interruption in the series of disturbances, and on 25 November the official inference was 'conditions remain favourable for the approach of further depressions from the Atlantic'; similarly on that evening: 'a new depression is approaching Ireland from the Atlantic. After a temporary improvement winds will again back to south-west and freshen to gale force'; and on the following day 'a renewal of gales generally is to be expected'. But, instead, the Azores anticyclone began to extend north-east, and by 27 November it covered the Atlantic; light northerly winds brought generally fair and cool weather to the British Isles—a complete change from

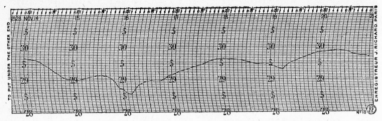

FIG. 119. Barogram, 14–21 November 1928, Oxford

the earlier south-westerly cyclonic type. The new spell continued for several days.

But the usual weather experienced in the Westerly type is less stormy. The intensity of winds and weather depends partly on the intensity of the depressions and largely on their tracks; the wildest storms are associated with deep depressions which cross our islands, particularly if they have secondaries sweeping round their southern outskirts.

Anticyclonic spells. Anticyclones have a strong tendency to remain almost stationary and give long spells of anticyclonic weather, not always of the same type, which is described in Chapter XXXIV.

Cyclonic weather, associated with a single depression, can hardly be considered as a 'spell' of weather, but it can be persistent and noteworthy. For an example, Fig. 120 shows the depression that gave a continuous spell of 72 hours of rain in much of south England; owing to the circular form of the track frontal rain fell without intermission over the south Midlands for 3 days. The rainfall at Oxford was 3·6 inches, and the widespread floods in the Thames Valley reached almost the highest levels ever recorded.

The mood of the weather. The weather may develop a 'mood', for reasons which are often obscure, and tend to maintain it for a month or more. The spells that have been described above are one aspect, based on the position and movement of pressure-systems. Another, of a different kind, is the tendency for rainy, or it may be dry, weather to continue for a considerable time, sometimes many weeks, though the isobaric systems do not seem to be specially favourable. During a rainy mood slight disturbances which at other periods would give only cloudy skies and little rain may spread heavy and continuous precipitation over large areas, and during a dry mood even depressions of a menacing appearance pass by without any notable deterioration in the weather. An inference is that the delineation of surface pressure-systems is far from being a complete picture of the atmospheric processes which produce weather.

Periodicity in Weather

Abnormalities in weather depend directly on variations in the general circulation of the atmosphere, that is, in the distribution of pressure, and 'spells' of weather are a manifestation of their persistence. In north-west Europe sometimes the Azores anticyclone spreads and the cyclone tracks are displaced northward of their normal position, giving Britain fine weather; sometimes the continental anticyclone dominates the weather, this being a frequent cause of abnormally cold winters. Or the cyclone tracks may be farther south than usual, and the British Isles have wet and stormy weather, mild in winter, cold in summer. Similar displacements may affect only a small area or a large part of the globe. They may persist for a week or two, or for a season. Possibly the immediate cause of the glacial periods was such a change persisting for thousands of years.

It is tempting to try to establish some periodicity in these changes, to discover cycles of a duration of some years, or pulsations covering centuries. The necessary basis for the quest is provided by series of instrumental records, some of which go back for over 100 years—the rainfall record at Padua starts in 1725—and for the more distant past by such self-registered natural phenomena as the growth-rings in trees of great age, especially the yellow pines of Arizona and the sequoias of the Sierra Nevada, California, in which 3,000

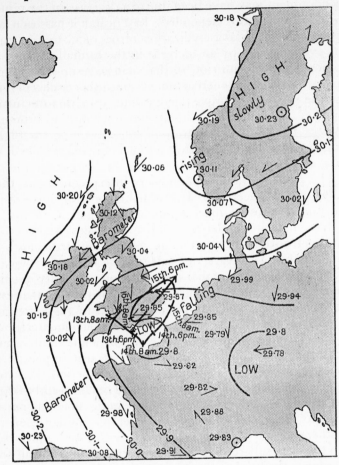

FIG. 120. Synoptic chart, 0700, 14 June 1903; the thick line shows the track of the depression

years of growth can be traced, from which Douglass[1] concludes that about 13 cycles, with a length from 7 to 300 years, can be distinguished in various regions, and the beaches which mark former levels of lakes.[2] The works

[1] *Climatic Cycles and Tree Growth*—Douglass, A. E. (Washington).
[2] See *The Climatic Factor as illustrated in Arid America*—Ellsworth Huntington (Washington); also, *Climate through the Ages*—Brooks, C. E. P. (London).

of man also contribute evidence; remains of deserted settlements are found in the deserts of Central Asia, and their abandonment may have been due to a decrease in the rainfall on which agriculture depended. In Yucatan it has been suggested that the Maya civilization of 600 B.C. to A.D. 1400 was overwhelmed by an increase in the rainfall causing the tropical forest to run riot, so that man gave up his unequal struggle against its encroachment; but other archaeologists find the evidence to prove the opposite, a stability of climate, and they attribute the decay of the civilization to economic distress, the result of progressive soil erosion on the higher ground, which reduced the arable land and blocked the lakes and rivers of the lowlands.[1]

The evidence, and especially its interpretation, in these latter cases is uncertain. The actual records of temperature and rainfall provide more solid material, and mathematical analysis indicates a large number of cycles with periods ranging from days to many years; Shaw tabulated some 130, ranging up to 260 years, in his *Manual of Meteorology*, vol. II, ch. vii. Their very number is one obvious difficulty in using them as a guide to the future. Another is the fact that even the best-marked cycles do not recur with any regularity and precision; the cold and dry part of a cycle may be interrupted by warm wet years, and a severe winter or a fine summer may break the succession of seasons of the opposite type. Many cycles seem to have continued for a long period, and then suddenly to have changed phase or died out. To add to these and other uncertainties, sundry sporadic phenomena are liable to supervene and have considerable influence on the weather; a great volcanic eruption may throw so much dust into the atmosphere that the temperature is lowered all over the globe; the level of the land may change, or the distribution of land and sea, with some resulting changes in the ocean currents which exercise a far-reaching influence on climate. It must be remembered, too, that changes in one region are related, directly and indirectly, to changes in the rest of the atmosphere. So it can be readily understood that cycles are of little if any value for the practical forecasting of seasonal weather.

[1] Cooke, C. W., *J. Washington Ac. Sci.*, 1931.

A well-known cycle is one with a mean period of about
35 years (the individual periods vary by many years) which
was worked out by Brückner[1] from the available evidence
of changes in the level of the Caspian Sea, advances and
retreats of the glaciers of the Alps, and other phenomena,
and was found to apply remarkably closely to many aspects
of life. The reality of this cycle seems to be well established,
though it is of little use for actual forecasting; it is a basis of
the choice of 35 years as the period estimated to give true
mean values of climatic elements. It is difficult to determine its underlying cause; probably it is merely a resultant
of many cycles.

The 11-year cycle of sunspot frequency seems to be more
or less reflected in the weather in parts of the world, though
not in north-west Europe. A short cycle of $12\frac{1}{3}$ months is
found by Brunt[2] in western Europe, and cycles of 12, 13, 18,
19, 24, 36, 48, and 72 days for barometric pressure are
claimed by C. E. P. Brooks, again an *embarras de richesse*.

Another interesting approach is the correlation of variations, simultaneous or consecutive, in different parts of the
globe. Hildebrandsson showed that the mean seasonal barometric pressure in the Icelandic region varies inversely with
that in the Azores in winter. The mean temperature at Oslo
in November and December varies very closely with that
at Berlin in the following March and April; and the rainfall in Java from October to March with the pressure at
Bombay in the following April to September. Shaw demon-
strated that the strength of the trade-wind at St. Helena
varies with the rainfall in the south of England. Walker[3]
established a connexion between the monsoonal rainfall in
India and the pressure at Cape Town and in the South
Orkneys in the following December–February. A great
number of such correlations have been worked out, but the
correlation is in no case complete, and a forecast based on
them is as liable to fail as one based on cycles.

---

[1] Brückner, *Klimaschwankungen seit 1700* (Vienna).
[2] *Q.J.R. Meteorological Society*, January 1927.
[3] See many papers by Sir Gilbert Walker in *Memoirs of Indian Meteorological
Dept.*, vols. xx and xxi, and in *Q.J.R. Meteorological Society*.

PART VI
SOME CLIMATIC TYPES

CHAPTER XXXIX
THE SUDAN

Seasonal Rhythm

EXCEPT in a few small areas near the equator the seasonal rhythm is one of the fundamentals of climate; description cannot be at all adequate unless it takes full account of the seasonal changes, and, in most countries, the weather changes characteristic of each season. In the inner and outer tropics the year is divided by rainfall and humidity into the rains and the dry season. In the trade-wind deserts temperature distinguishes summer from winter. In higher latitudes more elements are involved, rain and humidity, temperature, weather sequence, and length of day and night, a most prominent feature in the polar regions. Seasonal change seems to be favourable both directly and indirectly to the highest human development, except where it entails enervating moist heat or paralysing cold; the most advanced civilizations have evolved in lands where the year goes round with a strong, but not excessive, seasonal rhythm, punctuated by considerable weather changes. But at the equator the monotony tends to undermine civilizations that may be introduced. White men, lacking the stimulus of their invigorating native climate, lose their physical and mental energy, and are the more liable to succumb to parasitic and other diseases; the parasites that are the scourge of such lands seem to flourish in proportion as higher organisms are debilitated by the heat and moisture, the hot-house conditions without respite.

The following descriptions are given to illustrate and emphasize the significance of seasonal changes in countries where they are prominent.

The Sudan (or Outer Tropical) Type

Climatically we apply the term Sudan to a belt between 8° and 15° N. which crosses Africa from Abyssinia to French Guinea and Senegal, and includes the Anglo-Egyptian Sudan in the east, Nigeria (north of the Benue River), and the French Sudan in the west, as well as vast tracts still not developed. The seasonal rhythm is one of rainfall chiefly. The year is divided into three well-marked seasons, the cool, the hot and dry, and the rainy; and possibly September, October, and November should be classed as a fourth season, for after the rains temperature rises again under the cleared skies, making those months a minor hot season, but the land is still wet, and the weather is less dry than in the earlier hot months.

January is the middle of the cool dry season. The sun, and the equatorial low pressures for the most part, are in the south hemisphere. Asia and north Africa are dominated by the sub-tropical high pressures, and the trade blows steadily from the north-east over the thirsty sands of the Sahara; no pressure irregularities like those of the westerlies disturb the weather, and not a drop of rain falls; from the beginning of November till the end of March is a season of drought almost everywhere, and in the north the dry season starts a month earlier and continues a month later. The winds soon dry up the land, and by January most of the smaller streams have disappeared. The luxuriant summer-green vegetation withers and the leaves fall, baobab trees show their thick gaunt leafless boughs, and the savanna grasses are sere and brown; the ground is dry and dusty. But the season is cool only by contrast with the rest of the year, for here, within the tropic, the midday sun, even at its lowest, is 55° above the southern horizon, almost as high as in June in England, and frost is unknown. This is the resting season for plants, and many animals hibernate. When the sun shines brightly from a blue sky, the landscape, though dead, is not uncheerful. But at times the air is thick with haze and dust, and smoke from the burning grasses fired by the natives to improve the next year's growth. The savanna sometimes blazes and smoulders in patches over thousands of square miles, and the smoke darkens the air as far as the Guinea coast; even in a cloudless sky the sun is visible only as a pale disk in the grey haze, and serves rather to emphasize than brighten the lifeless and cheerless prospect.

As the year advances and the sun mounts higher day by day as it returns to the north hemisphere, the weather gets hotter, for the sky is still cloudless; March, April, and May are the hot dry season. In April the sun is overhead, and the heat is intense; the dry and dusty land is parched, and only the largest rivers still flow. No trees can survive except such as have provided themselves with effective devices to restrict desiccation. The mean temperature in April, May, and June exceeds 90°; the thermometer in the shade rises above 100° day after day, and though the nights are cooler the temperature does not fall much below 80°; the days become more and more furnace-like as the sun passes north in May.

June brings the rains. The equatorial low pressures have been creeping northward, invited by the intense heating of the arid lands, and by May the intertropical front is about 12° N., where the dry trade meets, moist, light and variable, monsoonal winds from beyond the equator. The arrival of the rains and the cooler air, which reach the Sudan in June, is hailed with delight by the natives.

In the west Sudan the rains usually begin with tornadoes (p. 205):

In a leaden and motionless sky appears a strange sign—a kind of dark-coloured dome rising from the horizon, taking unwonted and terrifying shapes; great semicircles of cloud rise and range themselves one above the other in thick and heavy, but clearly defined masses, the whole glowing beneath with metallic lustre; and all the while not a breath stirs. Then of a sudden comes a great and awful gust, a tremendous sweep that lays low trees, plants, and birds, and whirls the mad vultures round and round, overturning everything in its passage. The full force of the tornado is let loose; everything shakes and totters to its foundations; Nature writhes under the terrible might of the tempest. For the space of some twenty minutes all the windows of heaven are opened upon the earth, a deluge of rain revives the parched soil, and the wind blows furiously, strewing the earth with leaves,

branches, and wreckage of all kinds. And then suddenly the storm
subsides; the cyclone is past, and the sky is once more clear, motionless,
and blue. (P. LOTI.)

The air is vapour-laden; though the mornings are clear,
and the sky a pure deep blue, towards noon massive cumulus
clouds form and overspread the sky, and a torrential downpour begins, at times with vivid flashes of lightning and
peals of thunder—the convectional type of rainfall; but spells
of rain, lighter but still heavy by temperate standards, may

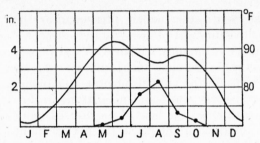

FIG. 121. Mean monthly rainfall and temperature, Khartoum

continue for 24 hours or longer. The landscape is trans-
formed, and even before the rains begin vegetation shows
signs of renewed life; the brown dusty ground becomes
green and the trees put forth their leaves. The air is heavy
with the smell of rank growths and the perfume of blooms.
The water-courses run brim-full with muddy rushing
torrents, and the low-lying land is waterlogged. The dense
clouds screen off the overhead sun, and the rain cools the air,
so that not only the midday temperature but also the
monthly means are considerably lower in the rainy season
(Fig. 121).

In October, with the southward retreat of the low-pressure
trough, north-east winds set in again, and the dry season
starts.

The duration and intensity of the rains decrease northwards; Timbuktu, 16·5° N., has 2 rainy months, July and
August, and an annual rainfall of only 9 inches, Khartoum
only 5 inches, these towns being near the farthest northward advance of the intertropical front. Lokoja, 7·5° N., at
the junction of the rivers Niger and Benue, has its rains

from April to October inclusive, and the mean total is 49 inches.

North from the Sudan the rain dies away in the Sahara, where even in July and August the cloudless skies offer clear passage to the rays of the overhead sun. No vegetation screens the ground, and the desert sands are too hot at mid-day to touch; although the nights are much cooler, a great area in the south of the Sahara has the hottest summers on the globe.

On the south the Sudan merges into the equatorial climate with rain most of the year. At Akassa in the Niger delta January is the only month with less than 3 inches; the rainiest months, October and June, have 25 and 19 inches respectively, and the annual mean is 144 inches. Thus the dry season is very short and no season can be called cool; but no month rivals the heat of the hot season of the Sudan; the mean temperature of April, the hottest month, is 80°, of August, the coolest, 76°, only 4° lower. The monotonous, enervating, hot-house conditions throughout most of the year are favourable to the growth of a rank vegetation, but are unpleasant and unhealthy for white men.

The Sudan type covers great areas on each side of the equatorial belt in both hemispheres. The monsoonal climates of India and the north of Australia resemble it, but have peculiarities of their own.

CHAPTER XL

THE MEDITERRANEAN TYPE
(SUB-TROPICAL WITH DRY SUMMER)

MOST of the lands round the Mediterranean Sea have a similar climate, which must have been favourable to the nurture of some of the earliest civilizations. The seasonal rhythm is strongly marked in respect of temperature, rainfall, and weather generally.

In summer pressure is high on the North Atlantic and west Europe, very low over the south of Asia and the south of the Sahara; the Mediterranean, lying between these great centres of action, is swept by north-west winds, strong and fresh like the trades. The sky is almost cloudless (Fig. 122), and the glare of the sun is thrown back from the white rocks; the air is clear save when hazy with dust, cyclonic disturbances are few in the west, almost unknown in the east; the air is dry, rain is rare and in most of the east practically absent. On the coasts the strong cool sea-breeze, which sets

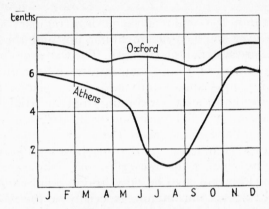

FIG. 122. Mean cloud amount

in about 0900, prevents excessively high temperatures despite the bright unclouded sun; the July mean is about 75°. The weather changes little day after day, but sometimes the wind blows stronger and great waves roll along with white crests. Inland it is much hotter, the mean exceeding 80°, hotter than in parts of the tropics, and work must be suspended during the middle of the day; the heat is most oppressive in places sheltered from the wind. All rivers but the largest dry up, and vegetation withers, except the evergreens which survive thanks to their small dark-green leaves carefully protected against evaporation by a hard glossy skin, and their deep roots; the land is dusty and the shrubs are grey rather than green. Summer, in the pronounced form just described, lasts in the west Mediterranean only through July and August, but in the east through June to September. The hot dry summers are the outstanding feature of the Mediterranean climate; the region is semi-arid, lying between well-watered central Europe and the arid Sahara, the chief drawback in his natural surroundings with which man has to contend being insufficiency of water. Agriculture demands artificial irrigation for success, and even the domestic architecture has sometimes been designed to collect and store the rain that falls, the roofs sloping inwards instead of outwards as in lands where the main object is to get rid of over-abundant water.

In autumn the winds become less regular; the low pressures over south Asia are filling up, and the Azores high-pressure system loses strength. The waters of the Mediterranean remain at a high temperature and the weather is warm and damp—unpleasantly so at many places. Depressions begin to appear, a few coming from the Atlantic, most forming over the Mediterranean itself, and they are soon both vigorous and numerous in the western basin; frequent lee depressions develop in the north-west; the weather is similar to that of the westerlies and gales are not uncommon. The rain may be very heavy, a fall of 4 inches in a day being not uncommon, especially on the mountains which overlook the Mediterranean. The land that was deep in dust in the parched summer months is soon saturated, and vegetation revives. But great damage is done by the violence of the rainstorms, for the watercourses which were wide channels of sand and pebbles in summer, quite dry or containing a few feeble trickles and small pools of water, are suddenly filled with torrents which bring down masses of soil and stones from the treeless mountain sides. On the Mediterranean littoral of France, north Spain, and north and central Italy, autumn is the rainiest season; winter also is damp and rainy, but less than autumn, and the rain increases again to a secondary (in some parts, a primary) maximum in spring. On the south shores and in all the east Mediterranean the rain begins in October, increases to a maximum in December, and decreases again through spring to the rainless summer (Fig. 123).

The winter half-year is the rainy period, yet it is the season for visitors who seek pleasure and health; the weather, though of the same type as in the westerlies, is more pleasant. The temperature is considerably higher during the day, the humidity very much lower, and the sunshine brighter and more abundant owing to the clearer air and less cloud; though the rain may fall heavily for a time the weather soon clears, and the sun shines the more brilliantly through air that has been washed.

The number of rain-days, too, is comparatively small— at Nice 81 in the year, though the rainfall is 33 inches; the south of England has a similar amount of rain, but the

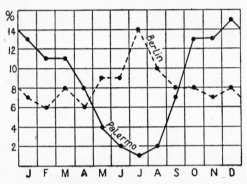

FIG. 123. Mean monthly precipitation (percentage of annual mean)

number of rain-days is more than twice as large. Frost and snow are by no means unknown even at sea-level on the north coasts, but the snow does not lie long; it is rare in the south, and though many of the ranges are snow-covered during the winter months, only the Sierra Nevada of the south of Spain retains a few patches throughout the year. The frost is not severe; temperature may occasionally fall 15° below freezing-point at night but rarely remains below all day. Sunshine is abundant, not only in summer, when high records are to be expected in view of the cloudless and rainless conditions, but also in winter.

The following table gives the mean daily solar energy in cal./cm.² received on a horizontal surface at Montpellier, south France, 44° N., and Stockholm, 59° N.; in summer the latter leads, thanks to its long days, but in winter Montpellier has a much greater advantage owing to its longer days, higher sun, drier air, and clear skies:

MEAN DAILY SOLAR ENERGY (cal./cm².)

	Montpellier Lat. 43° 36′ N.	Stockholm Lat. 59° 20′ N.
January	82	12
February	127	28
March	184	67
April	229	198
May	296	313
June	311	403
July	325	359
August	295	231
September	225	137
October	135	49
November	90	10
December	61	3

Health-resorts must be carefully chosen. Summer is too hot everywhere near sea-level, and even the natives would gladly seek relief in the mountains. In winter the north coasts are liable to strong polar winds and a mountain-shelter is needed; the French and Italian Rivieras are protected by the Maritime Alps and the Apennines, but the flat lands of the lower Rhone are often afflicted for days together by the piercing mistral (p. 161). These cold winds may be avoided by choosing a resort on the south coast of the Mediterranean, but at the risk of the unpleasantly dry, and at times hot, sirocco from the deserts of North Africa and Arabia (p. 159) which is most frequent and unpleasant in spring, when disturbances are still active and the deserts from which the air is derived are already heated by the approach of the overhead sun. The sirocco is not confined to the south coasts, but its passage over the sea, while reducing its temperature, increases its humidity, so that in the Aegean and the Adriatic it is damp and muggy, liable, with its high vapour-content, to give heavy precipitation on the mountains.

The Mediterranean climate, then, is distinguished by hot rainless summers, warm rainy autumns, cool rainy winters and springs, and bright skies and abundant sunshine mostly in summer but also in winter. It is restricted to the immediate littoral, generally not exceeding a width of 20 or 30 miles, of the sea from whose warmth and humidity it results; numerous local peculiarities depend largely on the nature of the shelter from winds. The mean annual rainfall ranges from under 10 inches a year on the Egyptian coast (where, however, the aridity precludes classification as Mediterranean) to over 180 inches in the mountains of Montenegro overlooking the Adriatic.

The main features are repeated in four other regions (all of small area but considerable importance for the valuable fruit and cereal products of their intensive agriculture), the coast of California, the south-west corner of Australia, the south-west of the Cape Province, and Central Chile.

CHAPTER XLI

THE WESTERLIES

Vancouver Island, British Columbia (Figs. 124 and 125)

THIS is chosen to represent the windward coasts of the continents in the westerlies—north-west Europe including the British Isles, the west of France, and most of Norway, the coasts and islands of British Columbia, the south of Chile, the South Island of New Zealand.

A mountainous island, most of the interior at an altitude of over 3,000 feet with a narrow coastal fringe, Vancouver is a remnant of a former coastal range. It lies in the course of the westerlies all the year, the seasonal change being one of temperature and of intensity of the weather type, not of wind system as in the Sudan and the Mediterranean.

In winter the westerlies blow strong under the control of the deep low-pressure system south of the Aleutian Islands; frequent depressions of the usual westerlies type give mild, damp, rainy weather, followed by blue skies, cumulus clouds, and showers in the polar current; winds are often of gale force. The mean rainfall in December at Victoria is 6 inches, and Victoria is on the lee side of the island; the west coast has 14 inches or more, and the mountains more than 30 inches. Frost is neither frequent nor severe on the west coast (zero has never been recorded), and snow does not lie long; it is colder in the east, and the mountains are snow-capped for several months. In January the mean temperature is about 40°, the same as in the British Isles; at night the thermometer usually sinks to near the freezing-point, and the day maxima occasionally reach 50°, high figures in view of the low sun and the short days in this latitude; at Winni-

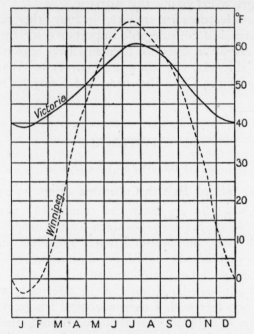

FIG. 124. Mean temperature

peg, in the same latitude but in the far interior, the mean for January is −4°, the mean daily minimum about −15°, and the mean daily maximum only 7°. The winter warmth of Vancouver is imported from the Pacific by the moist winds, it is not the result of direct local insolation.

March brings signs of spring, the days draw out and the sun rapidly gains power; but the wind is still strong and the ocean now keeps the temperature low. Moreover many returns to winter conditions give snow-flurries and cold north winds to nip the early vegetation. Winter and summer struggle for the mastery till at last towards the end of May summer is established; the sub-tropical high-pressures of the North Pacific extend far north, and the Aleutian depression almost disappears. The prevailing winds are still westerly and north-westerly, but disturbances are rare, the ocean breezes are fresh and invigorating, and the sky is clear. June, July, and August with their long summer days have very fine sunny weather, little rain (the July mean at Victoria is less than half an inch), and temperature never uncomfortably high, rarely exceeding 90°. Vancouver and its neighbourhood have much finer summers, with more sun and less rain, than the corresponding regions in the other continents.

In September autumn begins, the sun declines rapidly, the air is cooler, and damp at night. But many delightful, calm, cloudless, and warm days are enjoyed in September and October.

In November, with increasing cyclonic activity, the disturbed and rainy winter sets in, but the sea-air is still warm; on the west coast of Vancouver November, December, and January are the rainiest months of the year, each with more than 14 inches of rain. Even the coast of the mainland has 17 inches in the three months November, December, and January, together.

Vancouver and the similarly situated regions of other continents are the most favoured lands in the westerlies, for their windward position saves them from extreme cold in winter, and from aridity—the scourges of the interiors of continents; frost is never severe, and the sea is never frozen, thanks to the winds which have blown hundreds of miles over the warm ocean drift of the North Pacific. Labrador, in the same latitude but in the east of the continent, is snow-covered for 8 months, and the shore with its wide belt of ice-floes and bergs carried down from the Arctic by the cold Labrador current can hardly be reached by ships.

Manitoba (Figs. 124 and 125)

Manitoba is representative of the spacious plains in the interior of North America and Eurasia in temperate latitudes; the south hemisphere has no large land-mass in these latitudes. The outstanding features are the intensely cold winters, the dry air, and the moderate to scanty rainfall.

In winter the plains are snow-covered, and heat is lost rapidly by radiation during the long nights; the cold is intense in still, clear, anticyclonic weather, which is frequent; —46° has been recorded at Winnipeg. The cold air, even if saturated, can hold little vapour, and when warmed by contact with the body it becomes very dry, so that the weather, with bright sunshine by day, and brilliant starry skies at night, is pleasant and exhilarating.

But such weather does not always prevail, for the westerlies with their procession of cyclones and anticyclones pass right across North America. As a depression approaches, the southerly winds bring clouds, warmer weather (though the temperature is still below freezing-point), and often heavy snowfall, and behind it bitterly cold winds sweep down from the north-west. At such times a blinding blizzard may hide the landmarks; temperature, by the thermometer, is not so low as in the calm anticyclonic spells, but with the rapid air-movement the cold is more piercing. Owing to the low vapour-capacity of the cold air the precipitation, which consists entirely of snow, is not heavy, the mean depth of snow-fall in the year at Winnipeg being 49 inches; farther west it is rather less. Winter is the season of least precipitation.

In spite of the delights of the clear days, frosty air, bright skies, and snow sparkling in the sunshine, the long winter (5 months have a mean temperature far below freezing-point) must be admitted to be a tedious season, and life is hard, dull, and monotonous on the boundless prairie. Too often the cheerless grey sky descends on all sides to the featureless horizon, and even the blizzard may be a welcome break in the monotony. Throughout the winter lakes and rivers are frozen.

As the sun mounts in the heavens in spring temperature rises fast, though frost may be severe and is occasionally recorded even in June. The snow soon melts, the ground dries, and as oceanic influences are remote the curve of air temperature reflects with little lag that of the sun's altitude; spring is a short transition season from winter to summer. The land heats so rapidly that convection becomes active, the higher atmosphere being still cold, and heavy showers of rain, often thunderstorms, occur as early as April, when the wheat is sown. The rain increases in May and June, the latter month having the highest mean of the year (but at Winnipeg itself July has a slightly higher total than June); this early rain is ideal for the growth of wheat. Most of it falls in the hot hours and is soon over, so that the long summer days have high sunshine records on the wide wheat lands; the agricultural possibilities are almost as good along

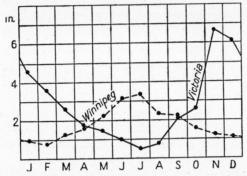

FIG. 125. Mean rainfall at Victoria, B.C. (west coast) and Winnipeg (interior)

the Peace River as on the international frontier owing to the longer sunny days in the higher latitude. The mean temperature in July is about 65°, some 5° higher than in Vancouver Island or in the south of England. Late summer has considerably less rain, and the heat can be oppressive when the ground is baked hard and dry. In September frost must be expected at night, and in October it may be severe; temperature falls rapidly, the mean being 13° lower in October than in September, and 20° lower in November than in October (a drop equal to that from July to January in England) but September and October often give delightful weather, warm lazy days followed by crisp, frosty nights. No efforts must be spared to get the wheat transported by water before the rivers and lakes freeze up in November and bring shipping to a standstill till the following April.

Manitoba, then, has a climate in which the seasonal

change of temperature is the most prominent feature, and controls most departments of life. In the intense cold of winter work on the land is suspended, but with the coming of spring outdoor activities are renewed and labour comes into great demand for sowing, and later for harvesting and transporting the crops.

A SHORT BIBLIOGRAPHY
(mostly of works in English)

METEOROLOGY

BRUNT, D., *Weather Study*. London, 1941.
—— *Physical and Dynamical Meteorology*. Cambridge, 1939.
BYERS, H. R., *General Meteorology*. New York, 1944.
GARBELL, M. A., *Tropical and Equatorial Meteorology*. London, 1947.
HANN-SURING, *Lehrbuch der Meteorologie*. Leipzig, 1937.
HUMPHREYS, W. J., *Physics of the Air*. New York, 1940.
LEMPFERT, R. G. K., *Meteorology*. London, 1920.
PETTERSSEN, S., *Weather Analysis and Forecasting*. New York, 1940.
SHAW, Sir N., *Forecasting Weather*. London, 1940.
—— with the assistance of ELAINE AUSTIN, *Manual of Meteorology*. Cambridge, 1936.
SUTCLIFFE, R. C., *Meteorology for Aviators*. London, 1939.

CLIMATOLOGY

ABERCROMBIE, R., and GOLDIE, A. H. R., *Weather*. London, 1934.
CONRAD, V., *Fundamentals of Physical Climatology*. Milton, Mass., 1942.
DE MARTONNE, E., *Traité de Géographie physique*, i. Paris, 1925.
HANN, J., *Handbuch der Klimatologie*. Stuttgart, 1908.
(Vol. i, translated into English by R. de C. Ward. New York. New edn., revised by K. Knoch. Stuttgart, 1932.)
HAURWITZ, B., and AUSTIN, J. M., *Climatology*. New York, 1944.
KÖPPEN, W., *Grundriss der Klimakunde*. Berlin, 1931.
KÖPPEN, W., u. GEIGER, R., *Handbuch der Klimatologie*. Berlin, 1930–.
MILLER, A., *Climatology*. London, 1947.
TREWARTHA, G. T., *An Introduction to Climate and Weather*. New York, 1943.
WARD, R. DE C., *Climate*. London, 1918.

CLIMATES OF REGIONS

BILHAM, E. G., *The Climate of the British Isles*. London, 1938.
BLANFORD, H. F., *The Climates and Weather of India, Ceylon, and Burma*. London, 1889.
BRAAK, C., *Het Klimaat van Nederlandsch-Indië*. Batavia, 1928.
BROOKS, C. E. P., *Le Climat du Sahara et de l'Arabie* in Hachisuka, *Le Sahara*. Paris, 1932.
KENDREW, W. G., *The Climates of the Continents*. Oxford, 1937.
KOEPPE, O. E., *The Canadian Climate*. Bloomington, Ill., 1931.
MAURER, BILWILLER, u. HESS, *Das Klima der Schweiz*. Frauenfeld, 1909.
MOHN, H., *The Norwegian North Polar Expedition 1893–6*. London, 1905.
PHILIPPSON, A., *Das Mittelmeergebiet*. Leipzig, 1922.

Problems of Polar Research. American Geogr. Soc., 1928.

SIMPSON, Sir G. C., *British Antarctic Expedition: Meteorology.* Calcutta, 1919.

SUTTON, L. J., *The Climate of Helwan.* Govt. Press, Cairo, 1926.

SVERDRUP, H. U., *Der nordatlantische Passat.* Veröff. Geoph. Inst., Leipzig, 1917.

—— The Norwegian North Polar Expedition with the 'Maud', Sci. Results, vol. ii, *Meteorology.* Bergen, 1933.

WARD, R. DE C., *The Climates of the United States.* New York, 1925.

GENERAL

American Meteorological Society, Bulletin (monthly).

BROOKS, C. E. P., *Climate through the Ages.* London, 1948.

CLARK, G. A., *Clouds.* London, 1920.

Climate and Man. United States Dept. of Agriculture, Washington, 1941.

ELLSWORTH HUNTINGTON, *The Climatic Factor as illustrated in Arid America.* Washington, 1914.

—— *The Pulse of Asia.* London, 1907.

Geophysical Memoirs, Meteorological Office. H.M. Stationery Office.

International Atlas of Clouds, Paris, 1932.

Monthly Weather Review, U.S.A. Weather Bureau.

NEWNHAM, E. V., *Hurricanes and Tropical Revolving Storms.* H.M. Stationery Office. London, 1922.

Royal Meteorological Society, Quarterly Journal.

The Observer's Handbook, Meteorological Office. H.M. Stationery Office, 1946.

ATLASES

BARTHOLOMEW, J., *Atlas of Meteorology.* Westminster, 1899.

Deutschland, Klimaatlas von. Berlin, 1921.

Egypt, Meteorological Atlas of. Giza, 1931.

India, Climatological Atlas of. Indian Meteorological Dept., 1906.

(Russia) *Klima der Union der Sozial. Sowjet-Republiken* (with Atlases). Leningrad, 1926–.

EQUIVALENTS
TEMPERATURE, °F. AND °C.

Fahr.	Cent.	Fahr.	Cent.	Fahr.	Cent.	Fahr.	Cent.	Fahr.	Cent.
−20·0	−28·9	+10·0	−12·2	+40·0	+ 4·4	+70·0	+21·1	+100·0	+37·8
19·5	28·6	10·5	11·9	40·5	4·7	70·5	21·4	100·5	38·1
19·0	28·3	11·0	11·7	41·0	5·0	71·0	21·7	101·0	38·3
18·5	28·1	11·5	11·4	41·5	5·3	71·5	21·9	101·5	38·6
18·0	27·8	12·0	11·1	42·0	5·6	72·0	22·2	102·0	38·9
17·5	27·5	12·5	10·8	42·5	5·8	72·5	22·5	102·5	39·2
17·0	27·2	13·0	10·6	43·0	6·1	73·0	22·8	103·0	39·4
16·5	26·9	13·5	10·3	43·5	6·4	73·5	23·1	103·5	39·7
16·0	26·7	14·0	10·0	44·0	6·7	74·0	23·3	104·0	40·0
15·5	26·4	14·5	9·7	44·5	6·9	74·5	23·6	104·5	40·3
15·0	26·1	15·0	9·4	45·0	7·2	75·0	23·9	105·0	40·6
14·5	25·8	15·5	9·2	45·5	7·5	75·5	24·2	105·5	40·8
14·0	25·6	16·0	8·9	46·0	7·8	76·0	24·4	106·0	41·1
13·5	25·3	16·5	8·6	46·5	8·1	76·5	24·7	106·5	41·4
13·0	25·0	17·0	8·3	47·0	8·3	77·0	25·0	107·0	41·7
12·5	24·7	17·5	8·1	47·5	8·6	77·5	25·3	107·5	41·9
12·0	24·4	18·0	7·8	48·0	8·9	78·0	25·6	108·0	42·2
11·5	24·2	18·5	7·5	48·5	9·2	78·5	25·8	108·5	42·5
11·0	23·9	19·0	7·2	49·0	9·4	79·0	26·1	109·0	42·8
10·5	23·6	19·5	6·9	49·5	9·7	79·5	26·4	109·5	43·1
10·0	23·3	20·0	6·7	50·0	10·0	80·0	26·7	110·0	43·3
9·5	23·1	20·5	6·4	50·5	10·3	80·5	26·9	110·5	43·6
9·0	22·8	21·0	6·1	51·0	10·6	81·0	27·2	111·0	43·9
8·5	22·5	21·5	5·8	51·5	10·8	81·5	27·5	111·5	44·2
8·0	22·2	22·0	5·6	52·0	11·1	82·0	27·8	112·0	44·4
7·5	21·9	22·5	5·3	52·5	11·4	82·5	28·1	112·5	44·7
7·0	21·7	23·0	5·0	53·0	11·7	83·0	28·3	113·0	45·0
6·5	21·4	23·5	4·7	53·5	11·9	83·5	28·6	113·5	45·3
6·0	21·1	24·0	4·4	54·0	12·2	84·0	28·9	114·0	45·6
5·5	20·8	24·5	4·2	54·5	12·5	84·5	29·2	114·5	45·8
5·0	20·6	25·0	3·9	55·0	12·8	85·0	29·4	115·0	46·1
4·5	20·3	25·5	3·6	55·5	13·1	85·5	29·7	115·5	46·4
4·0	20·0	26·0	3·3	56·0	13·3	86·0	30·0	116·0	46·7
3·5	19·7	26·5	3·1	56·5	13·6	86·5	30·3	116·5	46·9
3·0	19·4	27·0	2·8	57·0	13·9	87·0	30·6	117·0	47·2
2·5	19·2	27·5	2·5	57·5	14·2	87·5	30·8	117·5	47·5
2·0	18·9	28·0	2·2	58·0	14·4	88·0	31·1	118·0	47·8
1·5	18·6	28·5	1·9	58·5	14·7	88·5	31·4	118·5	48·1
1·0	18·3	29·0	1·7	59·0	15·0	89·0	31·7	119·0	48·3
−0·5	18·1	29·5	1·4	59·5	15·3	89·5	31·9	119·5	48·6
0·0	17·8	30·0	1·1	60·0	15·6	90·0	32·2	120·0	48·9
+0·5	17·5	30·5	0·8	60·5	15·8	90·5	32·5	120·5	49·2
1·0	17·2	31·0	0·6	61·0	16·1	91·0	32·8	121·0	49·4
1·5	16·9	31·5	−0·3	61·5	16·4	91·5	33·1	121·5	49·7
2·0	16·7	32·0	0·0	62·0	16·7	92·0	33·3	122·0	50·0
2·5	16·4	32·5	+0·3	62·5	16·9	92·5	33·6	122·5	50·3
3·0	16·1	33·0	0·6	63·0	17·2	93·0	33·9	123·0	50·6
3·5	15·8	33·5	0·8	63·5	17·5	93·5	34·2	123·5	50·8
4·0	15·6	34·0	1·1	64·0	17·8	94·0	34·4	124·0	51·1
4·5	15·3	34·5	1·4	64·5	18·1	94·5	34·7	124·5	51·4
5·0	15·0	35·0	1·7	65·0	18·3	95·0	35·0	125·0	51·7
5·5	14·7	35·5	1·9	65·5	18·6	95·5	35·3	125·5	51·9
6·0	14·4	36·0	2·2	66·0	18·9	96·0	35·6	126·0	52·2
6·5	14·2	36·5	2·5	66·5	19·2	96·5	35·8	126·5	52·5
7·0	13·9	37·0	2·8	67·0	19·4	97·0	36·1	127·0	52·8
7·5	13·6	37·5	3·1	67·5	19·7	97·5	36·4	127·5	53·1
8·0	13·3	38·0	3·3	68·0	20·0	98·0	36·7	128·0	53·3
8·5	13·1	38·5	3·6	68·5	20·3	98·5	36·9	128·5	53·6
9·0	12·8	39·0	3·9	69·0	20·6	99·0	37·2	129·0	53·9
9·5	12·5	39·5	4·2	69·5	20·8	99·5	37·5	129·5	54·2

INCHES AND MILLIMETRES

Inches	Milli-metres	Inches	Milli-metres	Inches	Milli-metres	Inches	Milli-metres	Inches	Milli-metres
0·05	1·3	3·3	83·8	6·6	167·6	9·9	251·5	30·3	769·6
0·1	2·5	3·4	86·4	6·7	170·2	10·0	254·0	30·4	772·2
0·2	5·1	3·5	88·9	6·8	172·7	11·0	279·4	30·5	774·7
0·3	7·6	3·6	91·4	6·9	175·3	12·0	304·8	31·0	787·4
0·4	10·2	3·7	94·0	7·0	177·8	13·0	330·2	32·0	812·8
0·5	12·7	3·8	96·5	7·1	180·3	14·0	355·6	33·0	838·2
0·6	15·2	3·9	99·1	7·2	182·9	15·0	381·0	34·0	863·6
0·7	17·8	4·0	101·6	7·3	185·4	16·0	406·4	35·0	889·0
0·8	20·3	4·1	104·1	7·4	188·0	17·0	431·8	36·0	914·4
0·9	22·9	4·2	106·7	7·5	190·5	18·0	457·2	37·0	939·8
1·0	25·4	4·3	109·2	7·6	193·0	19·0	482·6	38·0	965·2
1·1	27·9	4·4	111·8	7·7	195·6	20·0	508·0	39·0	990·6
1·2	30·5	4·5	114·3	7·8	198·1	21·0	533·4	40·0	1016·0
1·3	33·0	4·6	116·8	7·9	200·7	22·0	558·8	41·0	1041·4
1·4	35·6	4·7	119·4	8·0	203·2	23·0	584·2	42·0	1066·8
1·5	38·1	4·8	121·9	8·1	205·7	24·0	609·6	43·0	1092·2
1·6	40·6	4·9	124·5	8·2	208·3	25·0	635·0	44·0	1117·6
1·7	43·2	5·0	127·0	8·3	210·8	26·0	660·4	45·0	1143·0
1·8	45·7	5·1	129·5	8·4	213·4	27·0	685·8	46·0	1168·4
1·9	48·3	5·2	132·1	8·5	215·9	28·0	711·2	47·0	1193·8
2·0	50·8	5·3	134·6	8·6	218·4	29·0	736·6	48·0	1219·2
2·1	53·3	5·4	137·2	8·7	221·0	29·1	739·1	49·0	1244·6
2·2	55·9	5·5	139·7	8·8	223·5	29·2	741·7	50·0	1270·0
2·3	58·4	5·6	142·2	8·9	226·1	29·3	744·2	51·0	1295·4
2·4	61·0	5·7	144·8	9·0	228·6	29·4	746·8	52·0	1320·8
2·5	63·5	5·8	147·3	9·1	231·1	29·5	749·3	53·0	1346·2
2·6	66·0	5·9	149·9	9·2	233·7	29·6	751·8	54·0	1371·6
2·7	68·6	6·0	152·4	9·3	236·2	29·7	754·4	55·0	1397·0
2·8	71·1	6·1	154·9	9·4	238·8	29·8	756·9	56·0	1422·4
2·9	73·7	6·2	157·5	9·5	241·3	29·9	759·5	57·0	1447·8
3·0	76·2	6·3	160·0	9·6	243·8	30·0	762·0	58·0	1473·2
3·1	78·7	6·4	162·6	9·7	246·4	30·1	764·5	59·0	1498·6
3·2	81·3	6·5	165·1	9·8	248·9	30·2	767·1	60·0	1524·0

PRESSURE
INCHES AND MILLIBARS

Equivalents in Millibars of Inches of Mercury at 32° F., Latitude 45°

Mercury Inches	0·00	0·05
	Millibars	
28·0	948·2	949·9
28·1	951·6	953·2
28·2	954·9	956·6
28·3	958·3	960·0
28·4	961·7	963·4
28·5	965·1	966·8
28·6	968·5	970·2
28·7	971·9	973·6
28·8	975·3	977·0
28·9	978·6	980·3
29·0	982·0	983·7
29·1	985·4	987·1
29·2	988·8	990·5
29·3	992·2	993·9
29·4	995·6	997·3
29·5	999·0	1000·7
29·6	1002·4	1004·0
29·7	1005·7	1007·4
29·8	1009·1	1010·8
29·9	1012·5	1014·2
30·0	1015·9	1017·6
30·1	1019·3	1021·0
30·2	1022·7	1024·4
30·3	1026·1	1027·7
30·4	1029·4	1031·1
30·5	1032·8	1034·5
30·6	1036·2	1037·9
30·7	1039·6	1041·3
30·8	1943·0	1044·7
30·9	1046·4	1048·1

INDEX

PRINTED IN
GREAT BRITAIN
AT THE
UNIVERSITY PRESS
OXFORD
BY
CHARLES BATEY
PRINTER
TO THE
UNIVERSITY